D1090552

GRASSES &
GRASSLANDS

A grass flower (*Lolium temulentum*) at antithesis with the lemma drawn back
to disclose the ovary with its two feathery stigmas and swollen lodicules.

GRASSES & GRASSLANDS

Edited by
C. BARNARD

Division of Plant Industry, C.S.I.R.O., Canberra

LONDON · MELBOURNE
MACMILLAN & CO LTD
NEW YORK · ST MARTIN'S PRESS

MACMILLAN AND COMPANY LIMITED
St Martin's Street London WC 2
also Bombay Calcutta Madras Melbourne

THE MACMILLAN COMPANY OF CANADA LIMITED
Toronto

ST MARTIN'S PRESS INC
New York

PRINTED IN GREAT BRITAIN

Contributors

L. A. T. Ballard

C. Barnard

E. F. Biddiscombe

Nancy T. Burbidge

A. B. Costin

L. T. Evans

O. H. Frankel

B. D. H. Latter

J. F. Loneragan

J. R. McWilliam

C. W. E. Moore

R. M. Moore

I. F. Wardlaw

C. N. Williams

R. F. Williams

Preface

GRASSES and pastures have been important subjects in the research programme of the Commonwealth Scientific and Industrial Research Organization's Division of Plant Industry for just over thirty years. During this time a great deal of knowledge and experience of grasses and grasslands has been accumulated by the research officers of the Division, and many significant contributions have been made by them to an understanding of the biology of grasses and to the solution of problems of pasture establishment, maintenance, and improvement.

The present volume is essentially the result of an attempt to bring together under one cover some of this accumulated knowledge and experience for the benefit of students and teachers, and indeed all persons interested in the utilization of pastures and their improvement. It is in no way a record of the research achievements of its authors, nor is it concerned with all aspects of investigation into grasses undertaken in the Division's laboratories. It is a series of essays and documented essay-reviews on various aspects of the biology of grasses and grasslands upon which the contributors have been competent to write with special authority. Although treatment of subject varies somewhat from chapter to chapter, the motivation throughout has been to link the pure science disciplines and research with the general science and practical outlook of agriculture and to assess critically some past and present trends in agricultural research on grasses and grasslands. It is dedicated to the King of Brobdingnag who gave it for his opinion that whoever could make two ears of corn or two blades of grass to grow upon a spot of ground where only one grew before, would deserve better of mankind and do more essential service to his country than the whole race of politicians put together (Jonathan Swift, *Gulliver's Travels*, 1726).

The first chapter presents a picture of the historic development of grasses and grasslands in relation to the animals, including man, which feed upon them. The next nine chapters deal with different phases of the biology of grasses. In Chapter 2 their botanical classification and relationship are discussed whilst Chapter 3 deals with their distribution, and Chapter 4 their morphology and anatomy. Chapter 5 is concerned with the biology of the phenomenon of germination. This is followed by an essay on the quantitative analysis of growth in grasses and a review in Chapter 7 of knowledge on the relationships between their growth and environmental conditions. A comprehensive review of the nature of their reproductive mechanisms in Chapter 8 leads to a discussion of their cytogenetics in Chapter 9 and selection methods for species improvement in Chapter 10.

Chapters 11–14 deal with the plant communities of grasses or grasslands, their evolution and distribution, nutrition and utilization in grazing and soil conservation.

All contributors, except Dr. O. H. Frankel and Dr. Loneragan, are currently officers of the Division of Plant Industry of C.S.I.R.O., with head-quarters at Canberra. Dr. O. H. Frankel, Chief of the Division, 1952 to March 1962, is now an Executive Member of the Organization in Melbourne, and Dr. J. Loneragan who worked with the Division, 1953–1961, is at present a member of the Department of Soil Science of the Institute of Agriculture of the University of Western Australia.

Grateful acknowledgement is made to Miss S. M. White for assistance in preparing the manuscript, to Messrs. W. Goodwin and F. Dandridge for executing the majority of the drawings used as illustrations and to Mr. C. Totterdell for many of the photographs. The Editor and his colleagues also thank the various scientific journals which gave permission for the repro-duction of a number of illustrations and the Soil Conservation Service of New South Wales for the photographs used as plates.

C. BARNARD

12th May, 1963   Canberra

Contents

Grass, Grazing Animals, and Man in Historic Perspective

By C. Barnard and O. H. Frankel

THE establishment of grasses and grazing animals among dominant life forms on earth considerably preceded the advent of man.

The fossil record of grasses is rather meagre but there are fairly good grounds for assuming that they emerged as a distinct class of the Angiosperm complex during late Cretaceous times, or even earlier, when flowering plants were spreading throughout the world. By Miocene times, that is some 20 million years ago, grasses were probably assuming an important place in the earth's vegetation. Speciation of the grasses and development of grasslands has been occurring throughout the whole period from early Tertiary times to the present day.

It is estimated[8] that grasslands now extend over seventeen and three quarter million square miles and comprise 24 per cent of the world's vegetation cover. Many of the large grassland areas like the prairies and plains of North America, the pampas of South America, the steppes of Asia, and the velds of Africa, are believed to be of great antiquity and climax formations determined by soil and climate. The North American grassland area of prairie and great plains is believed[16] to date back to the Miocene times. The uplift which formed the Rocky Mountains resulted in changes of climate, especially of rainfall, over a large area of the continent. Dry summers and drier winters became a feature of this area making it unsuitable for the forests it previously carried. The forest disappeared and grasses took over. Many vicissitudes of climate have since occurred. During the ice ages of the Pleistocene, mass movements of grasslands must have accompanied the northward and southward pulsations as the ice sheets advanced and retreated. These migrations no doubt resulted in the mingling of populations and were coincident with periods of intensive evolution. The prairies of today are undoubtedly descended from the prairies of the Miocene. Other grasslands like those of Europe are of more recent origin and have replaced forests which have been destroyed by cutting and fire, and are maintained by man largely through his grazing animals.

The fossil record of the grazing mammals is much more complete, and the evolution of these animals is known in some detail. The two great ungulate orders of herbivorous mammals arose in early Tertiary times. The perissodactyls (e.g. horses, rhinoceros, tapirs), the non-ruminant artiodactyls (e.g. pigs, camels, hippopotami, and peccaries) and the ruminant artiodactyls (e.g. cattle, buffalo, sheep, goats, deer, and antelopes) all arose from a group of mammals known as the Condylarths which were abundant at the beginning of the Tertiary (Paleocene) in all continents except Australia.[9] The Condylarths were not fully herbivorous but were to some extent carnivorous and omnivorous and the early forms of the ungulates were all browsing rather than grazing herbivores.

The change from the early browsing ungulates to the later grazing types is best known in the evolution of the horse. The earliest known member of the horse family, *Eohippus* of the Eocene, was a small animal with five toes, more like a Condylarth than an *Equus*, and lived in both Europe and America. He was a primitive browser and probably lived on succulent leaves and fruits. Through the Tertiary the succession of animals derived from *Eohippus* gradually became more horselike; the body grew larger, toes gave way to the hoof, and the mouth changed, the lips becoming more mobile and the teeth high crowned.[10] Mouth and teeth characters became progressively better adapted to graze grass. During the Pliocene there were six genera of the horse family and all were grazers. Only *Equus*, however, survived through the Pleistocene to modern times.

Non-ruminant forms of Artiodactyla arose during the early Tertiary. Ruminant forms, particularly the Bovidae (cattle, sheep, etc.), appeared later during the Miocene. The rabbits arose in the early Tertiary and were well established by the Miocene.

The picture which therefore presents itself is of grasses commencing to appear in early Tertiary times followed by their diversification and spread over the earth by mid Tertiary. By Miocene times grasslands were becoming abundant and new environments had been created which had not existed before. The herbivorous mammals exploited these new environments by adaptation to a different kind of feeding. Every niche in the diverse ecological habitats of this new type of vegetation was filled by the radiating evolution of the grazing herbivores. Grasslands developed through varying vicissitudes of climate, but always in interaction with the animals which cropped them. The prairies of North America have been cropped and trampled and fertilized by the dung of herds of buffaloes and horses and their progenitors. On other grasslands cattle and deer and antelope roamed. In Australia where Condylarths were never present the marsupials gave rise to grazing types like the kangaroo.

While much has been written about the structural changes in mammals which accompanied their adaptation to feeding on herbs and grass, much less thought seems to have been given to the role of the grazing animal on the evolution of structural features in grasses. For some twenty million years grasses and grazing animals have been evolving together and must have acted as reciprocal factors in natural selection. There are among grasses many well known adaptations of the caryopsis and its investing palea and lemma for distribution of its seeds by animals. But, in addition, grasses are structurally well adapted for survival under the depredations of the animals which feed upon them.

The habit of forming short basal internodes and the mode of branching by basal tillering and rhizome formation (cf. Chapter 4) are very important factors in allowing grasses to withstand grazing. When the main shoot is cropped lateral shoots from basal buds take its place. This process may be repeated frequently and replenishment of leaves and aerial stems is constantly being made by growth from basal buds and underground rhizomes. These are features characteristic of grasses with both the tufted and creeping or prostrate habit.

The growth of the grass leaf by a basal meristem (cf. Chapter 4) also contributes largely to the suitability of grasses for grazing. As leaves are cropped they continue to grow from their bases. A great length of leaf may be produced; this is why a well kept lawn requires frequent mowing.

The shortness of the aerial stem internodes in all annual grasses, and in perennials with the tufted habit, during vegetative growth, and the investment of the stem apices by sheathing leaf bases are important in shielding the apical meristems from damage by both cropping and trampling. Elongation of the stem internodes occurs in most grasses only when the inflorescence commences to develop. This would seem to provide a useful mechanism for minimizing the time period during which the reproductive structures are vulnerable to the bite of the grazing animal.

The adventitious system of fibrous roots gives good anchorage, and it is usually difficult to pluck a tufted plant wholly from the soil. The long rhizome and stolon which root readily at most nodes also make it difficult for the grazing animal to destroy a plant entirely.

It is noteworthy that very few of the species of the large natural grassland areas, and particularly those of the American continent, are among the 40 odd grass species which are used in sown pastures today. The great majority are fringe forest species indigenous to Eurasia, and species from Africa. Hartley and Williams [6] have discussed the reasons for this. One important reason would seem to be the type of grazing animal that has been the dominant biotic factor in the evolution of the species. The family Bovidae to which domesticated cattle and sheep belong arose in Eurasia during Pliocene times and invaded Africa during the late Pliocene. Very few species reached North America and grasses there did not develop in interaction with these particular kinds of grazing animals.

Man arrived on the scene a long time after the fundamental evolutionary processes which allowed grasses and grazing animals to develop in relatively peaceful coexistence had been achieved. Estimates vary greatly of the time when articulate speech, the use of stone tools, and fire first distinguished man from other primates. It has been placed as far back as the beginning of the Pleistocene, one million years ago.[12] It has also been said 'There must have been some 200,000 years during which men were living a hunting, tool using, fire making complex life before men anatomically like ourselves appeared'.[15]

The staple foods of the great majority of mankind come from grass. The grains of grasses such as maize in the Americas, rice in Asia, wheat, rye, barley, and oats in Europe, and the sorghums in Africa, form the basis of man's carbohydrate diet while the flesh of animals that graze on pastures provides the main source of his proteins and fats. Thus the nurture of grasses and grasslands is a matter of great importance to him and has always been so. Many of his migrations and invasions have resulted from his search for grasslands. Increasing skill in growing cereal crops and maintaining grazing animals has been a fundamental feature of his progress in civilization. Indeed, the future of his present day civilization may depend largely on his ability to extend these basic sources of his nourishment.

Man's control and use of fire was a very important feature associated with his spread from the tropics throughout the world. His campfires and his practice of setting alight vegetation to rouse out game – a practice still prevalent among primitive peoples – introduced the factor of burning to the ecology of vegetation on a scale not previously experienced. Before man's advent the ignition of vegetation by lightning and other natural agencies had probably been relatively infrequent. Primitive man's firing of vegetation, particularly in the drier forest and shrub regions, undoubtedly led to an increase in the grassland areas (cf. Chapter 11).

In tropical forest areas where there is a sparse population of primitive people today, as in New Guinea, a shifting type of agriculture is practised. In the moister areas, the cultivated plots revert to forest as the population shifts camp. In the slightly drier areas, grassland patches develop. This change to grassland occurs since because of their structural characteristics grasses escape fire more easily than most shrubby and woody vegetation. Grasses also regenerate more quickly after fire. A great deal of the Central African equatorial forest has been turned into grassland by an agricultural system which employed fire. The activities of man, the hunter, therefore most likely considerably increased the area of grassland, and thus the environment of the grazing animals during thousands of years before animal husbandry and agriculture in even primitive forms arose.

The transition from a nomadic hunting life to a village and settled life occurred in different ways in different areas; and parallel development in both the domestication of animals and the growing of crops undoubtedly took place. We can presume that the collection of grain from wild grasses preceded their cultivation and that this happened in the temperate and drier regions of the earth. In some areas, especially those of the tropics, the collection and later cultivation of tuber crops originated agriculture. The domestication of animals and growing of cereal crops seem to have commenced between 8000 and 15,000 years ago, and these practices also tended to encourage grassland development. At this time man was undoubtedly learning that he could clear land for his crops by firing the vegetation and by the same means encourage the growth of grasslands for feeding his animals. Folk who used a stick and a dibble for planting could make use of fire as a tool for cultivation.

There is much evidence in Europe and Mediterranean countries, whose known histories date back some thousands of years, that great transformations have taken place in the vegetation during historic time. Large forest areas have been felled over the centuries for building and fuel, and burned for pastoral and agricultural purposes. Before the advent of fire cropping and domestic grazing, trees and perennial shrubs were the dominant component of the vegetation of large areas now occupied by grassland and crops in Europe.

It would seem therefore that both grazing and browsing animals probably contributed largely to the spread of grasslands and helped much in maintaining them in competition with shrub and woody vegetation during the later

part of the Tertiary period and before the advent of man. Primitive man and his practice of firing vegetation considerably increased the grassland areas. With the coming of the domestication of animals and the cultivation of cereal crops man further increased the extent of grassland areas and he became increasingly dependent upon grasses for his civilized life.

Haymaking must have been among the very earliest of the methods devised by man for more fully utilizing his grasslands. The adoption of a more or less settled way of life on the plains of the higher latitudes necessitated making provision for his animals as well as for his own food supplies during the winter season. He preserved both the straw of crops grown for grain and dried grass harvested from the fields. We know that haymaking was practised by the Romans, and during historic times it has been the traditional means of fodder conservation.

The next step was the sowing of particular grasses to form meadows for haymaking and grazing. It was probably not until late in the 16th century that farmers in Europe commenced this practice[3], and rye grass (*Lolium perenne* L.) seems to have been the first grass cultivated in England for this purpose.

It is difficult to say when farmers first became aware of the virtue and value of associating legumes with grasses for pasturage but it certainly was a discovery of the greatest importance. The introduction of red clover to pastures in England is usually attributed to Sir Richard Weston in 1613. To Townshend in 1730 is credited the introduction of four course farming which later developed into the practice of alternating arable land with a period under grass known as ley farming. In the early days the best leys seem to have been composed of red clover and rye grass and were of short duration. The adoption of this kind of practice for improving both crop and pasture land was the most outstanding development prior to the middle of the 19th century.

The origin of the use of fertilizers for promoting the growth of pastures is also shrouded in uncertainty but almost certainly this practice derived from the fertilization of cereal crops. Bones and bone dust had been used for many years as a fertilizer before the late 1880s when basic slag (which was available from the steel industries) was coming into general use. The major improvement in pastures in England and Europe at the end of the 19th century and for the first few decades of the 20th century resulted from the application of this phosphatic fertilizer to grass–clover pastures.

The modern era of research on grasslands and pastures had its origin in the establishment of the first agricultural experiment station in the world at Rothamsted in England in 1843. The first experiments were concerned with soil fertility and the rotation of agricultural crops, but a little later Gilbert and Lawes started an experiment which resulted in the publication of a paper in the Philosophical Transactions of the Royal Society of 1880–2, entitled *Agricultural, Botanical and Chemical results of experiments on the Mixed Herbage of permanent meadow conducted for more than 20 years in succession on the same land*. Plots had been treated with various fertilizers and the herbage mowed and weighed, and its botanical and chemical composition determined each year.

In 1889 fertilizer experiments on pastures were commenced in Germany and during the 'nineties similar projects were initiated in other European countries.

The second classic experiment in England was commenced in 1896 at Cockle Park in Northumberland. The results of these fertilizer experiments on pastures published in 1902 were noteworthy in that the results of treatments were gauged by measuring the weight of the sheep grazed upon them. They provided the first precise demonstration of the outstanding value of basic slag in developing wild clovers in the pastures and the effect of the improved pastures on the animals which grazed them. The next outstanding contribution also came from Cockle Park where, as a result of trials over a period of years with various clovers and grasses, a certain mixture was selected which proved eminently successful in Great Britain. Phosphates, white clover, and the best grasses were thus established as the basis of pasture farming.

The work at Rothamsted and Cockle Park was, however, pioneer work. The general realization that pastures and grasslands needed to be regarded in much the same way and given the same research attention as cereal crops did not come until later. Before 1917 there was no text-book on the subject of agricultural agrostology and such books as did exist on grasses were purely botanical in character. In the preface to his book on British grasses and their employment in agriculture published in 1917, S. F. Armstrong wrote, 'The enormous importance of our cereal grasses is apparent to everyone but apart from these our native grasses are worthy of the highest attention if only on account of the large proportion of agricultural land occupied by them.'

It was the impact of the First World War with its attendant food shortages, especially of animal products, in Great Britain and Western Europe that focused attention on the importance of high production from pastures. The need for research became more apparent and the modern era of institutional pasture research really began. Investigations were begun in 1914 by Dr. J. B. Orr at the Rowett Research Institute at Aberdeen in Scotland on the nutrition of the grazing animal. The chemical composition of pastures through a 12-month cycle and the effect of rotational grazing and frequent topdressing with fertilizers were related to the stock carrying capacity. During the 1920s a great deal of work was done at Cambridge and in New Zealand, Australia, and South Africa under the aegis of the Empire Marketing Board on the mineral deficiencies and feeding value of pastures.

In 1919 the Welsh Plant Breeding Station at Aberystwyth was established under Professor R. G. Stapledon. Here the breeding of herbage plants and the improvement and management of grassland were the main themes. The work at Aberystwyth on the breeding and selection of superior strains of pasture plants including grasses, and the development of seed mixtures and techniques for pasture investigation were eminently successful. Comparable development and interest in pasture research occurred in Europe, particularly in Sweden, during the same period.

The Rowett Research Institute and the Welsh Plant Breeding Station had a very significant effect on pasture research throughout the British

Commonwealth and the world, and this impact was facilitated by the establishment of the Imperial (now Commonwealth) Agricultural Bureaux in 1929. These bureaux were designed to act as clearing and exchange houses for information in their respective fields throughout the British Commonwealth, and the Bureau concerned with pastures contributed much to the concept and development of pasture research in the countries of the Commonwealth during the decade of the 1930s.

In 1945 the Food and Agriculture Organization of the United Nations was established with Sir John Orr (later Lord Boyd Orr), of the Rowett Research Institute, as its first Director General. Since then F.A.O. has engaged *inter alia* in survey work and dissemination of information relating to pastures and grasslands, and has stimulated research and development in under-developed countries. Of more recent years (since 1951) the Agricultural Committee of the Organization for European Co-operation has done somewhat similar work and disseminated information with respect to pasture and fodder development within Europe.

Pasture research thus commenced in the cool, temperate, humid, and long settled regions of Great Britain and north-west Europe where the grasslands had developed over a period of many hundreds of years on land that was originally forested. Grasslands of this kind were either permanent in so far as they were never cultivated and grazing alone prevented their reversion to a woody vegetation, or they were pastures of longer or shorter duration forming part of a rotational farming system. It was in this environment that the new outlook towards pastures had its origin during the second decade of the present century. It was this environment that led to the philosophy in Great Britain and Western Europe exemplified by Professor Stapledon when he wrote in 1945, 'In my view the era of permanent pasture as we know it has ended in this country and the grassland problems of the future centre almost wholly in the ley'. It was from this environment that the influence of Aberystwyth spread to other countries during the 'thirties. Only in certain restricted areas, however, in Australia and the New World, did comparable humid and cool temperate conditions obtain; it did not apply to the large natural climax grassland areas.

The large 'natural' grasslands of the world, particularly those of the drier areas, required a different approach for their proper utilization. In Australia, it was apparent before 1890 that periodic droughts combined with overgrazing and the spread of rabbits had resulted in a serious deterioration of the natural grasslands. F. Turner, the Government Botanist in Western Australia, wrote in 1897, 'For those areas that have deteriorated so much that animals have a difficulty to eke out an existence on them it would be a wise thing to rest them for a period until the better kinds of herbage recuperate'. He also advocated the preservation and cultivation of indigenous grasses by the establishment of reserves for raising seed of the better types for dissemination.

In America, the burning, overstocking, and abuse of the prairie areas and the great plains, which commenced with their exploitation in the middle of the 19th century, resulted in their continual deterioration. The botanical composition of these grasslands was changed, the more palatable species disappearing and worthless ones replacing them. In many places total ground

B

cover was seriously reduced or completely denuded. The great droughts of the early 1930s were the culminating point of nearly a century of deterioration.

It gradually became evident that these natural or climax grassland areas, particularly those of low rainfall and subject to periodic droughts, could only be restored and maintained by very careful management of the numbers and distribution of stock grazed on them. These areas could not be cultivated and sown to selected grass and legume species even if species suitable for the areas had been known. The rate of stocking needed to be adjusted so that not only was the area maintained as a grassland but its botanical composition was also preserved or controlled. This could only be done on the basis of a thorough knowledge of the ecology of each grassland area. Thus the necessity to stabilize the range areas on an ecological basis became fully recognized. Grassland ecology and studies in the management of these natural grassland or range areas have been major themes in grassland research in the United States and Australia during the last 25 to 30 years.

While, therefore, the value of organized research on pasture and grasslands problems began to be appreciated in the temperate regions of the Old World during the 'twenties it was not until the following decade that the particular problems of the drier natural grasslands of America and elsewhere came to be fully recognized. A great deal of knowledge has since been gained on the best methods of handling and managing these indigenous grasslands. However, the great rise in pastoral production which has taken place in Australia during the past 35 years has been in the main the result not of the improvement of the indigenous grasses, but of the development of more productive pastures based on introduced species.

When the need for more productive pasture species began to be realized, it was the legumes rather than the grasses which received principal attention. Under extensive conditions of grassland farming the application of fertilizer nitrogen can be economic only in rare circumstances. Hence farmers, even before the scientists, were looking for suitable pasture legumes, since the clovers to which they had been accustomed in their temperate, high-rainfall home countries failed in the harsher environment of southern Australia, and the native legumes adapted to a low soil phosphorus status gave only small responses to the application of superphosphate. It was indeed a South Australian farmer who pioneered the most outstanding of the exotic legumes, subterranean clover, *Trifolium subterraneum*.

By the time pasture research began in earnest, all the species which were to play an important part in the development of the pastures in the southern half of the continent had arrived, the majority without the will or the aid of man; subterranean clover, annual *Medicago* spp. among the legumes, and *Phalaris tuberosa* and a variety of annual species among the grasses. All had come from the Mediterranean region; and none had been regarded important pasture species in their countries of origin. Indeed, it is due to their success, one might almost say domestication, in Australia that some of them have come to be accepted as valuable pasture species elsewhere, and this, in recent years, includes even their native home.

However, with one notable exception, *Lolium rigidum*, very little genetic adaptation to their new and diverse environments has taken place among these grasses; little diversification has occurred through natural selection or through the efforts of the plant breeder. Among the legumes adaptation through natural selection was bound to be slow because the majority of species are, at least in their Australian environments, almost wholly self-fertilized. Deliberate selection has, in the main, been confined to a sorting-out of ecotypes collected in Australia; extensive plant breeding activities did not begin until the early 'fifties – no doubt owing to the range and satisfactory performance of types already established.

It is of interest to compare this relatively static evolutionary picture with the marked response to the new environment exhibited in New Zealand by the principal grass species, *Lolium perenne,* which evolved a number of distinctive ecotypes in response to the climatic, soil, and managment regimes in different regions, with plant breeders taking advantage of the material offered by natural selection. By contrast, even the cross-fertilized *Phalaris tuberosa,* in spite of considerable intra-population heterogeneity, has failed to develop distinctive ecotypes in Australia for reasons well discussed by Trumble and Cashmore,[13] and, although there are indications of 'local strains' of *Lolium perenne* in Australia, plant breeders have as yet failed to exploit this, and other temperate zone pasture species, to the limit of their ecological and genetic potentialities. (For a discussion of the introduction and evolution of some Australian and New Zealand pasture species see Frankel.[5])

On the other hand there appears to exist in subterranean clover a reservoir of naturally occurring variation which, for such adaptive characters as flowering time, exceeds the range of both extensive collections from the Mediterranean and plant breeders' hybrids.

It is then obvious that the chance introduction of actual and potential pasture species preceded planned scientific plant introduction. It was only when an ecological understanding of the potential of various regions had gradually accumulated, that plant collections of pasture types became increasingly appreciated and absorbed. When the time came for the development of tropical pastures, plant introduction as a scientific activity was in a position to play a leading part. A number of productive and climatically suitable grasses for these subtropical areas are now available and may be exploited as the particular mineral requirements of the various soils are determined. In the far north *Brachiaria mutica* (para grass) and *Panicum maximum* (guinea grass), in the southern sub-tropical areas *Paspalum scrobiculatum* and *Sorghum almum,* and in the hinterland areas *Chloris gayana* (Rhodes grass), and *Cenchrus ciliaris* (buffel grass) are being used. Suitable legumes, mainly species of *Stylosanthes, Glycine, Centrosema,* and *Phaseolus,* have also been established.

The spreading of introduced pasture species was assisted, and indeed made possible, by the growing understanding of the nutritional deficiencies of plants growing in the different Australian environments. Needless to say, interest in problems of plant nutrition preceded the cultivation of introduced plants (see review 4) but their greater apparent need of various mineral nutrients helped to highlight nutritional deficiencies. Indeed, the general acceptance of sub-clover as a pasture species and the practice of topdressing pastures closely followed the demonstration in 1920 that sub-clover could be satisfactorily established without cultivation by merely scratching the surface and sowing seed with superphosphate. By topdressing native grasslands with superphosphate, herbaceous legumes, which before the phosphate was applied were inconspicuous, developed much better, and the higher nitrogen status in the soil which resulted from the increased legume growth stimulated the growth of the grasses in succeeding years.

The discovery in 1938 by D. S. Riceman, C. M. Donald, and C. S. Piper[7] that the inability of one of the infertile soils in South Australia to grow pastures was due to a deficiency of copper ushered in a period of intense research on minor element deficiencies in grassland development. For the next 15 years these studies which were pioneered by Australian scientists were extraordinarily rewarding (see reviews (4) and (11)). In 1942 A. J. Anderson[1] demonstrated a deficiency of molybdenum in certain soils in South Australia and in the following year a deficiency of the same element was found in pasture soils in Tasmania. The deficiency of molybdenum affected the growth of clover by depressing nodule formation and nitrogen fixation; its effect upon the grasses of the pastures was therefore indirect. In 1943 it was found that zinc in addition to copper, was deficient in certain areas in South Australia. Thus in the early 'forties it was becoming apparent that deficiencies in certain trace elements were widespread throughout Australia. Copper and zinc deficiencies occurred in both Southern and Western Australia and molybdenum deficiency in south-eastern areas. These discoveries, together with a great deal of subsequent research during the later 'forties, resulted in the transformation of large tracts of infertile wastelands into productive pastoral areas. As a result of these studies the years immediately following the Second World War saw the development of much land which had become available for intensive land use; and even more importantly, over large areas of native grassland they rendered possible the replacement of low-producing native grasses by high-producing introduced grasses and clovers. In 1950 Anderson and Spencer[2] showed that a deficiency of sulphur occurred in soils on the southern tablelands of New South Wales. A similar deficiency was found on the Darling Downs in south-east Queensland and in Western Australia in 1952. Since then other areas have been found where the supply of this element markedly increases grass-legume growth.

The management of native pastures presented the grazier with the all-important problem of stock survival in dry periods and especially in drought years. But with the growing knowledge of the ecology of native grasslands it was realized that the pastures themselves were as vulnerable, but far less replaceable than the stock. Studies begun in the 'thirties and intensified in recent years have indicated the precarious balance of feed plants – and prominently of the native grasses – in the semi-arid and arid pasture zones. Similar conditions prevail at the other ecological extreme in the alpine grasslands, where deterioration through stocking and the concomitant burning has caused such widespread erosion damage that large areas in the alpine zone are now closed to grazing.

In the higher rainfall pastoral areas, introduced species at a high nutritional level presented very different management problems: systems of management, stocking rates, fodder conservation, drought feeding, and many more. A variety of management studies have shed a good deal of light on some of them, sufficient at any rate to appreciate their complexity; hence the recent intensification of research into pasture utilization (see Chapter 13).

Perhaps the most significant happenings in Australian grassland development during the 'forties and 'fifties was the increased attention given to the problems of the tropical and sub-tropical pastures of the summer rainfall areas of north-eastern Australia. This movement commenced in the late 'thirties and gained momentum during the 'forties and 'fifties. Considerable progress has been made, as already pointed out, towards the goal of providing a range of grasses and legumes for improved pastures under sub-tropical and tropical summer rainfall conditions and of determining the additional soil nutrients, including the appropriate strains of *Rhizobium*, necessary for their satisfactory performance.

During the past 100 years man's ingenuity has continually been increasing his ability to manage his grasslands and grazing animals more effectively. The use of wire fences, and later of barbed wire (1874), to confine his stock was an important step forward. The replacement of the horse on the farm by the internal combustion engine and the use of machinery for sowing, topdressing and haymaking have only taken place within the past 30 to 40 years. Commencing some 15 years ago aircraft have been increasingly used for both sowing and topdressing pastures. The use of aircraft for these purposes has been particularly advantageous in handling pastures in rough and hilly countries. In New Zealand in 1958, fertilizer was applied to some 4·2 million acres and 863 tons of grass and clover seed were sown over 163,000 acres from the air.[14] In Australia during 1960–61, 4·3 million acres were topdressed with superphosphate from the air, and pasture seed sown over 655,000 acres.

Although the great importance of grasslands to man lies in providing him with sustenance, grasses serve mankind in many other ways. In some parts of the world, grasses, particularly bamboos, are used for building homes; grasses make thatch roofs and are plaited into walls, and matting, brooms, and many other home conveniences are made from them. Gracious living among the more civilized nations today is inseparable from grassy swards. They form an essential feature of landscaping around homes, of parks and gardens, and racecourses and all recreational areas. Sporting and athletic fields with their soft expanse of green turf afford pleasure to millions during their leisure hours. In U.S.A. in 1961 there were 6185 standard golf courses occupying some 598,500 acres. In Australia, it is estimated that there are something like 1100 golf courses occupying some 91,000 acres. The attention of millions is focused from time to time upon the struggles of protagonists on the centre court of the Wimbledon Lawn Tennis Club and millions more become concerned at the condition of a small patch of turf upon which a cricket match is played. All these things help to make grass supremely important in the world today.

REFERENCES

[1] Anderson, A. J. (1942). Molybdenum deficiency on a South Australian ironstone soil. *J. Aust. Agric. Sci.*, **8**, 73–4.

[2] Anderson, A. J., and Spencer, D. (1950). Sulphur in nitrogen metabolism of legume and non-legume. *Aust. J. Sci. Res. B.*, **3**, 431–49.

[3] Arber, A. (1934). *The Gramineae. A Study of cereal, bamboo and grass.* Univ. Press, Cambridge.

[4] Davies, J. G. (1951). Contributions to Agricultural Research in Pastures. *J. Aust. Inst. Agric. Sci.*, **17**, 54–66.

[5] Frankel, O. H. (1954). Invasion and evolution of plants in Australia and New Zealand. *Caryologia*, **6** suppl., 600–19.

[6] Hartley, W., and Williams, R. J. (1956). Centres of distribution of cultivated pasture grasses and their significance for plant introduction. *Proc. Seventh Internat. Grassland Conf.*, 190–9.

[7] Riceman, D. S., Donald, C. M., and Piper, C. S. (1938). Responses to copper on a South Australian soil. *J. Aust. Inst. Agric. Sci.*, **4**, 41.

[8] Shantz, H. L. (1954). The place of grasslands in the earth's cover of vegetation. *Ecology*, **35**, 143–51.

[9] Simpson, G. G. (1950). *Meaning of evolution - A study of the history of life and of its significance to man.* Yale Univ. Press, New Haven.

[10] Simpson, G. G. (1951). *Horses.* Oxford Univ. Press, New York.

[11] Stephens, C. G., and Donald, C. M. (1958). Australian soils and their responses to fertilizers. *Advances in Agronomy*, **10**, 167–256.

[12] Stewart, O. C. (1956). Fire as the first great force employed by Man. In *Man's Role in Changing the Face of the Earth*, pp. 115–33. Univ. of Chicago Press.

[13] Trumble, H. C., and Cashmore, A. B. (1954). The variety concept in relation to *Phalaris tuberosa* and allied forms. *Herbage Reviews*, **2**, 1–4.

[14] Wallace, L. R. (1959). Animal production from grassland – present problems and future needs. *Aust. J. Sci.*, **21** (6a), 159–67.

[15] Washburn, J. L., and Avis, V. (1958). Evolution and Human Behaviour. In *Behaviour and Evolution*, edited Roe, A., and Simpson, G. G., pp. 421–36. Yale Univ. Press, New Haven.

[16] Weaver, J. E. (1954). *North American Prairie.* Johnson Publ. Co., Lincoln, Neb.

2

Grass Systematics

By N. T. Burbidge

THE present situation in the systematic arrangement of the Gramineae is not particularly satisfactory. There are a number of systems many of which are modifications of those published in the early 19th century though changed so as to incorporate both recent genera and recent data on interrelationships. The interpolation of this material results in a situation of considerable complexity and some confusion. It is difficult to select any one particular system as the best since selection must be influenced by the particular requirement and bias of the reader. For this reason no system is given in full detail here but the more important current arrangements are quoted.

The great stimulus given to botanical studies by the publication of Linne's sexual system of classification naturally involved the grasses or, to use Linne's own term, the 'Gramina'. This name has formed the basis of the accepted family name Gramineae which was first established by Jussieu[46] in 1789 though, as it is not in strict accordance with the provisions of the International Code of Botanical Nomenclature (edition of 1956), the name Poaceae[5] is preferred by some authors.

In the first edition of 1753 of his Species Plantarum,[54] the starting point for binomial nomenclature in the phanerogams, Linne listed his grass genera as follows: Monandria-Digynia: *Cinna*; Diandria-Digynia: *Anthoxanthum*; Triandria-Monogynia: *Eriophorum* (now placed in the Cyperaceae) *Nardus*; Triandria-Digynia: (28 genera including such diverse elements as *Phalaris* and *Aira, Panicum,* and *Hordeum*); Hexandria-Digynia: *Oryza*; Polygamia-Monoecia: *Andropogon, Holcus (Sorghum), Ischaemum, Cenchrus,* and *Aegilops*. This list was not greatly enlarged in the fourth edition (1805) of the Species Plantarum which was prepared by Willdenow.[84] The immense advances that have been made since the time of Linne can be readily gauged from the fact that the Gramineae is now recognized as one of the largest families and may include over 600 genera.

Many botanists disliked the rigidity of the system of classification which resulted from the application of Linne's methods of arranging plants according to the number of stamens and pistils. The strict use of these characters sometimes placed together plants which were obviously unalike or separated those which shared many features, as was the case with the grasses listed above. In a revolt against the Linnaean method a number of botanists sought to develop a 'natural system' in which 'related' and 'like' plants were grouped together. It should be emphasized that this 'natural system' was based on resemblances and not on phylogeny since the idea of evolutionary sequences and relationships had not yet been propounded. An important contributor to the idea of the natural classification was Jussieu in whose Genera Plantarum[46] there is an account of his arrangement.

Further, at the time Linne published his system, the structure of the spikelet was not properly understood. Following the earlier work of Tournefort[78]
which laid the principal emphasis on the floral structure rather than on that
of the reproductive organs, Linne considered the spikelet was homologous
with a flower. Thus the glumes were regarded as corresponding to the calyx,
and the lemma (or lemmas) and palea to the corolla. Consequently in the fifth
edition of the *Genera Plantarum*[55] in 1754 his description of *Poa* reads: 'CAL.
Gluma multiflora, bivalvis, mutica, flores in spicam disticham . . .' followed
by 'Cor. bivalvis: *Valvulae* ovato-acuminatae . . .' Obviously he was not
entirely clear as to whether the spikelet was a flower or an inflorescence.

The first satisfactory analysis of the grass spikelet was that of Robert
Brown.[11,12] He recognized that the spikelet is a modified inflorescence and
not a flower, and pointed out that the floral organs are enclosed in floral valves
which are subject to suppression in many genera. His 'outer envelope or
gluma' (the latter term taken from Jussieu) he equated with the bracts or
involucre. He noted that suppression at this level led to the loss of the lower
organ (quoting *Lolium* and *Lepturus* as examples). In the case of the 'inner
envelope or calyx of Jussieu' he noted that it is the inner valve (i.e. the palea)
which is more apt to be reduced or suppressed. He equated the lodicules or
'squamae' with the inner series of perianth members and suggested that the
palea represented two fused members of the outer perianth series. His interpretation of the homology of the various parts of the spikelet has been modified
by later workers but to him belongs the honour of first providing a clear
description of the organ itself.

Brown's keen powers of observation, in this case as in many others, enabled
him to perceive certain fundamental characters in the spikelet which he used
as the basis of his 'principal subdivisions' the Paniceae and Poaceae. To these
he gave tribal status though in modern usage they are equivalent to subfamilies. He defined the characters of these two subdivisions as follows:

> Paniceae: spikelet with two florets of which the lower is imperfect or
> reduced to a single 'valve'. He pointed out that the majority of the genera
> in this group occur in warm or tropical regions.
> Poaceae: spikelet of one to many florets, imperfect florets terminal not
> basal. Majority of genera occurring in temperate regions.

He also recognized a third group in which the spikelets are three flowered,
the terminal one (described by him as intermediate) is hermaphrodite and
the two lower ones (called lateral) are male or neuter. This group was later
called the Phalarideae by Link[53] and Kunth;[49] and Brown[13] uses the name
in a discussion of the nature of the lemma and palea under the description of
Ataxia horsfieldii Kunth (=*Hierochloe horsfieldii* (Kunth) Maxim.) in 1838.
The main features of Brown's principal subdivisions are still used today even
though there has been modification and further subgrouping.

During the earlier part of the 19th century botanists remained grouped
into those who followed the Linnaean system and those who, like Brown,
supported Jussieu's principles of a natural system. Moreover, botanical classification had not reached the unified state realized later, and it was open to

each compiler of a general work to propose a new classification or arrangement according to any set of principles he might care to select, with or without reference to those laid down by other and earlier workers. Thus we find Palisot de Beauvois published a new classification of the family which ignores Brown's description of the spikelet and his principal subdivisions. This may in part have been due to the fact that, at the time of publication of Beauvois' *Essai d'une nouvelle Agrostigraphie*[57] in 1812, England and France were at war and communication would have been difficult. Nevertheless Brown's *Prodomus*, at least, must have been seen by Beauvois who transferred various species described in it.[16] Beauvois' work is of major importance because of the large number of generic descriptions it contains but his system of classification was based on minor characters and was never widely accepted.

Another important worker of this early period was Trinius who discussed the Gramineae in his *Fundamenta Agrostographie*[79] and in *De Graminibus unifloris et sesquifloris*[80] and who prepared yet another arrangement of the family. Kunth[49,50] followed Brown's concept of the spikelet but arranged the grasses in thirteen tribes which, since they include the Paniceae, are not directly based on Brown's principal subdivisions. Kunth's arrangement of tribes was used by Endlicher in his Genera Plantarum[28] of 1836 and a number of his concepts are still used.

The whole situation was greatly clarified by Bentham[7] with the publication of his arrangement of the family in 1881. By this time knowledge of the grasses on a world scale, rather than on the more limited one known to Linne and the earlier workers of the 19th century, permitted a general treatment of the kind that Bentham was so well fitted to carry out. This treatment appears again in the third volume of the *Genera Plantarum*,[8] prepared by Bentham and J. D. Hooker, which was published in 1883. Bentham retained Brown's principal subdivisions as primary groupings and broke each into a number of tribes and subtribes which owe much to those described by Kunth[49] and by Dumortier;[25] in each case, however, he modified the circumscription by including other genera and in some he used new names rather than the older ones, the practice of strict priority not having yet been established.

As time has passed the size of the family has made the use of tribal subdivisions increasingly necessary. The synonymy of many tribal names and much bibliographical data relating to these are provided by Pilger[61] and need not be discussed here except to remark that far too many botanical works not only omit such information but fail to quote authorities for names so that the reader is left confused as to the exact concept being followed in a given instance.

Subsequent to the publication of Bentham's system a number of important floras appeared and in these, though his system was used as a base, it was subjected to certain changes. These modifications were largely due to the work of Hackel[33,34] whose views, especially those pertaining to the Andropogoneae, were of far reaching importance. Thus in Volume 7 of the *Flora of British India*,[41] published in 1897, Joseph Hooker states in a foreword that he has departed from Bentham's arrangement so as to comply with the views of

Hackel and with those of Stapf who was then working at Kew. Further modifications appear in Stapf's account of the family for the *Flora Capensis* (1898–1900) and in the *Flora of Tropical Africa* [72] where the account of the Gramineae was continued by C. E. Hubbard after Stapf's death. Hubbard has contributed a number of statements on affinities in the family and has given a system for it in Hutchinson's *Families of Flowering Plants*.[42] This system retains the older Paniceae and Poaceae as Panicoideae and Pooideae but there are a number of changes among the tribes. Further remarks on grass relationships are given by Hubbard in Hutchinson's *British Flowering Plants*.[44]

Just as Hackel's work followed closely after that of Bentham in the Gramineae so did the family arrangement of Engler and Prantl's *Die Natürlichen Pflanzenfamilien* [29] follow soon after that in the *Genera Plantarum* of Bentham and Hooker.[8] The systems provided in these two great works still greatly influence systematic treatments used by taxonomists despite the fact that in individual works there are modifications within families. Thus Wettstein's order of tribes of the Gramineae [83] deviates from that of both Bentham and Hackel, but there is less difference in generic content under each tribe. Hitchcock [39] and Hitchcock and Chase [40] made further modifications for their treatments of American grasses, and in the modern Russian Flora edited by Komarov [47] the system followed is basically the traditional one without subdivision into subfamilies.

Another recent arrangement of the Gramineae which is in a direct line of descent from earlier works is the one prepared by Pilger [61, 62] for the second edition of *Die Natürlichen Pflanzenfamilien*. Unfortunately this project remained unfinished at the time of his death though his general system was published posthumously in 1954. His scheme is not in strict accordance with results of recent research into generic inter-relationships and has not been well received. Nevertheless, by providing one of the few keys to all genera as well as a mass of bibliographical data relating to tribes, his work will remain an important reference source.

Thus, during the earlier part of the 19th century, there was a considerable amount of experimentation with systems of classification and this was followed in the later part of the century by the preparation of a large number of major works and comprehensive floras. Methods were developed which formed the basis of the international system of nomenclature that has made so great a contribution to the advance of biological science. A great change, however, occurred during the 20th century. Increasing knowledge and growing specialization with its almost inevitable channelization into limited fields of interest has resulted in few being competent or willing to undertake the great general works so characteristic of the earlier period. While the 20th century has seen the production of few major works in taxonomy a great deal of very important research significant to taxonomy has been carried out in the biological field during the past thirty years or more. This research has been concerned with fundamental aspects of evolutionary processes, phylogeny, and the species concept. Such work, whether theoretical or descriptive in its bias, commonly appears in specialist journals and usually records specific details for a limited range of material rather than the full and comprehensive treatment that might be expected in a major Flora or a monograph. Nevertheless, the sum total of this research is producing a revolution in our concepts of relationships among the Gramineae.

The natural classification of the Gramineae was made the subject of a special symposium held during the Ninth International Botanical Congress at Montreal in 1959, and the papers from this meeting were issued in a volume entitled *Recent Advances in Botany*, Volume 1, pp. 91–145, 1961. During the symposium (*loc. cit.*) the subject was considered under embryology, histology, cytology, anatomy, biogeography, physiology, and taxonomy, a selection of specialist fields which shows the great range in research, which has been and is being done, concerning grass affinities and interrelationships. The situation has been reviewed in recent papers by Stebbins,[73, 74] Tateoka [77] and Prat.[67] Prat includes a table of diagnostic characters based on that presented at the above symposium by Stebbins and Crampton[75] and which is divided into morphological and non-morphological features. The first includes the features of the inflorescence (spikelet) and floret, and the vegetative characters conventionally used by taxonomists. The non-morphological characters cover anatomical, histological, cytological, physiological, ecological, and chemical features, the study of which has lead to great changes in the arrangement of tribes and the placement of genera. The authors whose works are particularly relevant in their respective fields are listed as follows: *Anatomy of the Embryo*, Van Tieghem,[81] Reeder,[68, 69] Yakovlev;[85] *Anatomy of the leaf, culm and rhizome*, Duval-Jouve,[26,27] Avdulov,[4] Parodi,[58] Potztal,[63,64] and others; *Histology of leaf epidermis, root hairs and shoot apex*, Grob,[32] Prat,[65,66] Reeder and von Maltzahn,[70] Row and Reeder,[71] Brown,[14] and Brown, Heimsch, and Emery;[15] *Cytology*, Avdulov,[4] De Wet,[18,19,20] Stebbins,[73,74] Tateoka;[76,77] *Chemistry*, Fairbrothers and Johnson,[30] Al Aish;[2] *Physiology and Ecology*, Al Aish,[2] Al Aish and Brown,[3] Mez;[56] *Biogeography*, Beetle,[6] Bews,[9] Hartley,[35,36,37] Hartley and Slater.[38]

In bringing together work in all these fields Stebbins and Crampton[75] have prepared a very useful bridge between two groups of workers who have not always acknowledged their interdependence, and in so doing enabled us to gain a general view of the progress made.

That such interdependence exists must be obvious but, in practice, inter-communication between the groups of research workers has not always been as effective as could be wished. Those studying non-morphological characters that reveal relationships normally commence with named and taxonomically referable material. Inevitably they have a different approach from that of herbarium workers whose concern is the accurate placement of plants that are unknown or inadequately known at the commencement of study. Much of the work of the general taxonomist group is done by means of 'keys' and descriptions based on gross morphology since daily pressure of work demands rapid identification. In his research studies, however, the taxonomist aims to provide means by which his colleagues can not only place, i.e., identify, specimens of species, but also relate them or populations of them to recognized systems of classification and the fabric of the plant kingdom as a whole. He is concerned with arrangements by which masses of biological material can be

made comprehensible. To hold in the mind knowledge of hundreds of heterogeneous taxa would be impossible unless they are sorted into logical and
defined groups in a 'system'. Evolutionary theory gave, and still gives, stimulus
to the idea of producing a system truly based on phylogeny. The taxonomist
is quite aware that current systems of classification are imperfect but at the
same time he knows that while such systems have their limitations he still
needs 'keys' as tools for the process of identification. Placement of biological
material in a system under internationally recognized names is essential for
the correlation of research results and the communication of ideas in many
fields other than that of the herbarium. Unfortunately, at the present time,
both the naming and the characterization of taxonomic units may not be
simple. In this respect the remarks of Doroszewska[24] are particularly relevant.
She writes 'All that has been said . . . clearly shows how differently the
different workers approach the same phenomenon and what deplorable
effects this has on the systematics of the genus *Dactylis*. The question thus
arises what criterion should be given priority . . . the morphology of the
plants or the chromosome number? The discrimination between diploid and
tetraploid plants greatly facilitates the classification, but it seems illogical to
assign to different systematic units plants morphologically identical when
within the diploid and the tetraploid forms the taxonomic units are dis-
criminated according to the morphological traits alone'

The non-taxonomist commonly regards, or at least treats, systems of classification as essentially means by which the available information on inter-
relationships may be expressed; i.e., they are employed to indicate the latest
data concerning phylogenetic and evolutionary development. Where the
studies pertain to a limited number of taxa or involve re-assignment of genera
from one tribe to another, with consequent change in the circumscription of
these tribes, or where some previously overlooked character is shown to have
diagnostic significance, the reported conclusions may be applied by the author
in a limited sense; limited that is to the material he has studied or is discussing,
and the reader can be left without a clear idea of the possible consequences.
This problem is not restricted to the Gramineae but in so large and important
a family it raises peculiar difficulties. The great changes and advances made
in our knowledge of affinities and the range of characters by which these may
be traced have forced us to realize that modification of many of the earlier
concepts, especially among tribes, is unavoidable. The current situation is a
fluid one and for this reason alone the problem of tribal concepts is taxonomically and nomenclaturally difficult.

Jacques-Felix[45] comments that while Pilger's system[61] is still, despite the
discoveries made by recent workers, dominated by that of Bentham, the system
prepared by Prat,[66] though of great phylogenetical interest, is difficult to
apply under practical conditions that require identification of plant material.
In this comment Jacques-Felix highlights one of the principal features of
grass systematics of the present time. On the one hand we have systems based
directly on those of earlier times and provided with descriptions and keys,
while on the other we have arrangements, such as those of Prat[67] and of
Stebbins and Crampton,[75] in which every attempt has been made to sum-

marize and correlate the relationships revealed by both morphological and non-morphological research but in which only a minimum attention is given to definition and description through which taxa – – tribes, genera, and species can be correctly assigned even if not actually listed.

Under the International Code of Botanical Nomenclature (ed. Lanjouw 1956[52]) each taxon, whether subfamily, tribe, or subtribe, etc., should be accompanied by a latin description at the time of its original publication, unless it was published prior to 1st January, 1935, or unless it is validated by reference to a previously effectively published description. If the status of a taxon is changed, e.g. from tribe to subfamily, then the circumscription of the taxon in its new position must be indicated. Such circumscription cannot be provided merely by a quotation of the subordinate taxa included. There is also the principle of priority under which the first correctly published name must be used unless a later one has been conserved against it by the procedure laid down in the Code. In order that the usage of a name may be clearly understood it is customary for the name of the original author to be quoted, e.g. *Festuca* L., *Phalarideae* Link or, if emended, then as in the case *Andropogoneae* Presl emended Bentham. By such means the reader is advised as to the concept being followed and provided with evidence by which he can correlate the writings of diverse authors. It must be realized that adherence to the rules of nomenclature and of taxonomic practice is not a mere ritual. Unless there is a method by means of which an author can and does, within the limits set by current knowledge, clearly identify the biological material used in his work, or to which he refers in his text, there can be no efficient or effective communication of either his results or his conclusions.

It is curious and regrettable that, notwithstanding these rules, a number of grass tribe names have apparently never been validly published though they have been in use for some years. The common use of such names without indication of the authority adds to the difficulty of comprehending the concept being followed, the possible synonymy, or the intended changes in circumscription. For example, if a cytologist declares that genera A.B.C.D. belong in Tribe 1, whereas an anatomist states that C. and D. belong to Tribe 2 (leaving the position of A. and B. quite obscure), it is almost impossible without proper references to know whether the anatomist is using the same concept of the tribes as did the cytologist. Should A. and B. be transferred to Tribe 2? Was one of the genera the type for one of the tribes so that one name must lapse? In this case which tribal name has priority? Changing the subordinate taxa means emendation of concept and makes clarification by definition and by bibliographical reference essential. Taxonomic concepts are not boxes into which one can put subordinate taxa or from which one can remove taxa without altering the concept as used by another author. A reader should not be left to 'guess' what a writer means by his manner of using names of taxonomic units. The Code was prepared in order to express taxonomic facts and if new facts reveal errors in earlier work then the rules provide the procedures necessary for the resultant changes to be made in a manner that will prevent future confusion as to the nature of the entities concerned.

As was noted above, some difficulties arise because of the different approaches to the use of 'systems'.

Stebbins and Crampton[75] write, 'so long as the systematist recognizes the fact that an artificial key, which is intended to make identification as easy as possible, need have nothing to do with a natural system, which expresses probable genetic evolutionary relationships, he should not be disturbed by the fact that genera which are close together in the key are far apart in the system'. Taxonomists, however, are fully accustomed to the use of systems quite distinct from those keys which include the same taxa. Few, if any, would ever expect the two to be similar or that a key would give evidence as to evolutionary relationships – unless of course it should happen that the character associations used for convenience sake should also be those correlated with affinities. What the taxonomist does require, surely not unreasonably, is that if material can be sorted into a system then the categories in that system must have characters, or groups of characters, that can be defined and described. To be able to say that *Poa* is in the same tribe as *Festuca* is good enough if everyone knows what *Poa* and what *Festuca* are. It is quite unsatisfactory for someone with a plant unknown to him even though it happens to be a species of *Poa*. He requires a method by which he can personally ascertain the placement and identity of his material. It is irrelevant whether he does this by a laborious checking of characters of all tribes in a system, or whether he takes a short cut via a key even if this has a different arrangement, and uses characters that are convenient even if not phylogenetically significant. It is essential that however he reaches his conclusions he shall be able to comprehend the nature of the taxon, whether genus or tribe, and furthermore, that he shall be able to follow discussions of it by different authors.

Some of the complications that can arise through changing usage of names may be illustrated by the following example. Prat[67] gives a very useful table showing changes in grass systematics. In this it is indicated that the subfamily name Bambusoideae was established by Krause[48] in 1909. In 1931 Avdulov[4] referred the type genus *Bambusa* Schreb. to his taxon Phragmitiformes though it would seem that this cannot be nomenclaturally acceptable. In the Phragmitiformes Avdulov also included Arundineae, Oryzeae, Centotheceae, and Stipeae. In Hubbard's arrangement of the family[42] the Bambuseae is treated as a tribe and not as a subfamily. The name Bambusoideae was used by Parodi[58] who in 1946 limited it to the tribe Bambuseae but in a later paper[59] he includes Streptochaeteae, Olyreae, and Phareae. The subfamily was maintained by Jacques-Felix[45] and Pilger[61] though with some modification of the subordinates. Beetle[6] considered that four subfamilies should be recognized in the Gramineae of which two are the Bambusoideae and the Pharoideae (a new subfamily). He did not clearly define the Pharoideae though the subordinate tribes are listed as Streptochaeteae, Anomochloeae, Phareae, Parianeae, and Olyreae. Tateoka[76] accepted Beetle's name Pharoideae but errs in referring the Bambuseae to it since this would mean its reduction to synonymy under the earlier Bambusoideae unless it could be argued that the latter was nomenclaturally unacceptable. Furthermore, the name Pharoideae is also predated by the Oryzoideae of Parodi[58] if the tribe

Oryzeae is included as under the scheme proposed by Stebbins and Crampton.[75] Pilger[61] on the other hand refers the Streptochaeteae to the Bambusoideae and recognizes the subfamilies Oryzoideae and Olyroideae which means that if *Pharus* is treated as a subordinate genus of the latter then the Olyroideae has priority over Beetle's Pharoideae, unless Pilger's description in his key of 1954 is rejected in favour of that of 1956 in the second edition of *Die Natürlichen Pflanzenfamilien*.[29] It will be evident that such manipulation of the arrangement of subordinates without definitions and adequate references leaves the reader completely confused as to the concept of the Bambusoideae, Pharoideae, Oryzoideae, and Olyroideae that a particular author may be using, or how his concept may or may not be correlated with that of another. Furthermore, without consideration of the nomenclatural, as well as the taxonomic situation, the standing of a number of the names remains in doubt.

Another and simpler case of synonymy is that of the Eragrostoideae and Chloridoideae. In his earlier works Prat[65, 66] defined the 'Chloridoid type' of epidermis and leaf anatomy and used this more recently as the basis for the subfamily Chloridoideae. The Eragrostoideae was described by Pilger.[61, 62] Both Tateoka[77] and Prat himself[67] make it clear that the two are synonymous. Prat writes, 'Nous préférons appeler ce groupe "Chloridoidées" plutot qu' "Eragrostoidées" la tribu Chloridees an constituant la plus ancienne base.' This confuses the possible phylogenetical origin with the nomenclatural position and increases the difficulties of the reader who must in future ascertain whether a given author is using 'chloridoid' in the earlier anatomical sense or adjectival for the illegitimate name of a subfamily. Only in the latter case will the matter of synonymy with the Eragrostoideae arise.

Many of the difficulties arise from the manipulation of tribal concepts following critical research with representative genera. Unless the results from such work are properly related to their taxonomic context the light thrown on some aspects of problems of affinity may obscure rather than illuminate, and may merely intensify the surrounding shadows. This is not a criticism of the value of important and significant work done in recent years so much as a plea that results and discussions should be adequately correlated so that they may be fitted into wider problems through the conclusions of the reader. To illustrate this point in terms of work that does fulfil these requirements as well as work that fails to do so it may be useful to consider the case of the genus *Danthonia* and the tribe Danthonieae both of which have been critically studied in recent years.*

The genus *Danthonia* was originally described by De Candolle in the third edition of Lamarck and De Candolle *Flora Francaise*[51] of 1805. It was based on two species of which one has long been referred to *Sieglingia* Bernh. so that the other, *Danthonia provincialis* DC. (or more correctly *D. calycina* (Vill.) Reichb.) stands as the type of the genus as was noted by Bentham in

*Following remarks written prior to receipt of paper, 'Synopsis of the Grass Subfamily Arundoideae in New Zealand', V. D. Zotov, *N.Z. J. Bot.* 1, 78-136 (1963) in which New Zealand and Australia species, formerly referred to *Danthonia* are transferred to new genera and tribal nomenclature is rectified.

1881. This species thus becomes the type of the tribe Danthonieae, raised from subtribal status by Hubbard.[44] Early workers placed the genus in the Aveneae because of its relatively long glumes, awned lemmas and the number of florets per spikelet. Avdulov[4] divided the Aveneae into two groups in one of which the awn arises from the back of the lemma and in the other from the sinus. The first group, the Aveneae-Euaveninae, is mainly distributed in the cooler regions of the northern hemisphere; the second or Aveneae-Danthoninae, has a more southerly distribution. Avdulov reported that the basic chromosome number was seven in the first group and six in the second. In *Danthonia*, however, basic numbers of both six and seven have since been recorded.[1,10,17] In other genera of Avdulov's second group the numbers seven, nine, and twelve have been reported[19] so that this particular character cannot be regarded as a reliable one for the separation of these groups.

The affinities of *Danthonia* have been studied by De Wet,[18,19,20,21,23] and Tateoka[77] has reviewed the genera which in his opinion should be associated with it in the tribe Danthonieae. Previously Hubbard[44] had referred *Danthonia*, *Schismus* Beauv., *Sieglingia* Bernh. and (somewhat tentatively) *Molinia* Schrank to this tribe, but De Wet added *Alloeochaete* Hubb., *Asthenatherum* Nevski, *Pentaschistis* Stapf, *Chaetobromus* Nees, *Poagrostis* Stapf, *Pentameris* Beauv., and *Prionanthium* Desv., thus considerably enlarging the original concept. His study of the leaves of species of these genera[22] shows that some have epidermal and internal anatomical characters of the festucoid type as defined by Prat but others have panicoid epidermal characters associated with festucoid anatomy. These two types may occur within one genus as is the case in both *Danthonia* and *Pentaschistis*. The inference is that evolution has proceeded along parallel lines, but it also demonstrates the phylogenetic antiquity of the festucoid and panicoid characters and is a warning that these must be used with discretion as diagnostic features.

A different view of the affinities of the Danthonieae is taken by Brown.[14] Having described six basic types of leaf anatomy – Bambusoid, Festucoid, Arundoid, Panicoid, Aristoid, and Chloridoid, which he deliberately and expressly states are not intended for exact correlation with taxonomic categories – he includes the Danthonieae (concept not explained) under his Bambusoid group with the tribes Streptochaeteae, Unioleae, Bambuseae, Stipeae, and Oryzeae. However, in his table of affinities he splits the Bambusoid group into two, of which one includes the Streptochaeteae, Bambuseae, and Unioleae, and the other the Oryzeae, Danthonieae, and Stipeae. The association of tribes in this arrangement is not without interest but it is a pity that the author in attempting to sidestep nomenclatural responsibilities has added to those already existing since readers must take note of his groupings when trying to correlate his results with the systems proposed by other workers.

The genera included in the Danthonieae, following the work of De Wet and Tateoka, are linked with those of the Aveneae–Danthonieae of Avdulov. Tateoka[77] notes that the curious Australian genus *Micraira* F. Muell., which is one of those involved, is distinctive with its spiral phyllotaxy, multinerved palea and its mixed festucoid and panicoid anatomy,[60] and should, according to Potztal,[63] be removed from the tribe. Pilger[62] established for it a mono-generic subfamily, the Micrairoideae. For the rest De Wet has suggested that there are affinities between the Danthonieae and the Arundinelleae but Reeder,[69] as a result of his studies of the grass embryology, states that according to his formula *Danthonia* has an arundoid-danthonoid type embryo which is closely related to the panicoid type. To a taxonomist it would seem odd that *Danthonia* lacks a danthonoid embryo but the point, though minor, serves to emphasize the fact that while we now know a great deal more about relationships among the genera in or related to those included under the Danthonieae by various authors, we are left with no clear idea of either the characters or the content of the tribe since each author appears to have personal views which are rarely expressed through clear definitions of the circumscribing characters. A reader is forced to make a personal estimation of the author's meaning, a subjective process that must lead to confusion. Furthermore, while the character of the tribe has been studied by means of investigation of constituent genera and its separation from the Aveneae justified, the position of the tribe in a general system, is not so well established either in terms of the subordinate genera it should include or in terms of its intertribal affinities.

The most recent attempt to catalogue non-morphological data in a system for the whole family is that of Prat[67] who gives a full list of subfamilies, tribes, and genera (for major tribes) as well as tables illustrating the differences between other earlier systems. He omits authorities for the names of the taxa he uses and his concepts must be sought in his general text. His arrangement is as follows:

Subfamily: FESTUCOIDEAE
 Tribes: Festuceae, Hordeae, Agrostideae, Aveneae, Phalarideae,
   Stipeae, Monermeae, and the unplaced genus *Beckmannia*.
Subfamily: PANICOIDEAE
 Tribes: Paniceae, Andropogoneae, Maydeae, and also the "petites
   tribus" Arthropogoneae, Boivinelleae, Isachneae, Melini-
   dieae, and a number of unplaced genera.
Subfamily: CHLORIDOIDEAE
 Tribes: Chlorideae, Zoysieae, Eragrosteae, Pappophoreae, Sporobo-
   leae, and some unplaced genera.
Subfamily: BAMBUSOIDEAE
 Tribes: Bambuseae, Arundinarieae, Dendrocalameae, Melocaneae,
   and others not listed.
Subfamily: ORYZOIDEAE–OLYROIDEAE (PHAROIDEAE)
 Tribes: Oryzeae, Olyreae, and three unplaced genera:
   Orthoclada, *Pariana*, and *Streptochaeta*.
Subfamily: PHRAGMITIFORMES
 Tribes: Arundineae, Danthonieae, Arundinelleae, Aristideae, and
   fifteen unplaced genera including *Distichlis*, *Ehrharta*,
   Elytrophorus, *Micraira*, *Microlaena*, *Tetrarrhena*, and *Uniola*.

This systematic catalogue presents yet another resorting with consequent

c

changes in tribe circumscriptions but the coverage is enough to permit comparison with other treatments. Such a change as the separation of the Stipeae and the Aristideae, though still unfamiliar to those accustomed to older arrangements, is justified by recent work and the same applies to the placement of the Eragrosteae in the 'Chloridoideae' (=Eragrostoideae) rather than the Festucoideae. Prat differs from Stebbins and Crampton in maintaining the Sporoboleae as a distinct tribe instead of including it in the Eragrosteae as they have done, a point where they follow Pilger rather than Hubbard. Nomenclaturally it would seem that 'Triticeae (Dumortier, 1823)' has priority over 'Hordeae (Bentham, 1881)'. That *Pariana* and *Streptochaeta* are placed under the Oryzoideae indicates that the tribes Parianeae and Streptochaeteae of which they are both the types and the only representatives may also be placed here until such time as Prat may indicate that the tribes should be reduced to synonymy. The genus *Orthoclada* has long been placed in the subtribe Centotheceae of the Festuceae, as defined by Bentham, though this was treated as a tribe by Hubbard.[43]

Prat's reluctance to place *Ehrharta*, *Microlaena*, and *Tetrarrhena* in a distinct tribe indicates he does not recognize them in the tribal grouping proposed by Tateoka[76] and further discussed in a later paper.[77] This tribe is rather doubtfully retained by Parodi[59] under his Phragmitoideae, a modification of Avdulov's Phragmitiformes retained by Prat. Stebbins and Crampton place the Ehrharteae under the Oryzoideae, though they state that since the genera of the tribes they include in this subfamily are poorly represented in temperate North America their arrangement is subject to reconsideration because of the relationship with the Bambusoideae. Tateoka on the other hand prefers to place this tribe in his Arundoideae, for which Stebbins and Crampton use the name Arundinoideae, a change made for orthographic reasons, representing only a part of Avdulov's heterogeneous group, Phragmitiformes. The Arundinoideae is typified by the tribe Arundineae which in turn is typified by the genus *Arundo* and which also includes *Phragmites*.

Oryzoideae of Parodi[58] has priority over both Olyroideae of Pilger[61] and Pharoideae of Beetle,[6] even if there were not additional nomenclatural objections in the latter case, and it is accepted by Stebbins and Crampton. In his latest arrangement Parodi places the tribes Olyreae and Phareae in the Bambusoideae and it is obvious that a general satisfactory grouping of the taxa involved has not yet been reached.

These examples, without further delving into the comparable situation among other tribes of the family, are enough to illustrate the present situation with its confusion and its separation into the sphere of inter-relationships based on phylogenetical affinities and that of arrangement for purposes of identification and reference. The great problem is to what degree and in what manner should the various techniques and their resultant data be combined. Gilmour,[31] in discussing the influence of evolutionary thought on taxonomy, distinguishes between the search for a natural system based on phylogeny and one made possible by phylogeny. His point is that the processes of evolution are so complex and at present so little understood that while the second type of system is a reasonable goal the first is an impossibility. Accepting his view that a phylogenetical 'natural system' in the ultimate sense cannot be realized, one is lead to ask why this insistence on a 'natural system'? Walters[82] has recently written:

> Why should a two-dimensional hierarchical classification be able to express all the complexities of evolution? It is obvious, for example, from the little we know of allopolyploid micro-evolution, that polytopic origin and reticulation can occur, and may occur frequently; and no amount of juggling with the boundaries of taxa can hope to express a fraction of this possible evolutionary complexity alone.

We, therefore, are faced with a situation in which it is essential that research results be expressed in a form that will allow full realization of their potential effect in all related fields. In so far as these results can be correlated with normal taxonomic concepts then this course should be followed since these are a well established form of collating knowledge. To this extent at least the experimentalists should employ the correct and orthodox nomenclatural methods. But the position may well be different when the broader matter of whole systems of classification is concerned, since these involve philosophical issues. Walters[82] has also written:

> It seems important for the taxonomist . . . to make a strong plea for the continued recognition of an 'orthodox' morphologically-based taxonomy as providing a general purposes classification, and permitting a wide range of valuable generalisations to be made. In particular he must resist pressure from all specialists to alter radically this framework to suit their particular concern (evolutionary relationship, genetic similarity, 'biological significance'). . . . He should insist that they use special terminology and where necessary special classifications to express their particular interest.

To what extent would such procedure, unless severely limited and disciplined, be really advisable in our present situation? At a time when there are healthy signs of increasing collaboration among workers in diffuse fields, through which we may hope for real progress, would we not run a risk of erecting a new barrier if we were divided into those who used an 'orthodox' and those who employed a 'special' classification with its own esoteric terminology?

It would seem that in so far as search for a classification based on phylogenetical affinities results in a system which promotes advance in other biological fields then such a system must be accepted by the taxonomists with their responsibility for the organization of biological material into recognizable units. But if and where the evolutionary complexities are so great that results do not lend themselves to incorporation into 'orthodox' systems then some method of compromise must be found. It is essential that a means be provided by which ideas, concepts, and taxonomic entities can be clearly and unambiguously discussed, both within and between fields of specialist endeavour. If tabulation of results can be facilitated by the preparation of special treatments for specific purposes – whether these be for cytogenetics, biochemistry, ecology, anatomy, or physiology – let us ensure that the categories used are adequately defined and documented. The present fluid state in grass systematics is not wholly due to the wealth of new information; it is also due to poor nomenclatural practice and irresponsible manipulation of inadequately defined concepts. We await a new and comprehensive treatment, to the generic level, of the family on a world scale. In the meantime there is much that taxonomists and their colleagues in related fields can and should do to clarify the general issues.

REFERENCES

[1] Abele, K. (1959). Cytological studies in the genus *Danthonia*. *Trans. Roy. Soc. Aust.*, **82**, 163–73.

[2] Al Aish, M. (1956). The effect of isopropyl-N-phenol carbamate on the germination of grass seeds and its bearing upon systematics of the Gramineae. Ph.D. Thesis Univ. Texas (*non vidi*).

[3] Al Aish, M., and Brown, W. V. (1958). Grass germination responses to I.P.C. and classification. *Amer. J. Bot.*, **45**, 16–23.

[4] Avdulov, N. P. (1931). Karyo-systematische Untersuchungen der Familie Gramineen. *Bull. Appl. Bot.*, suppl. 44 (*non vidi*).

[5] Barnhart, J. H. (1895). Family nomenclature. *Bull. Torr. Bot. Cl.*, **22**, 1–24.

[6] Beetle, A. A. (1955). The four subfamilies of the Gramineae. *Bull. Torr. Bot. Cl.*, **82**, 196–7.

[7] Bentham, G. (1881). Notes on Gramineae. *J. Linn. Soc. Bot.*, **19**, 14–134.

[8] Bentham G., and Hooker, J. D. (1883). *Genera Plantarum*, Vol. 3, part 2, 1074–1215.

[9] Bews, J. G. (1929). *The World's Grasses. Their differentation, distribution, economics, and ecology*. Longmans Green & Co. London.

[10] Brock, R. D., and Brown, J. A. M. (1960). Cytotaxonomy of Australian *Danthonia*. *Aust. J. Bot.*, **9**, 62–91.

[11] Brown, R. (1810). *Produmus Florae Novae Hollandiae (facsimile edition*, 1960), p. 169.

[12] Brown, R. (1814). General remarks Geographical and Systematical on the Botany of Terra Australia, pp. 580–3 (app. to Matthew Flinders, *Voyage to Terra Australis*.

[13] Brown, R. (1838). Observations on *Ataxia horsfieldii* (Bennett and Brown, *Plantae Javanicae Rariores*, p. 8).

[14] Brown, W. V. (1958). Leaf anatomy in grass systematics. *Bot. Gaz.*, **119**, 170–8.

[15] Brown, W. V., Heimsch, C., and Emery, W. H. P. (1957). The organization of the grass shoot apex and systematics. *Amer. J. Bot.*, **44** (7), 590–5.

[16] Burbidge, N. T. (1941). A revision of the Australian species of *Enneapogon* Desv. *Proc. Linn. Soc. Lond.*, 153rd Sess., 52–91.

[17] Calder, J. W. (1937). A cytological study of some New Zealand species and varieties of *Danthonia*. *J. Linn. Soc. Lond. Bot.*, **51**, 1–9.

[18] De Wet, J. M. J. (1953). Nucleoli numbers in *Danthonia* polyploids. *Cytologia*, **18**, 229–34.

[19] De Wet, J. M. J. (1954). The genus *Danthonia* in grass phylogeny. *Amer. J. Bot.*, **41**, 204–11.

[20] De Wet, J. M. J. (1954). Stomatal size as cytological criterion in *Danthonia*. *Cytologia*, **19**, 176–81.

[21] De Wet, J. M. J. (1956). Leaf anatomy and phylogeny in the tribe Danthonieae. *Amer. J. Bot.*, **43**, 175–82.

[22] De Wet, J. M. J. (1960). Leaf anatomy of six South African grass genera. *Bothalia*, **7**, 299–301.

[23] De Wet, J. M. J. (1960). Leaf anatomy and morphology in South African species of *Danthonia*. *Bothalia*, **7**, 303–10.

[24] Doroszewska, A. (1961). A comparative study on *Dactylis slovenica* Domin and *D. glomerata* L. *Act. Soc. Bot. Pol.*, **30**, 775–82.

[25] Dumortier, B. C. (1823). Observations sur les Graminées de la flore Belgique.

[26] Duval-Jouve, M. J. (1865). Variations parallèles des types congénères. *Bull. Soc. Bot. Fr.*, **12**, 196 (*non vidi*).

[27] Duval-Jouve, M. J. (1875). Histotaxie des feuilles des Graminées. *Ann. Sc. Nat. Bot.*, ser. 6, **1**, 294–374 (*non vidi*).

[28] Endlicher, S. (1836). *Genera Plantarum*, Vol. 1, 77–109.

[29] Engler, A., and Prantl, K. (1887–1915). *Die Naturlichen Pflanzenfamilien.*

[30] Fairbrothers, D. E., and Johnson, M. A. (1961). The precipitin reaction as an indicator of relationship in some grasses (paper presented at Symposium on Natural classification of the Gramineae, IXth International Bot. Congr. Montreal 1959). *Recent Advances in Botany*, Vol.1, pp. 116–20.

[31] Gilmour, J. S. L. (1961). Taxonomy. *Contemporary Botanical Thought*, pp. 27–45. Oliver and Boyd, Edinburgh.

[32] Grob, S. (1896). Beitrage zur Anatomie des Epidermis der Gramineenblatter. *Biblio. Bot.*, **7**, 1–122.

[33] Hackel, E. (1887). Gramineae. In Engler and Prantl, *Die Pflanzenf*, II. teil 2, Abt.

[34] Hackel, E. (1889). Andropogoneae. In A. and C. Decandolle, *Monogr. Phan.*, **6**, 716.

[35] Hartley, W. (1950). The global distribution of tribes of the Gramineae in relation to historical and environmental factors. *Aust. J. Agric. Res.*, **1**, 355–73.

[36] Hartley, W. (1958). Studies in the origin, evolution, and distribution of the Gramineae. I. The tribe Andropogoneae. *Aust. J. Bot.*, **6**, 116–28.

[37] Hartley, W. (1958). Studies in the origin, evolution, and distribution of the Gramineae. II. The Tribe Paniceae. *Aust. J. Bot.*, **6**, 343–57.

[38] Hartley, W., and Slater, C. (1960). Studies in the origin, evolution, and distribution of the Gramineae. III. The tribes of the subfamily Eragrostoideae. *Aust. J. Bot.*, **8**, 256–76.

[39] Hitchcock, A. S. (1935). *Manual of the grasses of the United States.* U.S.D.A. Misc. Publ. 200.

[40] Hitchcock, A. S. (1951). *Manual of the grasses of the United States* (Second edition revised by Agnes Chase). U.S.D.A. Misc. Publ. 200.

[41] Hooker, J. D. (1896–7). *Flora of British India*, Vol. 7, 1–2.

[42] Hubbard, C. E. (1934). Gramineae. In Hutchinson, *Families of flowering plants.* Also as reprinted in 2nd ed. of the same (1959).

[43] Hubbard, C. E. (1940). Orthoclada africana C.E. Hubb. Hook. Ic. Plant. t. 3419.

[44] Hubbard, C. E. (1948). The genera of British grasses. In Hutchinson, *British flowering plants*, pp. 284–348.

[45] Jacques-Felix, H. (1955). La systematique des Graminées de Pilger et le principe de la sous-famille chez les Graminées. *J. D'Agric. trop.*, **11**, 207–11.

[46] Jussieu, A. L. (1789). *Genera Plantarum.*

[47] Komarov (Ed.) V. (1934). *Flora of the U.S.S.R.*, Vol. 2.

[48] Krause, E. H. L. (1909). Ein Besserungsversuch am System der Gramineen. *Beih Bot. Zentralbl.*, **25**, 421–89. (*non vidi*).

[49] Kunth, C. S. (1833). *Enumeratio Plantarum* 1. (Agrostographia synoptica sive enumeratio Graminearum).

[50] Kunth, C. S. (1835). *Enumeratio Plantarum* 2. (Agrostographie synoptica sive enumeratio Graminearum), supplement to volume 1.

[51] Lamarck, J. B., and De Candolle, A. P. (1805). *Flore Francaise*, 3rd edn. Vol. **3**, pp. 32–4.

[52] Lanjouw (Ed.) J. (1956). *International Code of Botanical Nomenclature. Int. Bur. for Plant Taxonomy and Nomenclature.   Utrecht.*

[53] Link, H. F. (1827). *Hortus regius botanicus Beroliensis*, **1**, 62.

[54] Linnaeus, C. (1753). *Species Plantarum*, 1st edn.

[55] Linnaeus, C. (1754). *Genera Plantarum*, 5th edn.

[56] Mez, C. (1926). Sero-diagnostik Bedeutung. *Bot. Arkiv*, **15**, 1.

[57] Palisot de Beauvois (1812). *Essai d'une nouvelle agrostographie.* Paris.

[58] Parodi, L. R. (1946). *Gramineas Bonariensis*, 4th edn.

[59] Parodi, L. R. (1961). La taxonomia de las Gramineae Argentinas a la luz de las investigationes mas recientes. (Symposium on the natural classification of the Gramineae, IXth International Bot. Congr. Montreal, 1959). *Recent Advances in Botany*, Vol. 1, 125–9.

[60] Phillipson, W. R. (1935). A grass with spiral phyllotaxy – *Micraira subulifolia. Kew Bull.* (1935), pp. 324–6.

[61] Pilger, R. (1954). Das system der Gramineae. *Bot. Jahrb.*, **76**, 281–384.

[62] Pilger, R. (1956). Gramineae II. Unterfamilien Micrairoideae, Eragrostoideae, Oryzoideae, Olyroideae. (Engler and Prantl, *Nat. Pflanzenf.*, aufl. 2, Bd. 14d.)

[63] Potztal, E. (1953). Ueber die Anatomie von *Micraira subulifolia. Bot. Jahrb.*, **76**, 134–8.

[64] Potztal, E. (1954). Die Anatomie der Gräser und ihre Bedeutung für die Systematik. *Ber. deutsch. bot. Gesellsch.*, **66**.

[65] Prat, H. (1931). L'epiderme des Graminées; étude anatomique et systematique. *Ann. Sc. Nat. Bot.*, **14**, 117–324.

[66] Prat, H. (1936). La systématique des Graminées. *Ann. Sc. Nat. Bot.*, **18**, 165–258.

[67] Prat, H. (1960). Vera une classification naturelle des Graminées. *Bull. Soc. Bot. Fr.*, **107**, 32–79.

[68] Reeder, J. R. (1953). Affinities of the grass genus *Beckmannia* Host. *Bull. Torr. Bot. Cl.*, **80**, 187–96.

[69] Reeder, J. R. (1957). The embryo in grass systematics. *Amer. J. Bot.*, **44**, 756–68.

[70] Reeder, J. R., and Maltzahn, K. von (1953). Taxonomic significance of root-hair development in the Gramineae. *Proc. Nat. Ac. Sc.*, **39**, 593–8.

[71] Row, H. C., and Reeder, J. R. (1957). Root-hair development as evidence of relationships among genera of Gramineae. *Amer. J. Bot.*, **44**, 596–601.

[72] Stapf, O. (1917–34). *Flora of Tropical Africa*, Vol. 9. Gramineae (continued by C. E. Hubbard).

[73] Stebbins, G. L. (1956). Taxonomy and the evolution of genera with special reference to the family Gramineae. *Evolution*, **10**, 235–45.

[74] Stebbins, G. L. (1956). Cytogenetics and the evolution of the grass family. *Amer. J. Bot.*, **43** (10), 890–905.

[75] Stebbins, G. L., and Crampton, B. (1961). A suggested revision of the grass genera of temperate North America. (Symposium on the natural classification of the Gramineae, IXth International Bot. Congr. Montreal, 1959). *Recent Advances in Botany*, Vol. 1, pp. 133–45.

[76] Tateoka, T. (1957). Miscellaneous papers on the phylogeny of Poaceae. 10: Proposition of a new phylogenetic system of Poaceae. *J. Jap. Bot.*, **32**, 275–87.

[77] Tateoka, R. (1960). Cytology in Grass Systematics: a critical review. *The Nucleus*, **3**, 81–110.

[78] Tournefort, J. P. (1694). *Elémens de Botanique*, 3 vols. Lyon.

[79] Trinius, C. B. (1820). *Fundamenta Agrostographiae*. Vienna.

[80] Trinius, C. B. (1824). *De graminibus unifloris et sesquifloris*. Petrograd.

[81] Van Tieghem, P. (1897). Morphologie de l'embryon et de la platule chez les Graminées et les Cyperacées. *Ann. Sc. Nat. Bot. ser.*, 8, **3**, 259–309.

[82] Walters, S. M. (1962). Generic and specific concepts in the European flora. *Preslia*, **34**, 207–26.

[83] Wettstein, R. (1935). Handbuch der Systematischen Botanik. 4th edn. Leipzig.

[84] Willdenow, C. (1805). Species Plantarum (4th edn. of Linnaeus, *Species Plantarum*). Berlin.

[85] Yakovlev, M. S. (1950). The structure of endosperm and embryo in cereals as a systematic feature. *Trud. Bot. Inst. Akad.*, **1**, 121–218 (*non vidi*).

3

The Distribution of the Grasses

By W. Hartley

Global and Regional Distribution of the Grass Family

THE grasses are one of the largest families of flowering plants in number of genera and species. Of an estimated total of 12,500 genera of flowering plants, 600 or 4·8 per cent are grasses, and of an estimated total of 225,000 species, 7500 or 3·3 per cent are grasses.[11] On a generic basis only the Compositae and the Orchidaceae, with 1000 and 700 genera respectively, are larger than the Gramineae, while in number of species the Leguminosae and Rubiaceae as well as the Compositae and Orchidaceae are larger. Since generic limits are rather arbitrarily drawn in the Gramineae, and have been the subject of some dispute among taxonomists, the most useful indication of the size of the family is given by the number of species. While the number, both of genera and species, has been increased substantially by more recent work, it is unlikely that this would have affected the relative position of the family.

These figures for family size do not fully reflect either the very wide distribution of the grasses, or their ecological significance.

Geographically, the grasses are ubiquitous, and the grass family is truly cosmopolitan. Grasses occur in all continents – including Antarctica – and there are no significant lacunae in the distribution pattern. Indeed it would be hard to find any area of substantial size from which grasses are absent, except those which are too barren or cold to support the growth of any higher plants. These characteristics are not fully shared by any other family, although the Cyperaceae, Ranunculaceae, Rosaceae, Leguminosae, Scrophulariaceae, and Compositae approach the Gramineae in overall range.[28]

Grasses are present in almost all types of vegetation, including not only the prairies and steppes where they are dominant, but also temperate and tropical forests, deserts, and swamps. Any account of the distribution of the grasses which is confined to consideration of the 'grasslands' would fail to reveal some of the most significant features of the family, for the grasses as a family are outstanding in their ability to adapt themselves to diverse ecological conditions.

This ability to adapt is surprising because both morphologically and biologically the grasses form a fairly homogeneous group. The limits of the family are well defined, and the Gramineae are not very closely related to other plant families, except, perhaps, the Cyperaceae. Floral characters are similar throughout the family, a feature which has led the grasses to be regarded as a 'difficult' group from the viewpoint of the taxonomist. With the exception of the bamboos, they are all herbaceous with relatively little variation in growth form. The species are virtually all wind-pollinated or cleistogamous, and hence their distribution is not dependent upon the presence of insect pollinators.

It is this combination of wide geographical and ecological distribution, with relative morphological and biological uniformity, which makes the grasses of special interest to students of plant geography and evolution.

As indicated above, a world map of the grass family is almost indistinguishable from a map of global land surfaces. However, such a map does not show if major differences occur in the relative floristic importance of the Gramineae in the Angiosperm flora of different regions, and it is of interest to consider whether this is the case.

Von Weihe[29] has published data on the percentage of grass species in 87 regional floras, mainly at high northern latitudes but including others ranging southward to the latitude of Morocco and Egypt. The percentages of grass species vary from 4·9 per cent to 26·1 per cent, 51 of the 87 being within the range of 6–14 per cent. Weihe shows that the percentage of grass species decreases in moving from high to low latitudes, at least north of 60° N, and suggests that this change may be related to progressive temperature changes. It is, however, difficult to separate any effect due to temperature from that associated with size of flora, since the total number of species in the floras covered also increases in moving from north to south. Table 3.1, based on the data given by Weihe, shows clearly the relationship between the size of the total flora and the percentage of grass species.

TABLE 3.1

Relationship Between Size of Flora and Percentage of Grasses at High Northern Latitudes (Data from Weihe [29])

Total no. of Angiosperm spp. in flora	Range of percentages of grass spp.		No. of floras in group
	Min.	Max.	
< 100 spp.	14·1	26·1	13
100– 150 spp.	10·3	21·0	16
151– 200 spp.	8·9	16·4	17
201–1000 spp.	9·2	12·8	9
1001–2000 spp.	7·8	9·7	13
2001–4000 spp.	7·0	9·7	9
>4000 spp.	4·9	9·0	10

There is a progressive fall in the percentage of grasses with increasing size of flora. All the regions with fewer than 100 species of flowering plants have more than 14 per cent of grasses, while on the other hand low percentages of grasses (below 7 per cent) occur only in regions with a total flora of more than 4000 spp. Floras of comparable size tend to have similar percentages of grasses, regardless of the geographical location and the climate of the regions to which they relate.

This relationship between percentage of grasses and size of flora appears to be a fairly general one, and is supported by data from other parts of the world, tropical as well as temperate. Thus, the cold Aleutian Islands (51°–55° N) and the tropical Curaçao group (11°–12° N), with 443 and 460 species of flowering plants respectively, each have 12·4 per cent of grasses.[20, 24] Similarly, the British Isles (1570 spp.) and Crete (1425 spp.) have respectively 8·1 per cent and 8·4 per cent of grasses.[6, 27]

There are, of course, many exceptions to this general relationship between the percentage of grasses and the size of the flora. In some regions there are more grasses than would be expected from the size of the total flora. Alberta and Arizona, with respectively 1530 and 3292 species of higher plants, have 11·3 per cent and 11·2 per cent of grasses. The flora of Buenos Aires and environs, with a total of 1349 species, is particularly rich in grasses, these numbering 234 or 17·4 per cent of the total.[5] Such high percentages occur predominantly in the floras of continental areas with few endemic species, including especially closely-settled regions.

On the other hand, relatively low percentages of grasses occur in regional floras with a high proportion of endemic species, including some island groups. This is well illustrated by the data of Turrill[27] on the flora of the Balkan Peninsula: a region of high endemism. Several floras of this region – Greece, Thessaly, Albania, Northern Macedonia, Athos, Northern Bulgaria, Rodhopi, and Hercegovina – have fewer grasses than would be expected from the relationship to total flora shown in Table 3.1. All these are regions with a high proportion of Balkan endemic species. Only Corfu, with few Balkan endemics in the flora, has *more* grasses than would be expected.

The paucity of grasses in floras of high endemism suggests that endemic species (i.e. those of restricted range) are relatively rarer in the Gramineae than in most other families of flowering plants. This conclusion is supported by the fact that, in almost all the Floras and floristic lists examined, the percentage of grass species is substantially higher than the percentage (3·3 per cent) for the world as a whole. This can only be explained by the fact that, compared with the generality of flowering plants, the species of grasses tend to be more wide spreading, with fewer local endemics. Their relative abundance in regional floras is not, however, greatly affected by geography and climate.

While, as already noted, grasses occur in varying degree in almost all types of vegetation, it is in those major vegetation types broadly classified as 'grassland' and 'savannah', that the grass family is of the greatest ecological significance. In these areas grasses are normally dominant, and give a characteristic aspect to the landscape.

Grasslands are very widely distributed throughout the world, and, in the aggregate, cover vast areas. They occur most typically in the interior of the great continental land masses, ranging northward to about 55° N in Asia and North America, and southward to 40° S in South America. Treeless prairies, steppes, and pampas predominate in the temperate regions, and are replaced by savannahs, with varying proportions of trees and shrubs, in the tropics and sub-tropics. They form the subject of numerous books and papers, and it is only possible to refer here to some points of interest in connection with their botanical composition.

It is noteworthy that the ecological dominance of the grasses in grassland vegetation is rarely, if ever, matched by a corresponding floristic predominance. In any considerable area of grassland it is usually found that a limited number of grass species are associated with a relatively large number of non-grass species, even though the latter may constitute only a small part of the ground cover. The percentage of grass species in the flora of forest vegetation may be as high as that in grassland vegetation, and does not bear any well-marked or universal relationship to the density of the three cover. This is illustrated by the data of Moore[21] on the floristic composition of various climax communities in the vegetation of the south-eastern Riverina, New South Wales.

TABLE 3.2

Grasses in Vegetation Types of the Riverina District, New South Wales, Australia (Data from Moore [21])

Alliance	Subformation	No. of species		Percentage of grass species
		Total	Grasses	
Eucalyptus dealbata	Dry sclerophyll forest	175	26	14·9
E. macrorrhyncha – E. rossii	Dry sclerophyll forest	85	17	20·0
E. camaldulensis	Closed swamp/sclerophyll forest and savannah woodland	65	19	29·2
E. woollsiana	Tall woodland	289	57	19·7
E. albens	Tall woodland	207	40	19·3
E. largiflorens	Savannah woodland	48	11	22·9
Acacia pendula – Atriplex nummularia	Shrub woodland	170	30	17·6

Excluding the *Eucalyptus camaldulensis* alliance, which occurs in distinct structural forms in different habitats, the percentage of grass species all fall within the range of 14·9–22·9 per cent although the tree canopy ranges from open to closed and the herbaceous stratum from continuous to discontinuous. It might be noted also that the relationship between the percentage of grass species and size of flora discussed above is again evident; those alliances with a total of less than 100 species all have 20 per cent or more of grasses, while those with more than 100 species have less than 20 per cent.

The picture which has been presented of relative uniformity of grass distribution, assessed in terms of the percentage frequency of grasses in the flora of different regions and of different vegetation types, is a purely floristic one. Ecologically the situation is very different. It is a far cry indeed from tropical forests where grasses may constitute less than 0·5 per cent of the ground cover – and this mainly where some natural or artificial breakage has occurred in the tree canopy – to the prairies and pampas where grasses may make up 99·5 per cent of the ground cover. In the former the grasses appear to have little obvious ecological significance; in the latter they are dominant and determine both the aspect and the economics of the vegetation.

The ecological factors associated with the occurrence of 'natural' grassland have been the subject of much dispute, and it appears certain that the relative importance of the different factors varies in different regions and in different types of grassland. While climatic factors are undoubtedly of some importance, they appear to be of significance mainly in determining the limits within which grassland may occur when other factors are favourable to its development. These limits are very broad indeed, both as regard temperature and rainfall, and there are few regions of the world, except those which are very cold or very arid, in which grasslands may not occur. Whether grasslands are in fact developed within these broad limits is determined by many other factors, including microclimate (especially as affected by local topography), soil differences, and the effects of fire and grazing. Since these factors operate differently from place to place, and indeed from time to time, it is hardly surprising that no very satisfactory general relationship has been determined between climate and grassland development, and it is questionable whether tropical grasslands, at least, can be regarded as climatically controlled.[22]

The distribution of grasslands in relation to environment factors and the effects of grazing on grassland are more fully discussed in Chapters 11 and 13.

The Distribution of Various Grass Taxa

The distribution of the grass tribes in relation to evolution and climate

The many genera of grasses are grouped together in tribes which in turn are grouped in a small number of subfamilies. The tribal and subfamily groupings have been the subject of much study in recent years in an effort to attain a more natural classification, and much progress has been made as shown in Chapter 2. Although there are still major differences of opinion about the relationships between tribes, there is a fair measure of agreement among taxonomists about the limits of the tribes themselves.

As presently conceived, the grass family is made up of a few large tribes, each with many genera, and of many more small tribes, some of which are monogeneric. The large tribes are of special interest from the viewpoint of plant geography as each of them has a wide distribution, but with definite climatic limits. Some are predominantly or exclusively tropical or subtropical in distribution, others are mainly developed in cold regions at high latitudes or altitudes. Thus the tribes of the grasses present especially favourable material for study of the relationships between distribution and climate. This was recognized some years ago by Bews[2] who, in his book *The World's Grasses*, discussed the ecology and distribution of the grasses in relation to their taxonomy. This book remains a mine of information on the subject, but the author was handicapped by the fact that publication of his book preceded recent work leading to a clearer definition of tribal limits, and he did not always distinguish clearly the floristic and ecological aspects of distribution.

Studies of the distribution of some of the larger tribes of grasses have been made by the present author, using the percentage of species of the tribe concerned in the total grass flora of any locality or region as the basis for mapping its distribution. An example of a map constructed on this basis is given in Figure 3.1, which shows the distribution of the tribe Andropogoneae on a world basis. The Andropogoneae is one of the larger grass tribes, some species of which are dominant in savannah and other types of grassland.

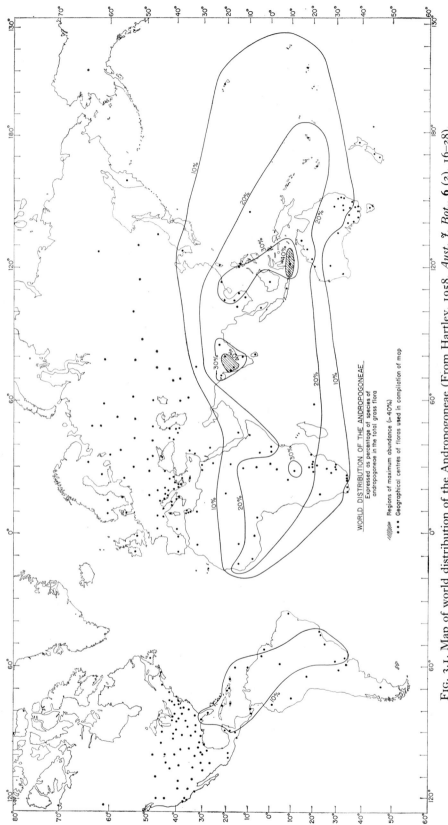

WORLD DISTRIBUTION OF THE ANDROPOGONEAE
Expressed as percentage of species of
andropogoneae in the total grass flora

///// Regions of maximum abundance (> 40%)

••• Geographical centres of floras used in compilation of map

FIG. 3.1. Map of world distribution of the Andropogoneae (From Hartley, 1958, *Aust. J. Bot.*, **6** (2), 16–28).

As is readily seen from the map, the tribe is predominantly tropical and subtropical in distribution, being poorly represented or absent from the temperate and cold regions. The distribution pattern is clearly defined, with centres of high relative specific concentration in parts of south-eastern Asia, India, and (to a lesser degree) central Africa. Closer study of the distribution pattern shows that the centres of high relative specific concentration occur in warm regions with high midsummer rainfall, that is in regions of monsoonal climate. This relationship between distribution and climate is shown not only by a comparison between Figure 3.1 and world maps of temperature and rainfall but also by a detailed study of grass distribution and climate along a longitudinal transect from Lapland in the north to South Africa in the south (*vide* 15). The relationship is modified, rather than substantially changed, by the effect of historical factors, as there is evidence to support the view that the Andropogoneae may have originated in tropical Africa or elsewhere in the Old World tropics, and spread to the American continent at a later stage of evolutionary development.

Distribution patterns showing a similar relationship to climatic factors have been demonstrated for other tribes and subfamilies of grasses, although the climatic factors concerned differ in each instance.[12,16,17] Thus the Paniceae attain their highest relative specific differentiation in regions of high winter temperature and high annual, rather than seasonal, rainfall. The grasses of the subfamily Eragrostoideae occur mainly in arid regions with high winter temperatures and summer or nonseasonal rainfall incidence.

The relationship between distribution and climate is less evident in the smaller tribes, or is concealed by the effect of other factors. Thus, the species of the tribe Oryzeae occur characteristically in marshes and other moist habitats, both in the tropical and temperate regions. Although species of this tribe comprise only about 0·6 per cent of all grasses,[2] they constitute 12 per cent and 25 per cent of the aquatic grasses of eastern U.S.A. and Amazonia respectively (data from[3,10]). Most of the smaller and especially the monogeneric tribes have a restricted geographical range, perhaps indicating a more recent origin, in marked contrast to the sub-cosmopolitan distribution of the larger tribes.

It is interesting to note that there is little or no relationship between the distribution of the grass tribes, as mapped on a floristic basis, and their ecological significance. The regions in which the Andropogoneae reach their greatest relative specific concentration, are regions of forest rather than grassland vegetation. On the other hand, three species of the tribe – the big and little bluestems (*Andropogon gerardi* and *A. scoparius*), and Indian grass (*Sorghastrum nutans*) – are, or were, dominant over vast areas of North American prairie in which the tribe is floristically poorly represented (cf. Figure 3.1). In regions such as Clinton County, Iowa, where species of Andropogoneae form only 5 per cent of the grass flora, two or three species of the tribe may originally have made up more than 80 per cent of the total vegetation cover.

In other regions, the dominants of the prairie vegetation are species of the smaller tribes, such as the Stipeae and the Hordeae, which constitute only a small percentage of the total grass flora of the regions concerned.

The factors which determine the ability of a species to become dominant in grassland offer a fascinating and little-explored field for study, but it is evident that they are quite different from those which account for the floristic success of the tribe to which the species belong.

The grass genus and its distribution

Discussion of the distribution of grass genera is complicated by different viewpoints among taxonomists regarding generic limits. Some of the very large genera, such as *Andropogon* and *Panicum*, have been split into smaller units by many botanists, while being retained by others. Nevertheless, it is possible to recognize the broad features of generic distribution.

The grass family includes a high proportion of cosmopolitan and sub-cosmopolitan genera, however these may be defined. Adopting somewhat different criteria, the following data are given by two authorities:

TABLE 3.3

Cosmopolitan and Sub-Cosmopolitan Genera

Grasses	Total flowering plants	Percentage of grasses	Source of data
52	403	12·9	Szymkiewiez [26]
21	130	16·2	Good [11]

As mentioned at the beginning of this chapter, grasses constitute about 4·8 per cent of the total number of genera of flowering plants, in contrast to the much higher proportion of widely distributed genera shown in this table. The cosmopolitan and sub-cosmopolitan grass genera listed by these authors include some which have been distributed through human agency as weeds, crop plants, or miscellaneous adventives. They also include others which would be excluded as a result of changed generic concepts. The lists nevertheless demonstrate the relative abundance of widely-distributed genera in the Gramineae.

As might be expected, the distribution patterns of the larger and more cosmopolitan genera bear some resemblance to those of the cosmopolitan tribes previously discussed. Figure 3.2, taken from Hartley,[18] shows the world distribution of the genus *Poa*, mapped on a similar basis to that used for the Andropogoneae in Figure 3.1.

Here again there is a close relationship between distribution and climate. The genus shows highest relative specific differentiation in regions of high latitude and high altitude. It is absent or rare in the tropics, except in mountainous regions with cool summers, and there is a close association between the occurrence of high percentage frequencies of species of *Poa* and cool summer temperatures. Climatic factors other than temperature appear to have little influence on the distribution pattern.

Among the less widely distributed grass genera, many types of distribution pattern occur, roughly comparable to those found in other families of flowering plants. In general, these distribution patterns reflect historical rather than

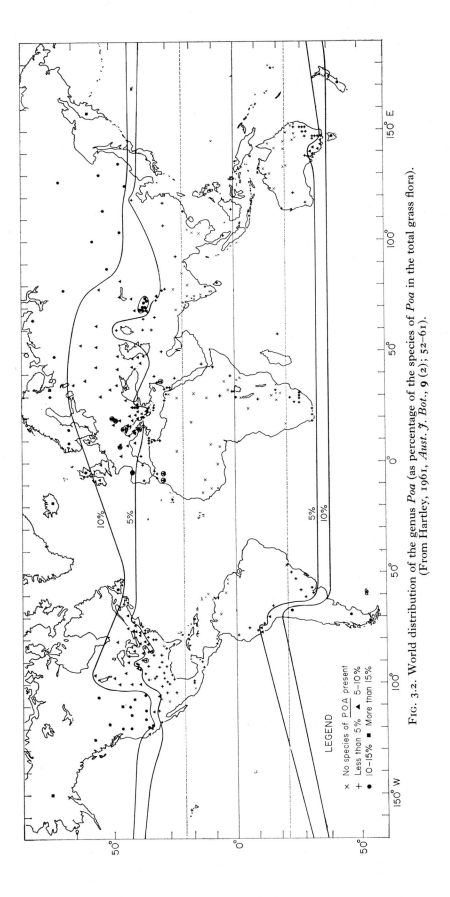

LEGEND
× No species of POA present
+ Less than 5%   ▲ 5–10%
● 10–15%   ■ More than 15%

FIG. 3.2. World distribution of the genus *Poa* (as percentage of the species of *Poa* in the total grass flora). (From Hartley, 1961, *Aust. J. Bot.*, **9** (2); 52–61).

climatic influence, since, in marked contrast to *Poa*, the genera have not reached all parts of the world where the climate is suitable for their development.

The distribution may be continuous or discontinuous, interesting examples of the latter being *Amphibromus*, *Distichlis*, and *Leptoloma* which occur in North and/or South America and in Australia or New Zealand.[25] The data of Good[11] (appendix B) do not, however, suggest that discontinuous genera are relatively more common in the Gramineae than in other families of flowering plants, except possibly in the tropical regions.

While there are many grass genera of very restricted distribution, such endemic genera appear to be relatively less common in the Gramineae than in most other families of flowering plants. Most grasses show good capacity for dispersal, and endemic genera occur mainly in regions isolated by major geographical barriers.

The ecological aspects of grass distribution at the generic level have been fully discussed by Bews.[2] While some of the smaller genera of grasses are associated with a particular habitat or vegetation type, most of the larger ones are not so restricted. Thus, species of *Poa* and *Festuca* occur in woodlands, marshes, wet meadows, dry pastures, and sandy seashores, as well as in mountain meadows and on arid ranges. The limitations to the distribution of large individual genera are, in most instances, climatic or geographic rather than ecological, and species have evolved which are able to occupy most of the ecological niches which exist within the overall limits of climatic tolerance.

Patterns of species distribution

Inevitably, as we move from a discussion of the distribution of tribes and genera to that of species, it becomes increasingly difficult to generalize about distribution patterns. Each species has developed through different evolutionary channels, in a different location, and in response to a different complex of environmental pressures. It is, therefore, all the more remarkable that some of the features of grass distribution which have already been discussed are still evident at the specific level.

As with the tribes and genera, many species of grasses have a very wide distribution. It has been claimed (cf. Good[11]) that the common reed, *Phragmites communis*, is 'the most widely distributed of all Angiosperms', being present in marshy places in almost all parts of the world. Other aquatic or moisture-loving species of very wide distribution cited by this author include the grasses *Glyceria fluitans* and *Phalaris arundinacea*. Grasses also figure prominently in his lists of wide-ranging but non-cosmopolitan species. While some of these 'wide' species might perhaps be better regarded as made up of several vicarious species, each of more restricted distribution, it is evident that widely-distributed species are relatively common in the grass family.

Many of these grasses owe their wide distribution largely to the effects of man and his grazing animals. These include species of *Bromus, and Cenchrus, Cynodon dactylon, Digitaria marginata*, and *D. sanguinalis, Echinochloa colonum*, and *E. crus-galli, Paspalum distichum, Poa annua, Setaria verticillata, Tragus racemosus*, and species of *Vulpia*. Many others could be added to this list, the distribution being now so wide that it is difficult to decide how far they may fairly be regarded as indigenous in any particular region.

At the other extreme, local endemics of very restricted range are relatively rare among the grasses. As previously noted, the flora of the Balkan Peninsula is particularly rich in endemic species, 26·9 per cent of all the flowering plants which occur there being confined to the Peninsula. However, only 33 of the 358 species of grasses, or 9·2 per cent are Balkan endemics.[27]

The generally wide range of individual grass species can perhaps be attributed mainly to the possession of good dispersal mechanisms which have enabled them to spread widely both with and without the aid of man and his grazing animals. The wide range also suggests that in many parts of the family at least the rate of dispersal is relatively rapid in relation to that of speciation. Thus, grasses are frequently able to spread widely and to occupy most of the habitats to which they are adapted before they are displaced by newly evolved species. Displacement, when it does occur, may again be a relatively rapid process, the old species being replaced by the new one throughout the whole or a major part of its range. It is then possible to understand the close relationship between tribal and generic distribution – *mapped on the basis of relative specific frequency* – and present climate. Within any region of relatively stable climate new grass species may develop and replace related ones without necessarily changing either the total number of species of the tribe or genus concerned in the region and without affecting its relative specific frequency. Speciation may proceed quickly in some taxa and slowly in others, without disturbing the relationship between distribution and climate, provided that dispersal is rapid. Similarly, in a region of changing climate, the capacity for rapid dispersal possessed by the grasses will enable existing species from surrounding regions as well as new ones to invade and occupy the changed habitats and to create a new floristic balance in accordance with the changed climate. With these postulates it is evident that the distribution of the tribes and genera of the grasses on the basis used, must be related to the present climates and does not show the effect of previous climatic changes.

It is of some interest to consider the distribution patterns of the grass species which occur along the 'climatic frontiers' of the tribes to which they belong. Such species might be local endemics which have developed in pockets of isolation around the boundary and which differ in their climatic adaptation from that which is characteristic of the tribe. Alternatively they might be older species which have been pushed out to the margin by the competition of more aggressive new species or as a result of climatic changes.

The limited evidence available suggests that the latter is the more common situation. Thus, as has been indicated above, the tribe Andropogoneae reaches its highest relative specific concentration in monsoonal climates with high summer rainfall. Species of the tribe are relatively rare in other climatic zones, and usually occur only in areas where the microclimate has been changed as a result of settlement or other human activities. Where species of the tribe do occur in relatively undisturbed habitats in such marginal zones, the species are typically those of wide, and often discontinuous, distribution. An example of this is *Hyparrhenia hirta* which is common in the Mediterranean region,

D

parts of east Africa, and parts of South Africa, i.e. in areas which are marginal to the main zone of Andropogoneae on the African continent. This marginal and highly disjunct distribution pattern suggests that it is a relatively old species which has been pushed out towards the climatic margins of the tribe, rather than a young species in a stage of active evolution leading to an extension of climatic limits. At the specific level, young marginal endemics appear to be comparatively rare in the Gramineae, and the limited evidence available suggests that centrifugal rather than marginal evolution is the more common pattern. This supports the claims made for speciation as a centrifugal process by Brown,[4] which are based entirely on zoological data.

If the overall range limits of grass species are primarily determined by climatic factors, the actual distribution of a species within these very wide limits (and even more its relative abundance) is affected rather by historical, biotic, and edaphic influence. Reference has already been made to some species which occur principally or solely in aquatic habitats, and to others which follow the paths of human settlement as weeds or ruderals. Many other instances could be given of grasses which are associated with particular habitats, including notably those, such as species of *Puccinellia*, *Cutandia*, and *Spartina*, which are halophytic. However, as pointed out by Bews,[2] the halophytic grasses form a somewhat ill-defined group as they are not sharply separated from hygrophilous and psammophilous grasses, and they occur at different levels in different phylogenetic lines.

Many other aspects of the distribution of grass species are discussed elsewhere in this book, with particular reference to the biotic and other factors which influence this distribution.

Grass Distribution as an Index of Environment Comparison

It is possible to compile a composite floristic index for any region, based on the percentages of species of each of the major climatically controlled taxa represented in the grass flora of the region concerned. Since each of the taxa responds differently to climatic factors, such a composite index may be expected to reflect the influence of most or all of the more important climatic factors which are significant for grass distribution. Further, insofar as the distribution patterns of the grass taxa utilized in the compilation of the index are relatively uninfluenced by factors other than climate, the composite index provides a method of comparing environments in different parts of the world which is likely to be of special value in studies of grass distribution, differentiation, and growth.

The 'agrostological index'[13] is a composite index of the type described above. In its compilation the percentage of grasses in each of the tribes Agrosteae, Andropogoneae, Eragrosteae, Festuceae, and Paniceae was calculated from floristic lists and regional floras from many parts of the world. The calculated percentages for each tribe were included in one of ten frequency groups, and the groups in turn were assembled to give the agrostological index for the locality or region concerned. Comparison of the agrostological indices for different localities provides a measure of the similarity of the tribal composition of their grass floras. It was shown that, in general, areas in different parts of the world with identical agrostological indices have similar latitude, climate, and topography, although some exceptions were noted. The index was of use mainly for the comparison of large, geographically separated regions, but could be used for smaller areas where the flora was well-known.

The agrostological index has proved to be a useful tool in the introduction and testing of pasture grasses, and in helping to define those regions of the world which would repay plant exploration in the search for better species and varieties of pasture plants. Its use is, however, limited by the unavailability of reliable floristic data for many parts of the world. For a fuller discussion of these and related problems, reference may be made to Hartley.[19]

At the other extreme from these broad environmental comparisons on a floristic basis, are those which are based on the presence or absence, or the relative frequency, of indicator species associated with particular ecological conditions. Examples of such indicator species are those which occur only or mainly in aquatic habitats, under saline conditions, and so on. Some grasses are included among the species which have proved to be useful indicators of the presence of heavy metal compounds in the soils of the metalliferous regions of the Congo.[8] While such indicator species may have either a broad or restricted geographical range, they are chiefly of value as indicators of the edaphic conditions rather than of the climate.

The naturalized grasses of any region, taken as a group, are of special interest, as they normally reflect the influence of many ecological factors. Partly because of their good dispersal mechanisms, grasses usually form a larger proportion of the exotic flora of a region than of its native flora. Many of these exotic species are very widely distributed as ruderals, while others are specially associated with grazing animals. They are therefore useful indicators of biotic conditions. However, the exotic grass flora of any large region tends to approach the native grass flora in its tribal composition. This is shown by the fact that the agrostological index of a region is not greatly affected by the inclusion or omission of naturalized grass species in its compilation. Where species of Festuceae, for example, are prominent in the indigenous grass flora, they will usually be found to form a high proportion of the exotic grass flora. Some of the smaller tribes, such as the Bromeae, appear to have an unusually high proportion of species which commonly occur as ruderals, and hence to be relatively highly represented in the exotic flora, but these form the exception rather than the rule. There appears to be considerable scope for the further study of the exotic grass flora as an indicator of environmental conditions.

The Major Cultivated Grasses and their Distribution

Discussion of the distribution of naturalized grasses leads on to consideration of the cultivated grasses. These are less dependent for their growth and survival on close adaptation to the natural environment, since this environment may be substantially changed in the cultivation processes. Hence grasses may be found in cultivation well outside the climatic limits of their natural distribution.

It is noteworthy that although sown pastures have been used, both in Europe and in other parts of the world, for some hundreds of years, only a few of the total of perhaps 10,000 grass species which are now known to occur in nature are used on any important scale as cultivated pasture plants. Hartley and Williams[14] estimate the number of such important cultivated pasture grasses as about 40. On a somewhat different basis, Whyte, Moir, and Cooper[30] list 36 grass species as adapted for cultivation in one or other of the main climatic regions. Most of these species have now been sown extensively far beyond their limits of natural distribution, but insofar as these natural limits may still be traced, they show definite regional groupings.

The cultivated pasture grasses occur as wild species in the indigenous flora of three main regions, viz.:

(a) The Eurasian Region, with about 24 of the 40 species listed by Hartley and Williams. This has two sub-regions, which are closely related botanically: (i) The northern Eurasian sub-region (ii) The Mediterranean sub-region;
(b) An East African Region, with 8 species;
(c) A subtropical South American region, with 4 species.

The other parts of the world, including North America, eastern and south-eastern Asia, and Australia, have contributed little or nothing to the world pool of cultivated grasses.

The origin of the cultivated pasture grasses in the regions listed above cannot be attributed solely to the effect of any single factor. The features which contribute to the success of a pasture grass under cultivation are themselves complex. They include high productivity, good nutritive value, the ability to withstand heavy grazing and trampling, good seed production and seedling vigour, and capacity to respond to improved soil fertility. There is some indication that grasses with these potentialities are most frequently found among those which occur naturally in and around the margins of forests and woodlands rather than in the prairies and steppes. Such is the natural habitat of most of the pasture grasses which are at present under cultivation in Europe and North America.

However they may have originated, the cultivated pasture grasses have certainly been exposed to varying periods of both natural and artificial selection. The regions in which they occur naturally coincide in part with the regions in which the great groups of grazing animals originated or to which they spread early in their evolutionary development.[14] Further, there is evidence of the existence of domesticated sheep and cattle about 11,000 and 7000 years ago, respectively, in northern Iraq.[1] From this centre they may have spread to other parts of Eurasia and elsewhere, taking with them propagules of the grasses on which they grazed.

The establishment of sown pastures has a much shorter history, both in Europe and other parts of the world. The grasses sown were mainly those – such as ryegrass and cocksfoot – which had come to be associated with man and his domestic stock, perhaps through the processes of semi-natural selection mentioned above. The cultivation process itself led to substantial changes in the plant population, especially through favouring those types with good seed production and seedling vigour. There are now frequently wide divergencies between the cultivars of the the pasture grasses and their wild ecotypes.

Even more significant has been the action of man, accidental and deliberate, in carrying seeds of pasture grasses far beyond the limits of their natural occurrence. There are no early historical records of the deliberate introduction of pasture species comparable with those which exist for crop plants, but the ease with which grass seeds become attached to human belongings of all kinds must have led to their chance introduction in prehistoric times. Some of these grasses have become established as weeds and ruderals, and, as noted above, it is often difficult to ascertain their region of origin.

The dispersal of pasture grasses has been greatly intensified during the last century, partly as an incidental effect of the general improvement in communications, and partly as a result of the deliberate action of governmental and other agencies. One of the most interesting results of this intensification is that several species of pasture grasses, which were not under cultivation in their regions of natural occurrence, have become widely cultivated in countries far removed from their original home. Examples include *Phalaris tuberosa*, uncultivated and considered of little value in its Mediterranean home, but now an important cultivated pasture grass in southern Australia, and *Agropyron desertorum*, introduced from western Asia and now widely cultivated in the western U.S.A. and Canada. Many other instances of similar successful introductions could be given. Frequently the circumstances or the original introduction are unknown. Their success does, however, indicate the great possibilities of adding to the world pool of cultivated pasture grasses through carefully planned introduction, making full use of all available phytogeographical knowledge in the selection of suitable introductions and of appropriate genetical techniques in their improvement.

The Significance of Grass Distribution for Ecology and Phytoclimatology

Throughout this chapter, emphasis has been placed on the significance of climatic factors in the distribution of the larger taxa of grasses. Two aspects of the relationship between distribution and climate merit special emphasis:

(i) Some, at least, of the larger tribes have distribution patterns which, while reflecting mainly the broad contrast between tropical and temperate conditions, also show clearly the effect of total quantity and seasonal distribution of rainfall.

(ii) The climatic factors show a close relationship with the *floristic* importance of the grass taxa concerned, rather than with their *ecological* importance.

Some authors have tended to discount the influence of annual and seasonal

rainfall on grass distribution. Thus Stebbins and Crampton,[23] while emphasiz-
ing the separation of the grasses into tropical and temperate groups write:

> On the other hand, the distribution of grass genera in relation to moisture
> shows no such sharp segregation. Many of the large genera, such as *Festuca*,
> *Elymus*, *Aristida*, *Eragrostis*, *Muhlenbergia*, and *Panicum*, contain strongly
> xeric species along with others typical of damp places.

While it is certainly true that the larger genera include species which differ in
their ability to withstand moisture stress, it is nevertheless also true that there
are major differences in this respect between genera and especially between
tribes. Thus, to cite only genera included in the above list, there is a marked
difference between *Aristida* in which 'all the species . . . are xerophytic and
relatively deep-rooted'[2] and *Panicum* in which 'many of the species occur in
marshes in different parts of the world and even in water'.[2] The occasional
exceptions should not mask the major differences between genera and tribes;
differences which are clearly shown when the distribution is mapped on the
basis of relative specific differentiation. 'The differing climatic responses are
in turn determined by differing patterns of physiological development, and it
appears that these patterns are no less characteristic of the tribes than are the
morphological features which form the basis of taxonomic classification'.[16]

The indices of grass distribution discussed in this chapter are exclusively
floristic, being based solely on the species present in any particular region
without regard to their relative or absolute abundance or their presumed
significance in the vegetation. While it is perhaps surprising that distribution
maps of the larger grass taxa show such a close relationship with climate, it is
less surprising that this is a relationship with the basic meteorological data
of temperature and rainfall rather than with the various derived climatic
indices which have been developed and mapped. Such indices have themselves
a vegetational basis; indeed, as noted by Daubenmire,[7] '. . . for half a century
the merits of most new climatic classifications have been judged according to
the closeness with which their application produces climatic provinces that
coincide with vegetation areas'.

The existence of a close relationship between vegetation and climate is
accepted as axiomatic by most ecologists. Thus Emberger,[9] in introducing a
biogeographic classification of climates, writes:

> Il convient, au debut de cet exposé, de faire une distinction fonda-
> mentale, celle entre géographie de la végetation et géographie botanique
> floristique. La première est l'expression biologique du milieu et avant tout,
> du climat, tandis que la seconde est le résultat des vicissitudes historiques
> du globe et de la phylogénèse.

However true this statement may be in general, it is subject to qualifications
when applied to grasses and grasslands. There is sufficient evidence to indicate
that some, at least, of the major grassland regions of the world are not
primarily climatically controlled. On the other hand, the distribution of some
of the larger grass taxa shows a close relationship to climate, and little or no
effect of the 'vicissitudes historiques du globe'.

It is only when one passes to consideration of the lower taxonomic categories, the smaller genera and the species, that the significance of factors other than climate becomes evident. In these taxa the present distribution is greatly affected by historical and prehistorical influences, by soils, and by the various biotic factors. Man and his grazing animals have largely determined the development and present distribution both of weeds and other ruderal grasses and of the cultivated pasture grasses.

Even in the smaller genera and the species of grasses the influence of climate on distribution is clearly marked. It is, indeed, noteworthy that attempts to correlate vegetation distribution with climate have been most successful when applied in restricted regions, and when the vegetation units used have a floristic base. When the climatic indices are extended on a wider, and especially on a global, scale they have usually failed to show much correlation with vegetation distribution, particularly if a physiognomic classification of vegetation is used.[19] The evidence from grass distribution suggests that further attempts to derive a satisfactory floristic base for inter-continental and inter-regional vegetation comparisons might be rewarding, and might lead ultimately to a system of vegetation classification which would show a better correlation with climate than those presently available.

REFERENCES

[1] Anon. (1962). Earliest sheep farmers. *New Scientist*, **14** (288), 419.
[2] Bews, J. M. (1929). *The World's Grasses*. Longmans, Green & Co. Ltd., London.
[3] Black, G. A. (1950). Os capins aquaticos da Amazonia. *Bol. Tech. Inst. Agron. do Norte.*, **19**, 53–94.
[4] Brown, W. L. (1957). Centrifugal speciation. *Quart. Rev. Biol.*, **32**, 247–77.
[5] Cabrera, A. L. (1953). *Manual de la Flora de los Abrededores de Buenos Aires*. Editorial Acme S.A., Buenos Aires.
[6] Clapham, A. R., Tutin, T. G., and Warburg, E. F. (1952). *Flora of the British Isles*. University Press, Cambridge.
[7] Daubenmire, R. (1956). Climate as a determinant of vegetation distribution in eastern Washington and northern Idaho. *Ecol. Monogr.*, **26**, 131–4.
[8] Duvigneaud, P. (1958). La végétation du Katanga et de sols métallifères. *Bull. Soc. Roy. Belg.*, **90**, 127–286.
[9] Emberger, L. (1955). Une classification biogeographique des climats. *Rec. trav. lab. Bot. Geol. et Zool., Fac. Sci. Univ. Montpellar; Ser. Botanique (Fasc. 7)*: 3–43.
[10] Fassett, N. C. (1957). *A Manual of Aquatic Plants*. Madison, Wisconsin.
[11] Good, R. (1953). *The Geography of the Flowering Plants*. 2nd edn. Longmans, Green & Co. Ltd., London.
[12] Hartley, W. (1950). The global distribution of tribes of the Gramineae in relation to historical and environmental factors. *Aust. J. Agric. Res.*, **1**, 355–73.
[13] Hartley, W. (1954). The agrostological index: a phytogeographical approach to the problems of pasture plant introduction. *Aust. J. Bot.*, **2**, 1–21.
[14] Hartley, W., and Williams, R. J. (1956). Centres of distribution of cultivated pasture grasses and their significance for plant introduction. *Proc. 7th Internat. Grassl. Congr.*, pp. 190–201.
[15] Hartley, W. (1958). Studies on the origin, evolution, and distribution of the Gramineae. I. The tribe Andropogoneae. *Aust. J. Bot.*, **6**, 115–28.
[16] Hartley, W. (1958). Studies on the origin, evolution, and distribution of the Gramineae. II. The tribe Paniceae. *Aust. J. Bot.*, **6**, 343–57.
[17] Hartley, W., and Slater, C. (1960). Studies on the origin, evolution, and distribution of the Gramineae. III. The tribes of the sub-family Eragrostoideae. *Aust. J. Bot.*, **8**, 256–76.
[18] Hartley, W. (1961). Studies on the origin, evolution, and distribution of the Gramineae. IV. The genus *Poa* L. *Aust. J. Bot.*, **9**, 152–61.

[19] Hartley, W. (1963). The phytogeographical basis of pasture plant introduction. Genetica Agraria (in press).

[20] Hulten, E. (1937). *Flora of the Aleutian Islands.* Bakforlags Aktiebolaget Thule, Stockholm.

[21] Moore, C. W. E. (1953). The vegetation of the south-eastern Riverina, New South Wales. *Aust. J. Bot.*, **1**, 485–547.

[22] Polunin, N. (1960). *Introduction to Plant Geography.* Longmans, Green and Co. Ltd., London.

[23] Stebbins, G. L., and Crampton, B. (1961). A suggested revision of the grass genera of temperate North America. In *Recent Advances in Botany*, Vol. 1, 133–45. Univ. of Toronto Press, Toronto.

[24] Stoffers, A. S. (1956). Studies on the flora of Curacao and other Caribbean Islands. Vol. 1. *The vegetation of the Netherlands Antilles.* Utrecht.

[25] Swallen, J. R. (1931). The grass genus *Amphibromus. Amer. J. Bot.*, **18**, 411–15.

[26] Szymkiewiez, D. (1947). Cinquième contribution statistique à la géographie floristique. *Bull. Acad. Polon. Sci.* Lett. B: Science Naturelles, **1**, 1–29.

[27] Turrill, W. B. (1929). *The Plant Life of the Balkan Peninsula.* Clarendon Press, Oxford.

[28] Vester, N. (1940). Die Areale und Arealtypen der Angiospermen – familien. I. *Bot. Archiv.*, **41**, 203–75.

[29] Weihe, K. von (1960). Uber die relative spezifishce Mannigfaltigkeit der Graminiden im holarktischen Raum. *Flora*, **148**, 595–611.

[30] Whyte, R. O., Moir, T. R. G., and Cooper, J. P. (1959). *Grasses in Agriculture.* F.A.O. Agricultural Studies, No. 42; (F.A.O., Rome).

4

Form and Structure

By C. Barnard

General Characters and Habit

GRASSES are easily recognized because they possess a particular combination of structural features. This combination comprises:

(a) cylindrical jointed stems with short basal internodes;

(b) branches of successive orders arranged in alternating planes at right angles;

(c) long narrow leaves with parallel veins and sheathing bases;

(d) distichous phyllotaxy;

(e) a fibrous root system consisting mainly of adventitious roots arising from nodes of the stem;

(f) flowers of an unusual and characteristic structure;

(g) albuminous seeds and caryopsis type fruits and;

(h) embryos of a characteristic structure.

The majority of grasses possess all these features and departure from some of them occurs in only a few species. For instance, in *Stenotaphrum secundatum* Kuntze the leaves of the axillary shoots are developed in the same plane as those of the main axis,[4] and the flowers in the spikelets of rye grass in the same plane as the axes of the spikelets; in *Micraira subulifolia* F. Muell., phyllotaxis is spiral. The most marked deviations in floral structure are found in the bamboos which usually have a greater number of stamens and lodicules. In bamboos also the fruit is often a nut or a berry. Because they may differ in so many respects from other tribes of the Gramineae, bamboos constitute a rather special group and will not be further discussed.

The combination of features listed above provides a picture of the basic architectural design of grasses. Differences in structure between genera and species represent variations in pattern within this overall design. A comparison of the main growth forms of grasses may be taken to illustrate this point. The major growth forms are the tufted or tussock, the prostrate or creeping and the straggling or ascending types. The mode of branching and stem structure are essentially the same in all types; the differences between them derive mainly from the pattern of development of the lateral shoots and the length of the stem internodes.

The tufted habit is found in all annual grasses and in many perennials. In annuals, the buds in the axils of the basal leaves of the main shoot give rise to primary lateral shoots and secondary laterals arise precociously from the basal nodes of the primary laterals. The internodes do not elongate during the vegetative phase of growth so the growing points of the axes remain near ground level though most of the leaves become fully expanded. These characteristics result in a crowding of the branches or tillers and a characteristic

tufted habit. Elongation of the internodes usually occurs only during inflorescence development when the axes become the flowering stems or culms.
Tufted perennials resemble annuals in their behaviour during the first year
except that some of the basal buds form underground stems or rhizomes instead of tillers. The rhizomes have short internodes and bear scale leaves in
place of foliage leaves. During the second season the apices of the rhizomes
turn upwards and develop foliage leaves and tillers, and buds in the axils of the
scale leaves produce new rhizomes. Because the internodes of the rhizomes
are very short a tussock habit is maintained.

The creeping habit results from the lengthening of the internodes of the
underground rhizomes or from the formation of prostrate tillers (stolons) with
long internodes. The main components of temperate meadow land and lawn
grasses are of this type. Long and short internodes may alternate or one long
internode alternate with several very short ones. Many different combinations
of internode length occur but the basal internodes of all axes are short and the
buds associated with the short internodes usually produce shoots. These
shoots may be sterile (innovations), terminate in an inflorescence, or grow as
rhizomes or stolons. In more xerophytic environments and particularly in
sandy habitats the long rhizome or stolon usually results in a straggling habit.
Forest margin and tropical grasses also frequently have this habit.

The differences between a tufted or tussock and a creeping or spreading
habit are thus primarily differences in internode elongation and the pattern of
development of lateral branches. The basic design of branching and development are the same.

The Embryo

The grass embryo is a highly specialized type (Fig. 4.1). It possesses the
primordia of the first two or more foliage leaves. In addition to the primary
root, the primordia of several adventitious roots may also be present. It
possesses a well developed provascular system in which the protoxylem elements are often lignified. The scutellum, being an organ entirely haustorial in
function, differs from the usual single cotyledon in other monocotyledons.
The coleoptile, epiblast and coleorhiza are also organs peculiar to the grass
embryo.

The embryo usually arises from the fertilized egg but it may develop par-
thogenetically or by apomixis (Chapter 9). Its early development follows a
well defined pattern of cell division and is similar to that of the usual monocotyledonous embryo. A large basal cell, a suspensor of elongated cells and a
more or less spherical or club shaped mass of small cells are formed. The
embryo then becomes pear shaped and the first indication of the differentiation of its parts is the appearance of a lateral prominence on one side of its
broader end.[1] This prominence develops into the shoot apex and the coleoptile
arises as a crescentic ridge of tissue around it. The remainder of the upper
portion of the embryo becomes flattened dorsiventrally and develops into the
scutellum. The primary root arises endogenously in the narrower portion of
the embryo and the tissue remaining external to it becomes the coleorhiza.
The first leaf primordium develops on the shoot meristem on the side distant

from the scutellum. The epiblast and adventitious root primordia when present are formed late in the embryo's development. The adventitious root primordia arise just above the level of the scutellar node, i.e. the point on the embryonic axis where the provascular strand from the scutellum enters the axis.

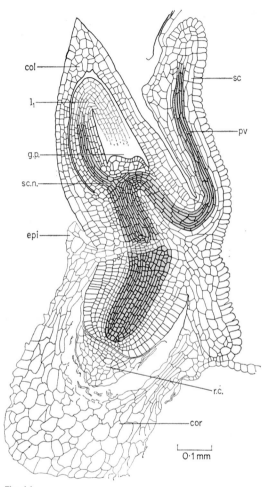

Fig. 4·1
    L.S. embryo of *Phalaris tuberosa*. col. = coleoptile; l_1 = first foliage leaf; g.p. = growing point; sc = scutellum; sc.n. = scutellar node; pv = provascular strand in scutellum; epi = epiblast; r.c. = root cap; cor = coleorhiza.

The coleoptile arises as an open sheath, but its edges unite to form a tube with a pore at its tip. In most festucoid grasses the coleoptile is inserted at the scutellar node (Fig. 4.1). In panicoid and chloridoid-eragrostoid grasses on the other hand the coleoptile is inserted above this point and there is a distinct 'internode' (the mesocotyl) between the scutellum and the coleoptile. This internode may lengthen at germination. In panicoid grasses there is a distinct cleft between the scutellum and the coleorhiza but in festucoid grasses the lower portion of the scutellum is fused to the coleorhiza.[20] The epiblast, which has no provascular strand, is developed only in some grasses, notably, in those of the festucoid type.

The most popular interpretation of the scutellum and coleoptile regards the scutellum as a single cotyledon, the coleoptile as the homologue of the first foliage leaf, and the mesocotyl as the first internode of the stem axis. Of the various other theories put forward from time to time, the best known, which is now strongly advocated by some morphologists, regards the scutellum and coleoptile as parts of a single cotyledon, the coleoptile representing its ligular portion and the scutellum its tip. The mesocotyl is interpreted as representing a fusion of the cotyledonary stalk and the hypocotyl. According to this view the separation of the two parts of the cotyledon by the mesocotyl must be regarded as a derived character. The festucoid type of embryo is thus interpreted as more primitive than the panicoid and chloridoid-eragrostoid type. The most widely held view regards the epiblast as a vestigial second cotyledon.

Few attempts have been made to homologize the coleorhiza. It is possible, however, that the coleorhiza is the true embryonic root or primary radicle and the structure now regarded as the primary root is really a lateral root arising endogenously from it. The coleorhiza, at germination, pushes through the wall of the caryopsis and produces a tuft of anchoring hairs which are very like root hairs. It may abort soon after emergence or form a club shaped tubercle which persists for some time (e.g. *Phalaris* and *Lolium*), or develop into a short cylindrical structure with evidence of a weak apical meristem. The so-called primary root arises endogenously, pushes through the side of the coleorhiza rather than through its tip and usually grows in a direction at right angles to the longitudinal axis of the embryo, i.e. even its direction of growth is that of a lateral organ. As pointed out later, it seems that the general trend in grasses is towards the early suppression of 'the primary root' and indeed of the adventitious seminal roots in favour of the later formed adventitious roots from higher stem nodes. The above suggestion with respect to the coleorhiza merely implies an earlier and more complete suppression of the embryonic radicle.

Development of Seedling to Adult Plant

The salient features of germination and the development of the embryo to the seedling have been described in Chapter 5. Suffice it here to remark that growth during germination results mainly from the elongation of existing embryonic cells and cell division in certain specific groups of cells or meristems. The principal meristematic areas are those of the shoot and root apices which are already well defined in the embryo. The coleoptile grows at first by meristematic activity and cell enlargement but later cell enlargement alone is almost entirely responsible for its elongation. The manner of elongation of the mesocotyl is similar to that of a stem internode which is described later. The first series of adventitious roots arises endogenously from tissue in the vicinity of the scutellar node and the second series from the coleoptilar node. This later series breaks through the base of the coleoptile.

From the time the seedling has become established until the end of the vegetative growth phase there are no basic changes in the plant's structural design and development. The plant grows in size and the number of its organ members; and these arise from meristems in which histogenetic patterns are repeated. New leaves arise in the same manner as older leaves and the organization of their tissues is similar. All branches originate in cell divisions which follow a well defined pattern and repeat the structure of the main stem. All roots originate in the same way and differentiate similar tissues. Each new member organ matures in succession. The growth of the plant during its vegetative phase is thus characterized by a repetitive development and maturation of organs.

The developmental pattern changes with the onset of the reproductive phase for the organs which arise from the apical meristem of the stem then develop in a different way. Three different morphogenetic patterns are evident during the reproductive phase. Firstly, there is the pattern of growth of the main axis and branches of the inflorescence in which the lateral buds form inflorescence branches instead of vegetative shoots. Secondly, there is the pattern of spikelet development in which the internodes are always extremely short and the lateral buds develop into flower primordia. In both of these patterns the characteristic architectural design of the vegetative phase is still apparent; the stems are jointed and the lateral appendages and axillary buds are distichously arranged. The third morphogenetic pattern which results in the development of flowers from the axillary buds of the spikelet is at first sight quite different. There are, however, as will be shown later, striking similarities in the histogenetic patterns which initiate vegetative buds and foliage leaves and those which initiate the flower primordia and the various parts of the flower.

The Root

Morphology of Roots

Grass roots generally are of comparable size, branch freely, and form a fibrous system. The seminal roots function throughout the life of some annuals but they become less important as the adventitious root system develops. More often the seminal roots function only for a short period before they die and are replaced entirely by adventitious roots.

In species with a tufted habit, adventitious roots usually originate only from the basal nodes of the main axis and tillers near ground level where the internodes are very short. In some, however, whorls of adventitious roots arise from nodes below which the internodes have elongated: in *Sorghum* spp. such roots may indeed develop from as high as four feet above ground level and are known as buttresses or prop roots. In species with stolons and long rhizomes, adventitious roots develop at nodes associated with short internodes. Thus stolons and long rhizomes serve as a means of vegetative propagation when they become severed by natural or artificial means. Without severance of the rooted nodes the individual may extend over a large area and consist of a number of practically independent units.

Root hairs are particularly large and long. They also tend to be persistent

and cover long lengths of root instead of being confined to a short region behind the tip. Only in those species in which a lignified exodermis is formed
and the piliferous layer becomes detached are the root hairs short-lived.

Histogenesis of the Root

The cells of the apical meristem of grass roots are organized in a clearly
defined histogenetic pattern (Fig. 4.2) which is remarkably constant in all
species. A single layered calyptrogen gives rise to the root cap. Beneath the
calyptrogen is another single layer. As the cells of this layer become laterally
displaced from the centre of the tip they divide by periclinal walls. The outer
cells then divide by anticlinal walls only and so remain as a single layer con-
stituting the dermatogen which gives rise to the epidermis; the inner cells give
rise to the periblem which has the form of a hollow cone and differentiates as
the cortex. The plerome is a cylindrical cone of cells within the periblem and

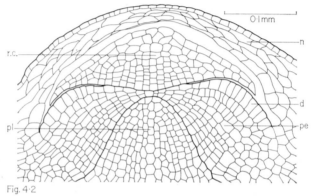

Fig. 4·2

L.S. root primordium at node in *Lolium perenne*.
n = node tissue; r.c. = root cap; d = dermatogen;
pe = periblem; pl = plerome.

gives rise to the vascular tissues and the pith. The divisions described above as
occurring at the apex take place early in the life of the root primordium when
all the cells of the meristem are active. Clowes[11, 12] has shown that there is an
area at the tip of the meristem where the cells rarely divide during the later
growth of the root. As cells all around are actively meristematic this quiescent
centre is passively carried forward. Goodwin and Avers[14] found that in
Phleum pratense L. most cell divisions occurred in the epidermis in the segment 150μ to 200μ behind the tip and ceased about 450μ from the tip.
Elongation ceased at 1150μ from the tip.

In panicoid grasses, all epidermal cells in the region of root hair development are alike in size and any one of them can give rise to a root hair; it
emerges from the mid-point of the cell and at right angles to the axis of the
root.[21] In festucoid grasses, the last division of the dermatogen cells produces
unequal daughter cells and the daughter cell nearest the apex of the root is
smaller and more densely protoplasmic than its sister cell. Root hairs arise
only from the shorter cells and emerge from near their distal ends at an angle
of about 45 degrees to the axis of the root.

Anatomy of the Root

The anatomy of the roots of grasses is typically monocotyledonous. In large roots a number (about 10–14) of exarch xylem groups alternate with groups of phloem around a central pith (Fig. 4.3). There are several small protoxylem elements to each large metaxylem vessel and two to six elements in each phloem group (Figs. 4.4 and 4.5). A one or two-layered pericycle is normally present (Figs. 4.4 and 4.5), but is not always clearly differentiated, and sometimes the protoxylem elements abut the cells of the endodermis. The deposi-

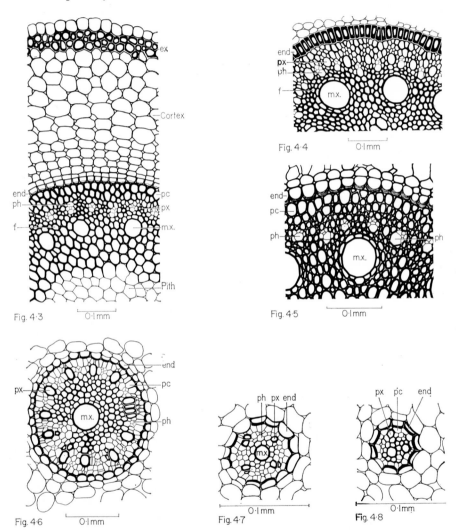

FIG. 4.3. T.S. sector root of *Andropogon gerardi*. FIG. 4.4. T.S. portion vascular tissues of root of *Panicum coloratum*. FIG. 4.5. T.S. portion vascular tissues of root of *Phalaris tuberosa*. ex = exodermis; c = cortex; end = endodermis; pc = pericycle; ph = phloem; px = protoxylem; f = fibres; mx = metaxylem vessel.

T.S. sections of vascular tissue on small roots of *Lolium perenne*. FIG. 4.6 of small root and FIG. 4.8 of a very small (adult) root. end = endodermis; ph = phloem; pc = pericycle; px = protoxylem; mx = metaxylem vessel.

tion of suberized lamellae causes the walls of the endodermal cells, particularly the radial and tangential walls, to thicken considerably as the root matures (Figs. 4.4 and 4.5); and casparian strips occur on the radial walls. Passage-cells may or may not be present. The parenchyma cells between the xylem and phloem and the cells of the pericycle and pith generally become lignified as the root matures. Cells of the layers immediately below the epidermis may also become suberized or lignified and form an exodermis (Fig. 4.3). The rest of the cortex remains parenchymatous and frequently lysigenous cavities develop; in older roots the cortex often breaks down completely.

In medium sized roots, there are fewer protoxylem, phloem groups and metaxylem vessels, and less pith. In small roots, the vascular tissues form a protostele with no pith and a single large centrally located metaxylem vessel (Figs. 4.6 and 4.7). In very small (but adult) roots, metaxylem vessels are absent and only protoxylem elements occur (Fig. 4.8). No attempts have been made to correlate differences in the anatomy of grass roots with the panicoid and festucoid groups.

The Stem

Morphology of stem apex

The growing point of the stem apex is dome shaped and leaf primordia arise as crescentic ridges alternately on either side of it (Plate 1(a)). Differences in the general form of the apex are associated with differences in the relative rate of leaf initiation and expansion. The apex may be very elongated with up to 30 leaf primordia between the tip and the cowling primordium. In other species only several leaf primordia may be present between the tip and the cowling primordium (Fig. 4.9); these apices are very short.[22] There seems to be no relation between the length of the vegetative apex and growth habit and it may differ markedly in related species.

Histogenesis of Stem Apex

The internal organization of the growing point and the histogenesis of both leaf primordia and axillary bud meristems are remarkably constant. In all grasses, there is a two-layered tunica surrounding a central core of cells or corpus. Some workers have mistakenly reported that the tunica comprised only a single layer. An attempt, indeed, has been made to relate the number of tunica layers to the systematic position of grass genera.[9] The cells of both the outer tunica layer (dermatogen) and the inner tunica layer (hypodermis) divide only by anticlinal walls, except where a leaf primordium is being initiated. These layers are therefore discrete and each maintains its histogenetic individuality in the growing point (Fig. 4.9a). The cells of the corpus arise from a small group of cells at the tip of the hollow cone formed by the dermatogen and hypodermis. No pattern of cell divisions can be discerned in this group but divisions just behind the tip are predominantly at right angles to the length of the stem axis and so result in longitudinal files of cells. The cells of the corpus become vacuolated early while those of the dermatogen and hypodermis do not.

A leaf primordium is initiated by the periclinal division of cells in the hypodermis; and these divisions are immediately followed by periclinal divisions in
adjacent cells of the dermatogen (Fig. 4.9a). Periclinal divisions occur in
hypodermal cells above and below those in which the first divisions took place
until a tier of some 3 or 4 cells have so divided. Similar divisions occur in the
hypodermis and the dermatogen in a horizontal plane extending at least half-
way around the axis. The crescentic protuberance which is the first external
manifestation of the primordium results from the divisions of these cells and
further growth of the primordium from their derivatives. In the area of mid-
insertion of the primordium, some cells of the outer layer of the corpus become

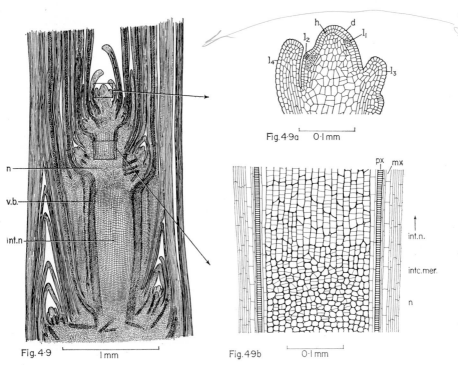

FIG. 4.9. L.S. through tip of stolon of *Cynodon dactylon*, diagrammatically illustrated; alternate internodes are elongating. FIG. 4.9a shows the histogenesis of the
apex. FIG. 4.9b shows an intercalary meristem and elongating internode. n = node;
v.b. = vascular bundle; int. n. = internode; d = dermatogen; h = hypodermis;
l_1, l_2 = leaf primordia; px = protoxylem; mx = metaxylem vessel.

elongated in the direction of the length of the axis and divide once or twice by
periclinal walls; these cells mark the site of the future provascular strand to
the midrib of the leaf. Growth of the primordium is most rapid opposite the
mid-point of its insertion and results in the formation of a tip. At first meristematic activity is mainly in this tip region and along the margins of the
primordium. Subsequently the locus of meristematic activity moves towards
the base of the primordium and a basal intercalary meristem is established.

The initiation of an axillary bud primordium is evident in periclinal divisions in a small group of cells of the outer layer (subhypodermis) of the

E

corpus just above the mid-point of insertion of a leaf primordium. These divisions result in radial files of cells converging to a point and directed towards the circumference of the axis. The cells of the dermatogen and hypodermis in this area continue to divide only by anticlinal walls and so these layers remain discrete (cf. Fig. 4.24a, b).

Thus there is a fundamental difference in the histogenesis of the leaf and the branch. The leaf arises from the two external layers of the growing point only; it is of superficial origin. The primordium of the lateral branch on the other hand is a duplication of the growing point of the main axis. The organization of the cells of its apical meristem is similar; its dermatogen is derived from the dermatogen of the parent axis; its hypodermis from the parent hypodermis and the cells of its central core from the parent corpus. Its origin is cauline.

Intercalary Meristem of the Stem

During their early development, successive leaf primordia are immediately above each other and are not separated by internodes (Fig. 4.9). The internodes are formed later by cell divisions in the axis between the leaf primordia. At first, these divisions occur throughout the area between the leaf primordia, but, as the internode grows, meristematic activity becomes increasingly restricted to its basal region, i.e. a basal intercalary meristem is established (Fig. 4.9b).

Different growth habits are due primarily to differences in the relative activity of these meristems. These differences may be in degree of activity and/or time of activity. In annual grasses for instance a number of mature leaves and lateral shoots may have been formed before the intercalary meristems initiate any appreciable elongation of the internodes. This elongation, which is due also of course to cell elongation following the meristematic activity, usually commences as the inflorescence is forming. It is this delay in the activity of the basal meristems which results in the tufted habit. On the other hand when intercalary activity occurs independently of inflorescence formation as in many perennial grasses, stolons or long rhizomes are produced.

Anatomy of the Stem

The vascular bundles of grass stems are the usual closed collateral monocotyledonous type and each is enclosed in a sheath of sclerenchymatous fibres. They may be scattered through the ground parenchyma of the internode which is solid; or occur in one or more often two (Figs. 4.10–4.12) or more concentric rings around a central portion of the ground tissue or pith which breaks down as the internode matures. Both types occur in annual and perennial species, the former in most tribes, the latter in all except the Andropogoneae and Paniceae. All bundles in the higher internodes come from leaves and a large number may enter the culm at each node from one leaf. The bundles from each leaf pass vertically down the internode, the midrib and larger ones tending to move to the centre of the axis or joining the inner ring while the smaller ones pursue a course nearer the periphery. They pass unbranched and in the same relative positions through one or more successive internodes. The number of bundles in successive internodes, however, remains approximately the same because some of them anastomize at each node and join with bundles coming from the same or other leaves. The branching and anastomoses of the bundles take place in the upper part of the nodes and result in a complex nodal plate. The bundles from an axillary shoot join the nodal complex and generally pursue a horizontal course across the node in so doing (Fig. 4.9). Details of this junction are not well known.

The epidermis consists of long and short cells and stomata arranged in

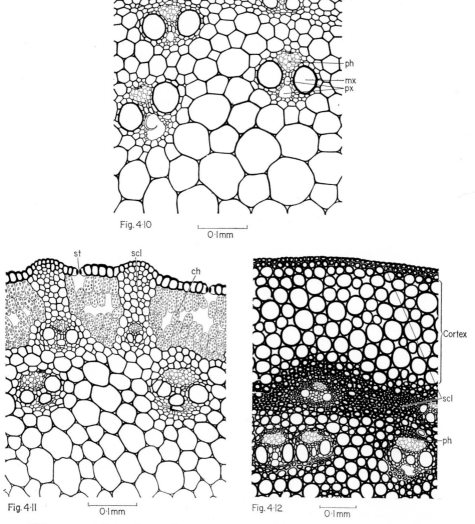

T.S. sectors of stem internodes. FIG. 4.10. *Digitaria sanguinalis.* FIG. 4.11. *Phalaris tuberosa.* FIG. 4.12. *Festuca arundinacea.* ph = phloem; px = protoxylem; mx = metaxylem vessel; ch = chlorenchyma; st = stomata; scl = sclerenchyma; c = cortex.

longitudinal rows in much the same way as in the leaf. Chlorenchyma is disposed in various ways in the young stem and frequently forms longitudinal
bands (Fig. 4.11). The cortical tissues become locally lignified as the stem
matures and different patterns of sclerenchyma are found in different grasses
(Figs. 4.10–4.12). The most marked difference between the anatomy of
different species lies in the disposition of these mechanical tissues and their
degree of lignification.

Sclerenchyma is formed at the base of the internode and at the node only
after elongation of the internode is complete. The protoxylem elements become lignified before elongation is complete and often break down leaving
lacunae. The other vascular elements differentiate basipetally during internode elongation: that is those at the distal end of the internode differentiate
first. Lignification occurs in the same sequence.

Adventitious roots arise endogenously in parenchymatous ground tissue at
the nodes just below the intercalary meristem. The cells in this zone at the
time of origin of adventitious roots are often arranged in radial rows strongly
suggesting origin from a cambial meristem. Subsequent to the formation of
the adventitious roots the cells in this area may become lignified and part of
the sclerenchymatous cylinder connecting the outer vascular bundles.

Junction of Stem and Root

The discrete polyarch vascular system of the primary root joins with the
separate vascular strands of the stem in a complex plate at the scutellar node.
The structure of the vascular tissue of the primary root is maintained right up
to its junction with this plate. The characteristics of the stem vasculature on
the other hand do not extend right down to the plate. In the first internode
above the plate (i.e. in the mesocotyl) the vascular structure is of a transitional
nature. A certain mixture of stem and root characters is also present in the
internode between the coleoptile and the first foliage leaf. It is not until the
third internode, that is between the 1st and 2nd foliage leaves, that the
arrangement of the vascular bundles and their structure become entirely
characteristic of the stem. The steles of adventitious roots join the lower side
of the vascular plate at the node of their origin.

The Leaf

Morphology of the Leaf

The first leaf or prophyll on each branch is different from other leaves. It is
always much smaller and is orientated at right angles to the plane of phyllotaxis of the succeeding leaves of the branch. It is often conical in shape and
resembles the coleoptile in having an apical opening through which the
succeeding leaves emerge and it envelops and protects the axillary bud. It has
been interpreted as a structure derived from the fusion of two leaves and also a
single leaf sheath.

The leaf is typically long, narrow, and non-petiolate, and consists of two
distinct parts, the sheath and the blade, with a ligule at the upper end of the
sheath. However, a great variety of form is exhibited in this organ. In some

tropical species the leaf is narrow-lanceolate or even ovate. In other grasses the blades are filiform as a result of the infolding of the margins. Large veins usually alternate with smaller ones and a mid-rib may or may not be particularly marked. In some species there are transverse connections between the parallel veins and these are often quite conspicuous in some broad-leafed types. The upper surface may be flat, or undulating, or grooved and ribbed, the ribs corresponding with the veins and the grooves with indentations between them. This furrowing is common in xerophytic grasses. The leaf sheath encircles and clasps the stem and encloses the bases of the leaves arising at the higher nodes. At the base of the culms where the internodes of the main axis as well as those of the basal tillers are short there is a series of leaf sheaths one inside the other.

The ligule has been interpreted as the distal part of the homologue of two fused stipules adnate to a petiole. This interpretation conceives the leaf sheath as representing a petiole to which the stipules have fused. The origin of the ligule from the adaxial epidermis of the top of the sheath (see below) and the fact that just above the ligule another pair of outgrowths (auricles) sometimes occur do not support this view.

Meristems of the Leaf

Meristematic activity in the leaf primordium becomes restricted quite early in its development to a zone of cells at its base. As a result of predominantly transverse divisions this intercalary meristem produces files of cells in the direction of the tip of the primordium and is responsible for further increase in length of the young primordium. There is at first no differentiation into blade and sheath but, when the primordium is still quite small (1 cm or more in length in *Lolium perenne* L.[25]), a narrow band of small compact parenchyma cells is differentiated which separates it into an upper and lower region. A new intercalary meristem arises above this band; it contributes to the growth of the blade, the lower meristem adding to the length of the sheath. The ligule arises as an outgrowth of the epidermis from the adaxial side of this band. Activity in the intercalary meristems may continue for a long period and produce a great length of leaf at a very rapid rate.

The Anatomy of the Leaf

The epidermis is composed of three or more kinds of cells which, together with the stomata, are arranged in longitudinal rows of various combinations; i.e. the distribution of each type of row is related to the veins. This is the overall design and within this design many different cell types and patterns of arrangement are found (Figs. 4.13–4.18). There are long cells which vary in size and wall thickness and whose walls may be either smooth (Fig. 4.13) or sinuous and 'rippled' (Fig. 4.16). Short cells of two types (silica cells and cork cells) also occur. The silica cell is almost completely filled with a single opaline silica body or phytolith which has characteristic shapes and the cork cells have suberized walls. Fibre cells which may be 200–375μ long often occur above the vascular bundles (Fig. 4.13) and large thin walled bulliform cells are frequently present (Figs. 4.20 and 4.22) in the intercostal areas. Most frequently

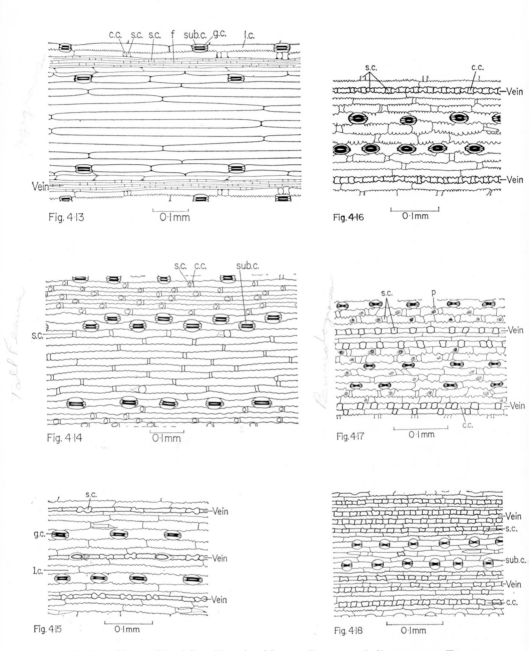

Strips of lower (abaxial) epidermis of leaves. FIG. 4.13. *Lolium perenne.* FIG. 4.14.
Festuca arundinacea. FIG. 4.15. *Andropogon gerardi.* FIG. 4.16. *Panicum coloratum.*
FIG. 4.17. *Cynodon dactylon.* FIG. 4.18. *Micraira subulifolia.* s.c. = silica cells; c.c. =
cork cell; l.c. = long cell; g.c. = guard cell; sub. c. = subsidiary cell of stomata;
f = fibres; p = papilla.

the bulliform cells are found at the base of the furrows on the adaxial surface of ridged leaves, but they may occur in the abaxial epidermis and in leaves which are not ridged. At one time it was believed that involution of the leaf in wilting was associated with a change in turgor in these cells but experimental evidence has not supported this view[24] and their function is not understood. The stomata have dumb-bell shaped guard cells and are accompanied by two accessory cells; they usually occur on both abaxial and adaxial surfaces. Hairs of different kinds are developed from the epidermal cells and usually arise in place of one of the short cork cells or pairs of cork-silica cells. Thus, even the hairs are not formed at random but their distribution conforms to a specific pattern.

Very early in the ontogeny of the leaf certain rows of epidermal cells differentiate as stomatal rows. These rows are indeed discernible in the first seedling leaves of the embryo of *Hordeum vulgare* L. before germination.[27] Cell divisions occur in these rows which are asymmetric resulting in a distal small cell with a large nucleus and proximal larger cell which quickly becomes vacuolated. The short cells are the stomatal or guard mother cells; the long cells become the intervening long type epidermal cell. The guard mother cell enlarges and while it is developing two small cells are cut out opposite it from adjacent cells of the adjoining rows. These cells are the result of asymmetric mitoses and are the subsidiary or accessory cells. The guard mother cell then divides longitudinally to form the two guard cells which differentiate to their mature shape and separate schizogenously between their opposing walls (cf. Figs. 4.13–4.18). Stebbins and Shar[27] have used the development of this stomatal complex to study the mechanisms associated with cell differentiation. They conclude that cytoplasmic polarization leads to the formation of the guard mother cells and the asymmetric divisions in adjacent epidermal cells are the result of an inductive force from the guard mother cell.

The mesophyll usually shows no differentiation into an upper palisade and lower spongy tissue. The leaf has an erect posture while its tissues are differentiating and do not lose this posture or emerge from the convolutions of older leaves and their clasping sheaths until it is relatively well developed. This may account for the lack of dorsiventrality in the mesophyll of the mature expanded leaf.

In the simplest types the mesophyll is rather compact and quite homogeneous (Fig. 4.20). In some of the simple types a layer of large cells develops in the centre of the mesophyll. As the leaf matures these cells lose their chlorophyll and break down leaving a series of large intercellular spaces running longitudinally in the centre of the mesophyll between the veins (Fig. 4.19). Page[18] has described this phenomenon in detail but there is some confusion in the literature about it. Where the cells do not break down completely they form the fusoid cells of Metcalfe[16] which are common in bamboo leaves.

Differences in cell shape and the chloroplast content of cells occur in more complex types and the mesophyll is orientated around the vascular bundles. The chlorenchyma cells around the vascular bundles tend to be radially arranged and palisade-like in the first stages of specialization (Fig. 4.21). In the most specialized, the chloroplast-bearing cells of the mesophyll are restricted to a layer of palisade shaped cells radially arranged about each bundle and separated by clear cells of a bulliform nature (Fig. 4.22).

The provascular strand of the midrib of the leaf is first apparent in divisions in the outer cells of the corpus of the stem behind the young leaf primordium. The strand differentiates down the axis from this site and development is coincident with the elongation of the internodes (cf. Fig. 4.9); it also differentiates upwards into the leaf primordium. The main lateral bundles develop in the same way, but intermediate and smaller veins originate later in the leaf primordium itself. The smallest veins arise near the tip and differentiate down through the blade and sheath to the axis through vacuolated pseudo-parenchymatous tissue.[22] The marginal bundles are last to form and usually do not extend into the sheath but fuse at the base of the blade with adjacent bundles. Any transverse connecting bundles arise later by the tangential division of cells of the ground tissue which appear no different from their neighbours.[19] They may consist only of several vascular elements.

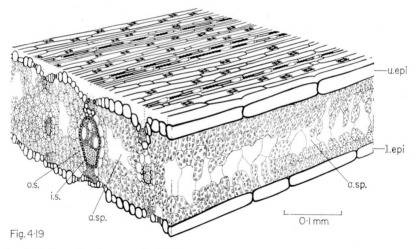

Fig. 4·19

Leaf of *Dactylis glomerata* in T.S. and L.S. and showing the upper epidermis in surface view. a.sp. = air space; o.s. = outer bundle sheath; i.s. = inner bundle sheath.

The vascular bundles are enclosed in one or two sheaths (Figs. 4.19–4.22). The inner sheath consists of small thick walled cells which often have their inner and radial walls heavily sclerized like endodermal cells, while the outer sheath is made up of large cells which are usually thin walled (Fig. 4.20). If only one sheath is present then it is the outer one of large cells. Sometimes the inner sheath is not well defined from the small sclerized cells of the bundles and is only developed on the phloem side of the larger bundles. For these reasons the discrimination made between one and two bundle sheath categories of grasses is not quite as definite as the literature often suggests. The cells of the outer sheath generally contain chloroplasts. They are often large and, indeed, the most active in starch formation in leaves with radially arranged mesophyll (Fig. 4.22).

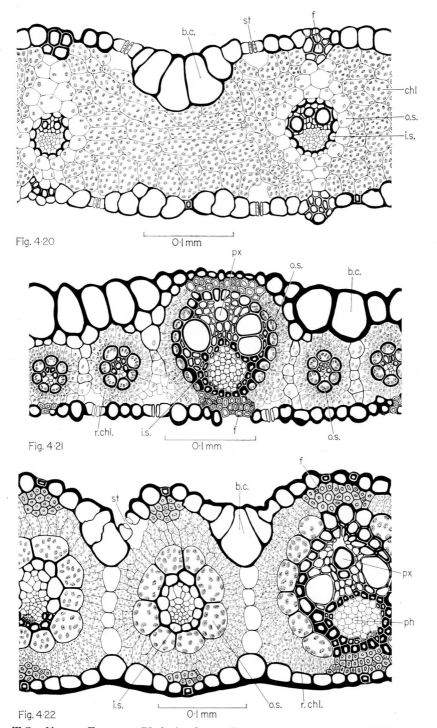

T.S. of leaves. Fig. 4.20. *Phalaris tuberosa*. Fig. 4.21. *Andropogon gerardi*. Fig. 4.22. *Panicum coloratum*. st = stomata; chl = chlorenchyma; r.chl. = radial chlorenchyma; b.c. = bulliform cells; o.s. = outer bundle sheath; i.s. = inner bundle sheath; px = protoxylem; f = fibres.

There is xylem and phloem of the normal type and arrangement in the larger vascular bundles but in the smaller ones there may be only tracheids in the xylem and very few elements in the phloem (Fig. 4.21). Indeed gradations are found between small bundles with a small amount of vascular tissue to small groups of parenchyma surrounded by a bundle sheath of a few very large parenchymatous cells (Tateoka[28] in *Arundinella*; Soper and Mitchell[25] in *Lolium perenne* L.).

It has long been known that differences in the organization of the epidermal cells, chlorenchyma, and bundle sheaths were associated with the two major taxonomic grouping of the grasses (*vide* Chapter 2). More recently four, and later six, combinations of anatomical characters with taxonomic significance have been claimed.[10,26] The three principal groupings are:

(*a*) the festucoid type which is the least specialized;
(*b*) the panicoid; and
(*c*) the chloridoid which is the most specialized.

In (*a*) the epidermis is relatively simple and shows little diversification of cell type; the inner bundle sheath is well developed and the outer not very clearly differentiated from the rest of the mesophyll, and the mesophyll tissue is almost homogeneous. In (*b*) there is more diversification of epidermal cells, the inner bundle sheath is usually absent, or present around larger bundles only, and the parenchyma sheath is well developed; while the chlorenchyma tends to be radially disposed around the bundles. In (*c*) the epidermal cell arrangement is again complex and the inner bundle sheath absent; the chlorenchyma of the mesophyll consists of narrow cells arranged radially in a layer around the bundles and its cells contain only small chloroplasts; large chloroplasts and starch formation are concentrated in the sheath cells; each bundle and ring of chlorenchyma is separated from the next by a longitudinal file of bulliform-like cells.

A high degree of suberization, lignification, and silicification is characteristic of grass leaves. Sclerenchyma fibres are nearly always developed above and below the vascular bundles (Figs. 4.19–4.22) and frequently form long mechanical girders extending from the bundles to the epidermis. Heavy strands of fibres also develop along the margins of the leaf. A substantial part of the silica absorbed by the plant is precipitated as silica bodies and these bodies are concentrated in the silica cells. The walls of most cells are, however, also heavily impregnated with silica. With suitable technique all other components of the cell walls may be removed and a silica skeleton of the cellular structure of the leaf obtained.[8,15]

The Inflorescence

Morphology of the Inflorescence

In all grasses, the branches of the inflorescence are arranged distichously and the origin of each successive order is at right angles to the preceding order (except in *Lolium*). In all cases where the branches appear to be arranged polystichously, investigation has shown[13] that they arise distichously. Thus the branching pattern is the same as in the vegetative body.

A spreading panicle in which spikelets represent the ultimate units is regarded as the most primitive form of inflorescence and the main evolutionary trend seems to have been towards contraction, condensation, and reduction. By contraction and reduction of the branches a simple panicle, a raceme, and finally a spike is formed; by contraction of the main axis as well as condensation of the branches a capitate inflorescence results. Differences in the form of the inflorescence are thus mainly due to the number of times branching is repeated before spikelet differentiation and the relative lengths of the internodes of the various orders of branches. Even the highly specialized female inflorescence of *Zea mays* is paniculate. The massive axis or rachis has resulted from the telescoping of the primary axis plus adnation to it of the prophylls borne on the secondary or spikelet axes.[17] The conspicuous cupules and rachis flaps are really adnate prophylls.

The spikelets may be many or few flowered and, in some cases, consist only of a single flower. The 'typical' spikelet consists of an axis bearing two empty or sterile glumes and a number of lemmas or flowering glumes each of which subtends a flower. The general evolutionary trend appears to have been from the many to the few and single flowered types and reduction has come about by loss of distal florets in some cases and of basal florets in others.[7] Sterile lemmas are found both above and below the fertile ones. Bews[7] concluded that reduction by loss of distal florets is most prevalent among the more primitive groups of grasses and that in the more advanced tribes and genera loss of the lowermost florets represents the last stage in the evolutionary trend.

Departures from the normal spikelet and floral pattern do occur. Spikelets for instance may be unisexual and monoecious (e.g. *Zea mays*) and very occasionally dioecious. An unusual spikelet which deserves special mention is found in *Anthoxanthum odoratum* L. It consists of four sterile glumes and two lemmas each of which subtends a single stamen. The gynaeceum forms directly from the apex of the spikelet axis and there are no lodicules. Sharman[23] has shown that the two stamens are borne in the same plane as the lemmas and appear axillary to them. It is possible that here the 'floret' is actually a spikelet consisting of two basal male flowers each of which has been reduced to a single stamen and a single distal ebracteate female flower.

In some grasses, e.g. *Pennisetum, Setaria, Cenchrus*, bristles which may be either free or united in a kind of involucre are found associated with the spikelets. Arber[3] interprets these bristles as sterile spikelet axes.

Ontogeny of the Inflorescence

Transition from the vegetative to the reproductive growth phase is first evident in a rapid elongation of the growing point of the shoot. Leaf initials continue to form on the growing point; they form rapidly and in close succession but their further development progressively diminishes in each succeeding leaf primordium. The elongated apex thus bears a number of leaf initials which may be no more than crescentic ridges (Plate 1(b) and (c)) and this change in form of the apex is most sudden and marked in vegetative apices of the short type.

When the inflorescence is a spike or simple panicle, lateral bud (i.e. spike-

PLATE I. Development of the inflorescence of wheat.   (a) and (b) ($\times 58$) show the elongation of the vegetative apex; (c) and (d) ($\times 58$) the appearance of spikelet primordia in the double ridge stage; (e)–(j) ($\times 40$) the early development of the spikelets; (k) ($\times 58$) and (l) ($\times 32$) the development of flower primordia on the spikelet. (From Barnard, 1955, in Aust. J. Bot., 3 (1), 1–20. Plate I.)

let) primordia arise in rapid succession or almost simultaneously in the axils of the leaf initials, and the bud primordia and leaf initials form double ridges (Plate 1(d) and (e)). This simultaneous appearance of organs on the axis is evidence of evolutionary condensation. The axillary buds and the growing point of the main axis develop into spikelets (Plate 1(e)–(l)). Between the last expanded foliage leaf of the culm and the leaf initial which subtends the basal branch of the inflorescence there are often a number of leaf primordia which have no axillary structures and which fail to develop beyond the primordium stage (Plate 1(h)). The internodes between these leaf primordia, which are only discernible during early development, fail to elongate.

In inflorescences with secondary branches, the axillary primordia may be less numerous than in the spike and generally develop more obviously in acropetal succession. Tertiary and subsequent branches are formed in the same way although the subtending leaf initials may not be so easily discerned. The apex of an ultimate branch invariably forms a spikelet.

In many-flowered spikelets some of the distal flower primordia usually abort. In two flowered spikelets the apex of the spikelet is often aborted but the lateral origin of the most distal floret is apparent during early development. This is also true of some single flowered spikelets though in others (e.g. *Ehrharta erecta* Lam. and *Stipa hyaline* Ness.), the primordium of the single flower develops directly from the apical meristem of the spikelet and there is no histogenetic evidence of derivation from an axillary position. Occasionally, as in certain varieties of *Triticum aestivum*, flower primordia are initiated and often reach maturity in the axils of the two basal glumes.[5] The two basal empty glumes are therefore probably to be interpreted as sterile lemmas.

Histogenesis of the Inflorescence

The primordia which grow into branches of the inflorescence and into spikelets arise in the same manner as the primordia of lateral vegetative shoots. Their cells are organized in a two layered tunica and central corpus like the apical meristem from which they arise. Glumes and lemmas originate from the growing point of the spikelet axis by periclinal divisions in the cells of the hypodermis and dermatogen in the 'foliar' manner (Fig. 4.23). Their growth is first apical and marginal but meristematic activity subsequently becomes concentrated in a basal zone in the same way as in the foliage leaves. The lemma is probably homologous with the sheath of the foliage leaf and its awn with the blade.[19] The flower primordia arise in the same manner as the spikelet primordia and vegetative buds by periclinal divisions in the corpus (Fig. 4.23); periclinal divisions never occur in the dermatogen; their origin is cauline.

The Flower

Ontogeny of the Flower

The flower primordium before the differentiation of its parts is a hemispherical structure (Plate 1(j)). The palea arises as a narrow ridge of tissue along the posterior side of the primordium and is followed by the formation of four papillae which represent the rudiments of the stamens and carpel (Plate

2(1)). The papillae of the two lateral stamens arise first, followed by those of the anterior stamen and carpel. The papilla of the carpel rudiment is actually a horseshoe shaped ridge of tissue encircling the apex of the flower primordium; it arises and grows at first rapidly on the anterior side of the apex and then encircles the apex extending right around to the posterior side (Plate 2(2)). As the carpel primordium develops it completely encloses the apex of the flower primordium which becomes the ovule. The lodicules (Plate 2(3))

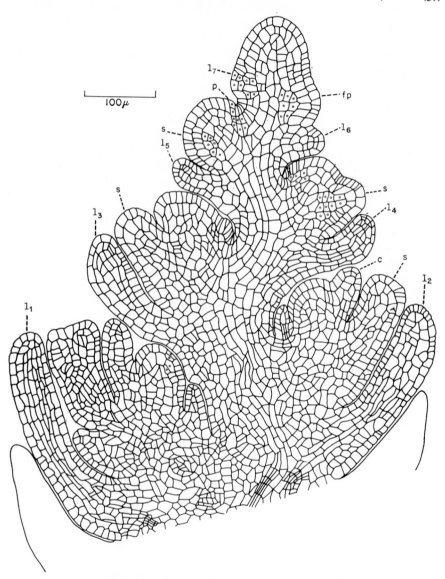

FIG. 4.23. L.S. spikelet *Triticum aestivum*. The seventh lemma is arising at l_7; and the origin of the youngest flower primordium is shown at fp. In the older flower primordia, p = palea; s = anterior stamen; c = carpel. (From Barnard, 1955, *Aust. J. Bot.*, **3** (1), 1–20. Fig. 5.)

are usually the last of the floral organs to appear though sometimes (e.g. *Stipa hyalina*) the palea may not be initiated until after the carpellary ridge is evident.

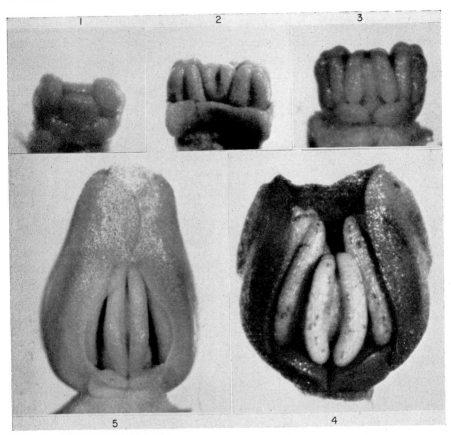

PLATE 2. Development of flower primordium in wheat. (1) ($\times$140) is an anterior view of a very young primordium; (2) is a posterior and (3) an anterior view of slightly older primordia. In (2) ($\times$100) the young palea is visible, in (3) ($\times$108) the lodicules are seen. (4) ($\times$85) and (5) ($\times$48) are anterior views of older primordia in which the palea overtops the stamens. (From Barnard, 1955, in *Aust. J. Bot.*, **3** (1); 1–20. Plate 1.)

Histogenesis of the Flower

The cells of the flower primordium are organized into the usual two layered tunica and central corpus (Figs. 4.23–4.24). The palea arises in the foliar manner through periclinal divisions in the hypodermis and dermatogen (Figs. 4.24d–g). Usually there are only several divisions of hypodermal cells and the palea is composed almost entirely of derivatives of the dermatogen. The lodicules also arise in the foliar manner. The stamens on the other hand arise by periclinal divisions in the outer layer of the corpus (Figs. 4.24d–g). Periclinal divisions occur also in the hypodermis; the inner cell from such divisions being incorporated in the corpus, the outer becoming a hypodermal cell and thereafter dividing only by anticlinal walls. The mode of initiation, however, is essentially of the cauline type. The carpel is initiated in the foliar manner and, as in the palea, divisions in hypodermal cells are few (Figs. 4.24g–j); it is derived almost entirely from the dermatogen of the flower primordium. The divisions in the dermatogen commence on the anterior side of the apex and then extend circumferentially around it in an obliquely transverse plane; that is, the divisions occur higher on the axis on the posterior side. Growth on the anterior side is most rapid so that the young carpel primordium soon forms a cowl-shaped structure; marginal growth closes the cowl to form the loculus of the ovary. The tip or peak of the cowl becomes bifid and develops into the style and stigmas.

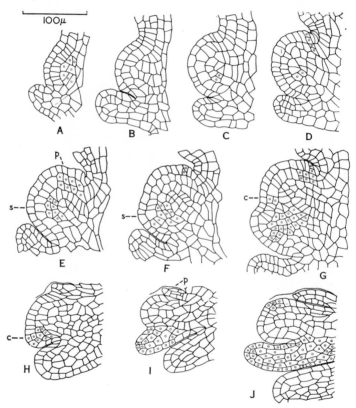

FIG. 4.24. Histogenesis of flower primordium. p = palea; s = anterior stamen; c = carpel. (From Barnard, 1955, *Aust. J. Bot.*, **3** (1), 1–20. Figs. 6–8.)

The apex of the flower primordium, after the genesis of the encircling carpel, is very small and has a diameter of only 7 or 8 dermatogen cells (Figs. 4.24g–j). The organization of the cells into dermatogen, hypodermis, and central corpus is still, however, clearly apparent in this diminutive growing point. It increases rapidly in size. Growth is most rapid on its posterior side and it thus becomes gradually turned towards the anterior side of the flower or the lemma, first assuming a horizontal position and finally pointing downwards. A hypodermal cell at the tip of the growing point divides by a periclinal wall to give rise to the megaspore mother cell and a parietal cell. At the same time the outer integument is initiated by periclinal divisions in hypodermal and dermatogen cells on the adaxial side of the young ovule. The inner integument also arises in the foliar manner. The parietal and other hypodermal cells divide by periclinal walls to add to the nucellus. Megasporogenesis and microsporogenesis are normal. The megaspore mother cell divides to form a linear tetrad of megaspores three of which abort and the one at the chalazal end forms the embryo sac.

The histogenesis and meristematic patterns of the floral structures are thus comparable with those of the vegetative organs. The mode of origin of the spikelet primordia, the flower primordia and the stamens, is similar to that of vegetative axes. The glumes, lemma, palea, lodicules, and carpel on the other hand all arise in the foliar manner as appendages; their mode of growth by apical and marginal meristems at first, and by basal intercalary meristems later, is similar to that of foliage leaves. The flower therefore may be interpreted as a reduced branch system axillary to the lemma. The bikeeled palea is the homologue of the prophyll and the lodicules and carpel are also foliar appendages developed on the main axis of the system. The stamens represent lateral branches terminating in microsporangia and the ovule or megasporangium is terminal on the main axis. This concept needs a little modification for there is evidence that the apparent single carpel may in fact be composed of three or possibly more fused foliar structures,[2,6] and the ovule, while now appearing terminal, has been derived from a position originally axillary to one of these foliar structures.

REFERENCES

[1] Abbe, E. C., and Stein, O. L. (1954). The growth of the shoot apex in maize – embryogeny. *Amer. J. Bot.*, **41** (4), 285–93.

[2] Arber, A. (1929). Studies in the Gramineae. VIII. On the organization of the flower in the bamboo. *Ann. Bot.*, **43**, 765–81.

[3] Arber, A. (1931). Studies in the Gramineae. X (1) *Pennisetum, Setaria*, and *Cenchrus*. (2) *Alopecurus*. (3) *Lepturus*. *Ann. Bot.*, **45**, 401–20.

[4] Arber, A. (1934). *The Gramineae*. Univ. Press, Cambridge.

[5] Barnard, C. (1955). Histogenesis of the inflorescence and flower of *Triticum aestivum* L. *Aust. J. Bot.*, **3** (1), 1–20.

[6] Barnard, C. (1957). Floral histogenesis in the monocotyledons. I. The Gramineae. *Aust. J. Bot.*, **5** (1), 1–20.

[7] Bews, J. W. (1929). *The world's grasses. Their differentiation, distribution, economics, and ecology*. Longmans, Green & Co., London.

[8] Bonnett, O. T. (1961). The oat plant. Its histology and development. Bull. 672. *Agric. Exp. Stat.*, Univ. of Illinois. 1–112.

[9] Brown, W. V., Heimsch, C., and Emery, W. H. P. (1957). The organization of the grass shoot apex and systematics. *Amer. J. Bot.*, **44** (7), 590–95.

[10] Brown, W. V. (1958). Leaf anatomy in grass systematics. *Bot. Gaz.*, **119**, 170–78.

[11] Clowes, F. A. L. (1959). Apical meristems of roots. *Biol. Revs.*, **34**, 501–29.

[12] Clowes, F. A. L. (1961). Duration of the mitotic cycle in a meristem. *Exp. Bot.*, **12**, 283–93.

[13] Evans, M. W., and Grover, F. O. (1940). Developmental morphology of the growing point of the shoot and the inflorescence in grasses. *J. Agric. Res.*, **61**, 481–520.

[14] Goodwin, R. H., and Avers, C. S. (1956). Studies on roots. III. An analysis of root growth in *Phleum pratense* using photomicrographic records. *Amer. J. Bot.*, **43**, 479–87.

[15] Jones, L. H. P., Milne, A. A., and Wadham, S. M. (1963). Studies of silica from the oat plant. II. Distribution of the silica in the plant. *Plant and Soil* **18** (3), 358–71.

F

[16] Metcalfe, C. R. (1960). *Anatomy of the Monocotyledons. I. Gramineae.* Oxford Univ. Press.

[17] Nickerson, N. H. (1954). Morphological analysis of the maize ear. *Amer. J. Bot.,* **41** (2), 87–91.

[18] Page, V. M. (1947). Leaf anatomy of *Streptochaeta* and the relation of this family to the Bamboos. *Torrey Bot. Club Bull.,* **74**, 232–39.

[19] Philipson, W. R. (1934). The morphology of the lemma in grasses. *The New Phytologist,* **33** (5), 359–71.

[20] Reeder, J. R. (1957). The embryo in grass systematics. *Amer. J. Bot.,* **44**, 756–68.

[21] Row, H. C., and Reeder, J. R. (1957). Root hair development as evidence of relationships among genera of Gramineae. *Amer. J. Bot.,* **44**, 596–601.

[22] Sharman, B. C. (1942). Developmental anatomy of the shoot of *Zea mays.* L. *Annals of Bot. N.S.,* **6**, 245–81.

[23] Sharman, B. C. (1960). Developmental anatomy of the stamen and carpel primordia in *Anthoxanthum odoratum. Bot. Gaz.,* **121** (3), 192–98.

[24] Shields, L. M. (1951). The involution mechanism in leaves of certain xeric grasses. *Phytomorphology,* **1** (1), 225–41.

[25] Soper, K., and Mitchell, K. J. (1956). The developmental anatomy of perennial rye grass (*Lolium perenne*). *N.Z. J. Sci. Tech.,* A **37**, 484–504.

[26] Stebbins, G. L. (1956). Cytogenetics and evolution of the grass family. *Amer. J. Bot.,* **43** (10), 890–905.

[27] Stebbins, G. L., and Shah, S. S. (1960). Developmental studies of cell differentiation in the epidermis of Monocotyledons. II. Cytological features of stomatal development in the Gramineae. *Developmental Biology,* **2**, 477–500.

[28] Tateoka, T. (1958). Notes on some grasses. VIII. On leaf structure of *Arundinella* and *Garnotia. Bot. Gaz.,* **120** (2), 101–9.

5

Germination

By L. A. T. Ballard

THE information available about germination of grasses falls sharply into two categories, one dealing with methods of inducing and measuring germination and the other with details of the germination process itself. It should be appreciated that these two types of information have largely been secured on two different types of material, and the reasons for this are of interest.

Surprisingly few species of grasses currently play a major role in the improved pastures of the world (Chapter 3), but potential contributors are rapidly being added to the list, and more are being investigated. In many of these, difficulties and irregularities in germination associated with the brevity of their domestication are marked – as witness titles such as *Grass seed testing is tricky*,[59] *Buffel grass hits snags*.[5] Much has been done to derive empirical methods for overcoming these difficulties, and the findings are valuable, both for the purposes of establishing sound methods required in commercial certification, and as an aid to further investigations by agronomists. Journals of some international and national bodies (e.g. Proceedings of the International Seed Testing Association, Proceedings of the Association of Official Seed Analysts) are devoted largely to the publication of such information.

On the other hand, during the much longer domestication of the staple cereals, conscious or unconscious selection has operated to increase the readiness and uniformity of the germination of their seeds to a very high level, and thus to meet requirements imposed by their culture and their use in industry. The extreme uniformity of germination of barley for the malting industry is a classic example. Although it is not implied that no problems in this direction remain, they do not assume the same significance as among the pasture grasses. Investigations aimed at obtaining a greater understanding of germination processes, as distinct from deriving methods of germination, have thus largely been undertaken with cereal seeds. The availability of stocks of greater genetic homogeneity, as well as the advantages attaching to the use of larger seeds for experimental purposes, have probably been responsible for this choice.

It must therefore remain a matter of judgement whether all or any of the basic information derived from physiological and biochemical studies of cereals is of relevance to problems in the germination of pasture grasses. Some of the evidence reviewed later in this chapter suggests that, at the least, considerable caution should be exercised in such extrapolations.

The Nature and Events of Germination

Most plants have incorporated in their life cycles a relatively resistant and quiescent stage of reduced water content in which they survive unfavourable periods, and in which dispersal usually occurs. In the Spermatophyta this stage is commonly the seed, and, broadly speaking, germination is the resumption of activity of the young sporophyte.

However, the precise meaning to be attached to the term 'germination' remains a matter of definition. The term could be used for those initial steps which are assumed to succeed the restoration of an appropriate water content. Unfortunately we have little information about these processes, and recognition and measurement of them is as yet scarcely possible. Germination is thus usually taken to mean the appearance of the radicle outside the seed coats. (Some workers require the radicle to exhibit geotropism in order to exclude 'false germination' caused merely by imbibitional swelling). It is important to recognize that this wider meaning embraces an element of growth, and that here germination could fail because of failure in the requisite subsequent growth processes. Perhaps the most profitable outlook is to regard the whole germination process as a series of reactions, each of which may exercise control.

For special purposes further restrictions have been attached to the concept. Thus, for legal and commercial certification needs, a seed is not deemed to have germinated unless, from its apparent early growth, it may also be judged able to grow into a normal plant.

While there is a place for each of these shades of meaning there can be little justification for confusion between *germination* (even field germination) and *establishment*. Failure to establish in the field may be due to causes quite unconnected with germination, and some greater precision in referring to these two phases of early seedling growth seems called for.

Both seed* structure and the first visible events in germination are very uniform throughout the grasses.

During maturation, both on and off the parent plant, the seeds exchange water vapour with the environment, the equilibrium reached being mainly dependent on the diffusion pressure deficit of the environment. Grass seeds usually contain about 10 per cent water in atmospheres of 40–50 per cent R.H.,[32,43] the exact value being dependent on the amount of chaffy matter associated with the grain proper.

In the first step towards germination the seeds may absorb water, either as liquid from sufficiently dilute solutions, or as vapour from sufficiently saturated atmospheres, though Owen's results with wheat indicate that little germination can be expected below 97 per cent R.H. at 20°C.[67,68] In uncomplicated cases absorption from water is very rapid, up to 80 per cent of the saturation amount being taken up during a few hours' immersion, and the maximum rate of uptake is achieved within the first hour. The first water is absorbed by imbibition. Then, as free water becomes available, solution occurs, accompanied by vacuolation and the generation of a further diffusion pressure deficit. Finally, more water is absorbed as growth commences. When fully saturated and before radicle protrusion has occurred, the water absorbed

---

* With the exception of the Bamboos whose germination is not treated here, the fruit of the grasses is a caryopsis. In this chapter it will be referred to as seed or grain. The remains of testa, the pericarp, and, where relevant, lemmas and glumes will collectively be called seed coats.

by grass seeds is 40–60 per cent of their air-dry weight, and that absorbed by the embryos perhaps two to three times as much.

In cereals, at least, cell extension precedes cell division,[23, 77, 80] suggesting that the greater part of the observed early growth is to be attributed to the former process. It also suggests that the earliest step in the germination sequence is the induction of some special activity in existing cells of the embryo, rather than the introduction of new functions in newly created cells. Indeed, Haber and Luippold[38] have shown (for lettuce seeds) that germination, as indicated by radicle protrusion, may occur in the absence of any mitotic activity.

In grasses, the first organ to undergo extension is the coleorhiza, through which the primary root emerges. At the other end of the embryonic axis the coleoptile with the enclosed first foliage leaf also emerges. Even on any extended interpretation of the term, germination is then completed.

The most obvious of the chemical events which accompany these morphological changes are a sharp rise in the respiration rate, associated more with the embryo than the endosperm, and a degradation of the starchy endosperm. An array of enzymes must be either activated or synthesized to catalyse these reactions. It has only recently been re-emphasized that these steps follow the initial activation of the embryo, and are directed by it.[23, 24, 49, 69, 70, 71] Thus there is justification for regarding some of the events discussed in the following paragraph as post-germinal.[23, 24]

Because of the obvious significance of the starch reserves most attention has been directed to carbohydrate changes. Dry cereal grains possess very low amylase activity and this is due entirely to β-amylase, whereas the great rise in activity during germination is due substantially to α-amylase. The scutellum has long been associated with the functions of rendering soluble and absorbing the endosperm reserves, and it is interesting to recall that it was in this grass tissue that Horning and Petrie[45] made one of the earliest demonstrations of plant mitochondria, and combined this with suggestions on their metabolic function. These authors observed a great increase in mitochondrial numbers during germination, and believed they were secreted from the scutellar epithelial cells into the endosperm. From the fact that they clustered round starch grains which then were eroded away, they believed that mitochondria secreted amylase (Fig. 5.1). Although the increase in numbers has been confirmed,[40] amylase is no longer believed to be localized in mitochondria. A later suggestion[24] that α-amylase protein may be synthesized by mitochondria requires confirmation, in view of the role currently allotted to ribosomes in protein synthesis. In fact, several aspects of the origin and role of mitochondria during germination invite further study. As a result of some elegant studies on barley endosperm, Paleg[69, 70, 71] has presented an attractive alternative concept for the rise in α-amylase activity. Briefly, his results support the view that the embryo produces and secretes into the endosperm a gibberellin-like hormone causing release of proteins into solution, the appearance of α-amylase and cytase representing special cases of this. The low respiratory activity of endosperm tissue during germination suggests that synthetic processes are at a minimum. The enzymes are thus unlikely to be synthesized in the endosperm

Fig. 5.1. Portion of a transverse section of a maize grain fixed in Champy-Kull solution on the sixth day of germination. Mitochondria are seen accumulated at the peripheral ends of the epithelial cells and in process of passage into the adjacent endosperm. Some are embedded in the mass of crushed cell-walls bounding the endosperm, and in the cells immediately within they occur in profusion. The more peripheral endosperm cells are practically depleted except for a few starch grains in process of solution and show numerous mitochondria accumulated for the most part round their walls. The cells farther in contain more starch grains which have not yet commenced to corrode, and round these mitochondria are clustered in numbers; starch grains which are in process of corrosion are, on the contrary, generally free from mitochondria (×1200). (From Horning and Petrie, 1927, *Roy. Soc. Proc.*, B, **102**, Pl. 9,Fig. 3.)

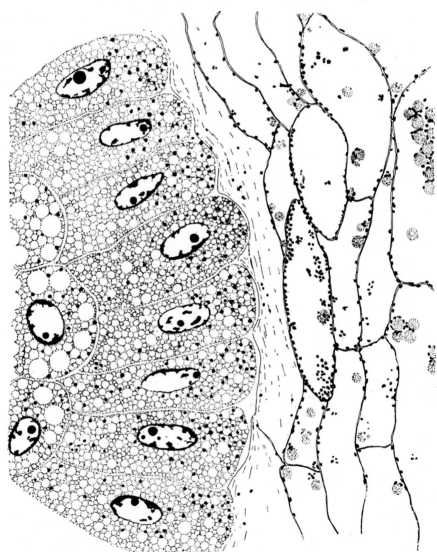

from precursors; more probably they are activated in some way. These findings and views are fully consistent with observations on the facilitating and hastening effects of gibberellic acid on germination in other cereals.[28, 44, 50, 64]

Time Relationships

Although there is uniformity in the morphological events of germination, there are very considerable differences in the readiness with which the process starts and is consummated.

Generally, the grass embryo is capable of continued development quite shortly after pollination, if removed from the grain and suitably cultured.[37, 53, 61, 62] Even immature grains, if removed from the parent plant sufficiently early, have some low capacity for germination. Germinability then usually declines, reaching a low value at morphological ripeness, and sub-

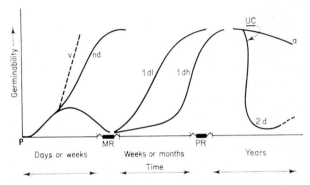

FIG. 5.2. Schematic presentation of some simple time relationships. Modified and simplified, partly after Grahl (1961). P = pollination; MR = morphological ripeness; PR = pysiological ripeness; UC = unfavourable condition; v = vivipary; nd = non-dormant; 1 dl = low primary dormancy; 1 dh = higher primary dormancy; 2 d = secondary dormancy; a = decline in an aged sample.

sequently rises with or without the interpolation of a refractory (dormant) period, as discussed later. Less frequently it increases steadily till full germinibility is achieved at morphological ripeness (Fig. 5.2).

As in other species, true vivipary, i.e. the germination of seeds in advance of morphological ripeness and while still attached to the parent plant, is found naturally very rarely in grasses [8] though it may be induced experimentally.[72, 73] Thus mechanisms preventing development after the germinable phase has been reached, and before reduction of water content stops all activity, must have been incorporated. Two possible mechanisms are lowering of oxygen tension by the resistance to diffusion offered by the developing seed coats, and the accumulation of inhibitors.

Brown[15] has shown (in *Cucurbita pepo*) that the imbibed seed coat membranes do restrict diffusion, but since the oxygen requirements for isolated embryos are generally very low it seems improbable that the loss of germinability is due to reduction of respiration below some threshold. However,

Wareing and associates[12, 83, 84] have produced evidence that oxygen is required to reduce the level of an inhibitor (in *Xanthium* and *Betula* seeds): it now seems likely that a similar mechanism may occur in grasses. The effect of increased pressure on the germination of *Cenchrus ciliaris* (buffel grass)[46] could be interpreted on this basis, and Black[13] has more directly established a decrease in inhibitor content (and dormancy) in *Avena fatua* seeds following treatment with oxygen. In other cases there is no evidence for this mechanism, and Durham and Wellington,[25] studying the germination of red and white wheats, conclude that 'diffusion of oxygen through the covering layers is not a critical factor in the germination of either variety under normal conditions, and the varietal difference in germination behaviour cannot be attributed to differences in the permeability of the covering layers to oxygen'.

There is more evidence for inhibitors located either in the grass seed or in some associated structure. The favourable effects on germination of leaching have been widely observed, inhibitory extracts have been obtained,[13, 26] and in at least one instance, that of wheat, very considerable progress has been made in the purification and identification of the inhibitory substances.[62]

Whatever the suppressive mechanism may be, its removal or deactivation results in the expression of vivipary. Heavy selection pressure against vivipary would be expected in nature, and it is interesting that in the Gramineae most of the recorded cases have been from the staple cereals,[27, 56, 57, 58, 78] where the mutants concerned would have been preserved under domestication, especially for genetic studies.[76]

At morphological ripeness many grass seeds are readily germinable, others when held under ordinarily favourable conditions are not. Such seeds are said to be dormant (primary dormancy), and the processes occurring while normal germinability builds up are spoken of as post-harvest ripening. Even when seed samples are physiologically mature some species may germinate in a few days (*Lolium italicum*, *Phleum pratense*, *Festuca pratensis*) while others take weeks or months (*Cenchrus ciliaris*, *Paspalum* spp.). It is, however, in the time taken for the sample generally to reach a favourable state that the major differences occur. In addition, many grass seeds having reached physiological maturity, become dormant again (secondary dormancy) if held under unfavourable conditions.

On the other hand, processes leading to loss of viability take place in mature seeds, and may also occur before maximum germinability is reached, thus lowering its value. The nature of these processes is not well understood; but their speed is highly dependent on seed moisture content, and hence on the R.H. and temperature of the storage environment. Figures for longevity therefore have little meaning unless these conditions are stated. Viability and seedling vigour may be satisfactorily retained by drying seeds to moisture contents in equilibrium with 15–20 per cent R.H., and holding them in sealed, moisture-proof containers at temperatures not exceeding 32°C.[43, 48] For most grasses this corresponds to 6–8 per cent seed moisture, though certain sensitive species require lower values e.g. *Festuca rubra* (creeping red fescue) requires 3 per cent. Other aspects of storage and longevity are discussed by Owen[66] and Barton.[10]

These time relationships are presented schematically in Fig. 5.2, and several variants are discussed by Grahl.[34]

A great part of this diversity of behaviour is probably to be related to the duration of domestication. It is generally agreed that there is biological advantage attaching to delayed and irregular germination; it insures the species against some seasonal catastrophic condition, it allows for dispersal and for the building-in of mechanisms ensuring the possibility of germination only when conditions are favourable for survival.[88]

Is There a Characteristic Gramineous Pattern of Germination?

In view of the paucity of knowledge on mechanisms of germination in general, this is probably an ambitious query, though the uniformity of seed characteristics and first appearances of germination give point to it. A more specific approach may be through the subsidiary questions: Are there aspects of germination present in grasses, but not paralleled by members of other families? Are there any features present in other families which are not represented somewhere among the grasses? It is necessary only to note that grass seeds exhibit all degrees of dormancy and light sensitivity, possess inhibitors, have the same range and type of temperature requirements and are stimulated by the same range of chemicals and growth regulators as other seeds, to be satisfied that these two questions may be answered in the negative.

A similar situation holds amongst the grasses themselves. On the one hand closely related species may show divergent behaviour, as the following examples demonstrate.

Sorghum halepense	Dormant, temperature selective early in post-harvest life	(42)
S. sudanense	Non-dormant, temperature tolerant	
Festuca pratensis	No light requirement	
F. rubra	No light requirement	(17)
F. elatior	Greatly promoted by light	
Poa pratensis	Unresponsive to KNO_3	
P. trivialis	Unresponsive to KNO_3	(20)
P. compressa	Very responsive to KNO_3	
Panicum maximum	Promoted by light	(6)
P. miliaceum	Light not required	
Phalaris arundinacea	Promoted by light	(6, 7)
Ph. canariensis	Light not required	

On the other hand the same feature or requirement for germination may be shown by quite distantly related species, e.g. light sensitivity is found in members of most of the tribes of the Festucoideae, Panicoideae, and Chloridoideae.

Only between temperature requirement and systematic position does there seem to be some relation. As Went[88] has pointed out, members of the Andropogoneae and Chlorideae fairly consistently have higher optima than those with more temperate distribution; but even here the relationship is by no means as rigorous as implied by Went.

There are two consequences of this situation. First, germination characteristics seem to offer little aid for taxonomic purposes. Prat[74, 75] has forecast that the time course of heat evolution following the wetting of seeds – his thermograms – may be useful for this purpose; but this suggestion is, at best, speculative, in view of the paucity of examples presently available. A more important practical consequence is that detailed knowledge of favourable conditions for germinating one species, and particularly a treatment effective in overcoming a difficulty, is not necessarily of value in forecasting a successful condition or treatment for another. The only valuable rule is that there is no rule. The most that can be said is that an awareness of the range of effective treatments provides a guide.

Helpful Procedures in Germinating Grasses

If the conclusions of the previous section are sound it should be unnecessary to examine here in detail the operation of the major requirements for germination. In common with those of other groups, grass seeds require adequate moisture and an appropriate temperature; they have certain oxygen requirements, and, in some cases, special requirements such as light. Full discussion of these features for germination in general is available in text books and larger reviews.[19, 52, 54, 82]

The intention in this section is to list the chief treatments which have been found empirically useful in grass germination and to comment on mechanisms involved where information is available. It is not intended to imply that the treatments are useful only for grasses.

The treatments may be grouped as follows:

1. *Provision of a Favourable Temperature Regime*

(*a*) Selection of correct optimum. When a single constant temperature is employed, its optimum for most grasses lies between 15° and 25°C. (As noted above, it is higher in the Andropogoneae and Chlorideae where it may be 30–35°C). Shortly after morphological ripeness the optimum is usually lower than later in storage life.

(*b*) Temperature alternation, that is, holding imbibed seed for a portion of each 24 hours at a lower temperature, and at a higher temperature for the remainder. Harrington[41] has recorded the origin of the adoption of this measure as a germination technique. It was suggested from the results of a controversy among 19th century botanists as to whether the favourable effects of light on germination should be attributed to the radiation *per se*, or to the concomitant temperature variations.

The treatment is widely favourable and the conditions it produces appear even to be obligatory for some species e.g. *Poa pratensis, Bromus inermis.* When first used, the amplitude of the alternations found valuable was not more than 10°C, with the higher temperature being restricted to 6–8 hours of the 24-hour cycle.[41] Wider amplitudes, up to 20–25°C, have now been reported as successful,[4, 7, 18] in some cases with the higher temperature being maintained for the longer portion of the cycle.[7, 21]

The alternation itself, and its sharpness, are clearly the effective features. Many of the suggestions concerning the mechanism responsible (e.g. promotion of gas exchange) are neither convincing nor experimentally supported. Toole et al.[81] have provided an analysis in general terms (based on results with non-gramineous species) wherein it is assumed that one temperature regime may generate a balance of reactants favourable for the reaction rates involved at a different temperature.

(c) Pre-chilling, that is, holding imbibed seeds at a low temperature, usually 5–10°C, for a few days to a few weeks, followed by transfer to a higher temperature.

(d) High-temperature dry storage, that is, heating dry seeds to 40–50°C for some weeks. There is a tendency for this treatment to be the more effective the earlier it is applied in post-harvest life, and for it to induce secondary dormancy at a later stage.

Whether the favourable result arises from the heating per se, or from the accompanying reduction in seed moisture content, is not known, since experiments designed to contrast drying achieved by desiccants or low temperature drying under reduced pressure have given variable results. Moreover, there are cases where after-ripening proceeds while seed moisture content remains constant.

2. Modification of Seed Coats

This may be done by cutting, wounding or pricking seeds, by removal of some or all of the covering structures by hand or by milling, or by treatment with abrasives or concentrated H_2SO_4. The method is used by cereal breeders, even on immature seed, to reduce delays in breeding programmes to a minimum. While it is far from infallible, it may be recommended as the single treatment with greatest prospects of success, particularly in cases where only a few seeds of special interest are available, making individual hand treatment feasible.

The general efficacy of the treatment is probably due to it exercising a number of separate effects. It may (a) remove inhibitors, or facilitate their leaching from the coats, endosperm or embryo; (b) facilitate gas exchange; and (c) promote favourable water absorption. Grass seeds do not have hard, impermeable coats, as is common for example in legumes. It appears to be mechanical strength which is important here. It has been shown in some varieties of wheat that the coats are sufficiently strong to resist rupture by the amount of swelling induced by imbibitional water uptake. Further uptake by vacuolation and growth is restricted and thus germination is impaired.[85, 86, 87] A similar situation may obtain in other cases e.g. Paspalum notatum.[1, 3, 16, 60]

3. Inhibitor Removal

This may be done by pre-washing, by leaching with water or acid, or by placing seeds on beds of activated carbon.

4. Light Treatments

(a) Effective intensities are usually within the range of 5–100 f.c. In all species of other families which have been investigated, whether the light be promotive or inhibitory, the effect has been found to be mediated by the phytochrome system. This has now been shown to be true for *Eragrostis ferruginea* also, [30, 31] and may therefore be considered likely for other grass species. The grasses exhibit very clearly a feature shown perhaps less distinctly in other groups. Some species, or even some samples within a species, may either be virtually light indifferent or light obligate, while others appear to be favoured only in their germination by light. A possible explanation for this feature (which has been found to hold in *Anagallis arvensis* subsp. *foemina* (Ballard and Grant Lipp, unpublished)) is the existence of a number of populations, each with a differing sensitivity to light, within apparently homogeneous samples. Even deliberate selection for uniformity of other characters need not necessarily result in increased homogeneity in this one.

Although germination, even on any extended interpretation, is completed by the time of coleoptile emergence, it is interesting to recall that extension of the first internode of grasses is also controlled by the phytochrome system. First internode extension is related inversely to growth of the coleoptile and the enclosed first leaf. In combination, these two features have selective advantage in ensuring maximum survival from buried seeds.

(b) The germination of many non-gramineous species is controlled by the photoperiod. Among grasses this appears to be demonstrated only for *Eragrostis ferruginea*, which behaves as a short-day germinator.[30, 31] However, in many other grass species different amounts of germination are obtained according to whether light is applied for the longer or shorter portion, or at the lower or higher temperature, during alternation. Therefore it seems possible that photoperiod control is exercised in such cases, and that its use might be extended.

5. Manipulation of Oxygen Tension

This has been done by appropriate additions to containers or gas streams, or by variation of pressure. Morinaga[63] reported the favourable effect of lower than atmospheric oxygen tensions for *Cynodon dactylon*; most other positive reports indicate favourable results with enhanced oxygen. The information, however, is scattered and not entirely consistent, and it is difficult to judge how widely useful the treatment may be. Among the grasses, *Poa compressa* appears to be the only case where increased CO_2 tension is promotive.[2]

6. Treatment with Chemicals

Effective compounds include the following: potassium nitrate, thiourea, potassium thiocyanate, potassium cyanide, cupric sulphate, iodo-acetic acid, ethyl alcohol, ethylene chlorohydrin and related substances. The very nature of the list precludes the likelihood that they all act similarly. The first two are used more widely than the remainder – potassium nitrate at 0·1–0·2 per cent, and thiourea at 0·1–1·0 per cent. In view of the fact that the use of potassium nitrate, with or without light, is a prescribed rule of several official seed-testing agencies for a large number of grass species, it is surprising that no detailed information on its action is available. Toole et al.[81] have provided a general analysis analogous to that given for the action of alternating temperatures.

7. Treatment with Growth Regulators

Reference has already been made to the dormancy-breaking or hastening of germination in cereals by gibberellic acid (GA). Less information is available about its action on other grass seeds. Reduction in dormancy has been reported for *Eremochloa ophiuroides* at 1000 mg/l,[22] and for *Avena fatua* at 25–100 mg/l.[36] The latter case illustrates a principle seemingly worthy of further exploitation, that is the controlling of germination to ensure greater

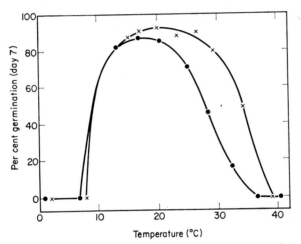

FIG. 5.3. Temperature response of *Lolium rigidum* Gaud. (Wimmera ryegrass). ●—● = 6 weeks after harvest. x — x = 18 months after harvest.

efficiency of subsequent herbicidal treatment. The seeds of *Avena fatua* appear to be particularly responsive to GA treatment, in fact Black and Naylor[14] have prevented the appearance of dormancy in them by GA application during maturation. Here it is suggested that GA antagonizes an inhibitor.[65]

In non-gramineous species the promotive effects of GA on germination are not restricted to cases where it appears to substitute for light (i.e. in effect, not necessarily in mechanism). Particularly among the Rosaceae, GA also replaces a chilling requirement, and relieves epicotyl dormancy. Descriptions of seedling abnormalities produced from unchilled Sudan grass seeds[41] suggest an epicotyl dormancy of a similar nature. It would be of interest to learn whether such cases are more widespread in grasses than is at present appreciated, and whether these also would respond to GA treatment.

There is yet little evidence to suggest that effects of practical significance in germinating grass seeds may be obtained with either auxins or kinins. In higher concentrations indole-acetic acid (IAA) is usually inhibitory, presumably because of its well known inhibitory action on radicle extension. IAA has been found to break dormancy in lettuce seeds, but not in *Poa*.

Kinetin does substitute for, or render less stringent, the light requirement of light-sensitive seeds, but in only a few cases has it been found stimulating where light is not. *Oryzopsis miliacea*, the germination of which is inhibited by light, is such a case.[55] However, it is interesting to note that the best analysis of kinetin's action in germination (of lettuce) indicates that, although it does induce cell division, its promotive action is due solely to its stimulation of cell expansion.[39]

Two general features, the first of which is implicit in the above list, merit comment at this point. Several of the effective treatments apparently act in different ways on different seeds; but germination in any one species may be achieved by different treatments. The other feature is that in the grasses, as indeed in other groups, germination behaviour markedly depends on the physiological age of the seed. The nature of the drift is such that in all cases the stringency of the requirement of a particular condition becomes less with time. This is particularly well illustrated in the case of temperature. The necessity for pre-chilling declines as the seed ages,[47] the optimum becomes higher and broader[9,33] (See Fig. 5.3), and alternation may cease to be obligatory.[41,79] Similarly, light may cease to be obligatory or even promotive,[11,31,33,35] inhibitors decay or are removed, and secondary dormancy becomes more difficult to induce.[29] As an extension of this situation it would be logical to imagine that in some seeds there could be a multiplicity of blockages to germination. If these disappeared sequentially different germination techniques would yield different results on the same seed at different times (as has been shown in subterranean clover (Ballard and Grant Lipp, unpublished)).

There are frequent examples of conflict in the literature on the germination of grasses and inconsistency in findings and recommendations. Age of samples worked on is suggested as the prime source of these discrepancies, closely followed by varietal and population differences within the species.

Finally, it may be remarked that it is implicit in such an analysis that, provided a seed is alive or viable, it will germinate if appropriate conditions are supplied, or, stated conversely, that failure to germinate is due to the absence of some requirement. This type of thinking has led to criticism of the term 'dormant', which seems to discriminate about the seed, whereas the relevant feature is its environment.[19,51] This is a logical position to take, though the term itself has value in a loosely descriptive sense.

Appraisal

Germination is undoubtedly a very critical stage both for the individual and the species. It is just this circumstance, however, which renders so efficient the operation of controlling features which have become incorporated as part of its mechanism.

The preceding sections of this chapter have presented the view that the grass family does not differ essentially from other families in the nature of the individual mechanisms which are found to control the germination of their seeds. But it could be suggested that they have exploited more widely and efficiently the *range* of mechanisms which have been evolved. Even in caryposis weight the range is great, a factor of 10^4 being involved from smallest to largest.

It seems plausible that methods of control became established via the selective advantage in avoidance of vivipary. Variation in time of inactivation or decay of these mechanisms, together with the adoption of others, may then have been incorporated adaptively. However, the very stringency of some of the requirements imposed, would carry the serious disadvantage of possible loss of reproductive material, should the particular condition not be met before viability was lost. Escape from this predicament has been achieved by ensuring gradual loss of control by the mechanisms throughout post-harvest life.

REFERENCES

[1] Akamine, E. K. (1944). Germination of Hawaiian range grass seeds. *Hawaii Agr. Exp. Sta. Tech. Bull.*, No. 2.

[2] Anderson, A. M. (1933). The effect of carbon dioxide and some other gases on the germination of seeds of *Poa compressa*. *Amer. J. Bot.*, **20**, 678–9.

[3] Anderson, A. M. (1953). The effect of the glumes of *Paspalum notatum* Flügge on germination. *Proc. Assoc. Off. Seed Anal.* 43rd Annual Meeting, 93–100.

[4] Anderson, A. M. (1961). A study of dormant and firm seeds of browntop millet. *Proc. Assoc. Off. Seed Anal.*, **51**, 92–8.

[5] Anon. (1952). Buffel grass hits snags. *Southern Seedsman*, **15**, 40–1.

[6] Anon. (1959). International rules for seed testing. *Proc. Int. Seed Test. Assoc.*, **24**, No. 3.

[7] Anon. (1960). Rules for testing seeds. *Proc. Assoc. Off. Seed Anal.*, **49**, No. 2.

[8] Arber, A. (1925). *Monocotyledons, A Morphological Study*. University Press, Cambridge.

[9] Ballard, L. A. T., and Grant Lipp, A. E. (1960). Dormancy and optimum temperatures in Wimmera rye grass. *Aust. Seed Testing Newsletter*, No. 1, 11–13.

[10] Barton, L. V. (1961). *Seed preservation and longevity*. Plant Science Monographs. Leonard Hill (Books) Ltd., London.

[11] Bass, L. N. (1951). Effect of light intensity and other factors on germination of seeds of Kentucky bluegrass (*Poa pratensis* L.). *Proc. Assoc. Off. Seed Anal.*, 41st Annual Meeting, 83–6.

[12] Black, M. (1956). Interrelationships of germination inhibitors and oxygen in the dormancy of seed of *Betula*. *Nature*, **178**, 924–5.

[13] Black, M. (1959). Dormancy studies in seed of *Avena fatua*. I. The possible role of germination inhibitors. *Can. J. Bot.*, **37**, 393–402.

[14] Black, M., and Naylor, J. M. (1959). Prevention of the onset of seed dormancy by gibberellic acid. *Nature*, **184**, 468–9.

[15] Brown, R. (1940). An experimental study of the permeability to gases of the seed-coat membranes of *Cucurbita pepo*. *Ann. Bot. N.S.*, **4**, 379–95.

[16] Burton, G. W. (1939). Scarification studies on southern grass seed. *J. Amer. Soc. Agron.*, **31**, 179–87.

[17] Chippindale, H. G. (1949). Environment and germination in grass seeds. *J. Brit. Grassl. Soc.*, **4**, 57–61.

[18] Colbry, V. L. (1953). Factors affecting the germination of reed canary grass seed. *Proc. Assoc. Off. Seed Anal.* 43rd Annual Meeting, 50–6.

[19] Crocker, W., and Barton, L. V. (1953). *Physiology of seeds: an introduction to the experimental study of seed and germination problems*. Chronica Botanica: Waltham, Mass.

[20] Crosier, W., and Cullinan, B. (1941). Some observations in the germination of grass seed. *Proc. Ass. Off. Seed Anal.*, 33rd Annual Meeting, 69–74.

[21] Cullinan, B. (1941). Germinating seeds of southern grasses. *Proc. Assoc. Off. Seed Anal.*, 33rd Annual Meeting, 74–6.

22 Delouche, J. C. (1961). Effect of gibberellin and light on germination in centipede grass (*Eremochloa ophiuroides*). *Proc. Assoc. Off. Seed Anal.*, **51**, 147–50.

23 Drennan, D. S. H. (1962). Physiological studies of germination in the genus *Avena*. II. Changes in some metabolites during the germination of grains of *Avena sativa*. *New Phytol.*, **61**, 261–5.

24 Drennan, D. S. H., and Berrie, A. M. M. (1962). Physiological studies of germination in the genus *Avena*. I. The development of amylase activity. *New Phytol.*, **61**, 1–9.

25 Durham, V. M., and Wellington, P. S. (1961). Studies on the germination of cereals. 4. The oxygen requirements for germination of wheat grains during maturation. *Ann. Bot. N.S.*, **25**, 197–205.

26 Evenari, M., and Koller, D. (1956). Desert agriculture: problems and results in Israel. In *The Future of Arid Lands*, ed. G. F. White. Amer. Assoc. Adv. Sci. Publicn. 43, 390–413.

27 Eyster, W. H. (1931). Vivipary in maize. *Genetics*, **16**, 574–90.

28 Fischnich, O., Thielebein, M., and Grahl, A. (1957). Brechung der Keimruhe bei Gerste durch Gibberellinsäure und Rindite. *Naturwiss.*, **44**, 642.

29 Fischnich, O., Thielebein, M., and Grahl, A. (1961). Sekundäre Keimruhe bei Getreide. *Proc. Int. Seed Test Ass.*, **26**, 89–114.

30 Fujii, T. (1962). Studies on photoperiodic responses involved in the germination of *Eragrostis* seeds. *Bot. Mag. Tokyo.*, **75**, 56–62.

31 Fujii, T., and Isikawa, S. (1962). Effects of after-ripening on photoperiodic control of seed germination in *Eragrostis ferruginea* Beauv. *Bot. Mag. Tokyo*, **75**, 296–301.

32 Gane, R. (1948). The water content of the seeds of peas, soy, linseed, grass, onion, and carrot as a function of the temperature and humidity of the atmosphere. *J. Ag. Sci.*, **38**, 81–3.

33 Gordon, E. M. (1951). Light- and temperature-sensitiveness in germinating seed of timothy (*Phleum pratense* L.) *Sci. Agric.*, **31**, 71–84.

34 Grahl, A. (1961). Über Keimruhe bei Saatgut. I. Die primäre Keimruhe bei Getreide. *Kali-Briefe*, **5**. Fachgebiet 3, Folge 2: 7.

35 Grahl, A., and Thielebein, M. (1960). Wirkung von Licht und Dunkelheit auf die Keimung von Saatgut. *Mitteilungsblatt der Forschungsanstalt für Landwirtschaft Braunschweig – Völkenrode*, **10** (4), 100–3.

36 Green, J. G., and Helgeson, E. A. (1957). The effect of gibberellic acid on dormant seed of wild oat (Abstract). *Proc. North Central Weed Control Conf.*, **14**, 39.

37 Haagen-Smit, A. J., Siu, R., and Wilson, G. (1945). A method for the culturing of excised, immature corn embryos *in vitro*. *Science*, **101**, 234.

38 Haber, A. H., and Luippold, H. J. (1960a). Separation of mechanisms initiating cell division and cell expansion in lettuce seed germination. *Plant Physiol.*, **35**, 168–73.

39 Haber, A. H., and Luippold, H. J. (1960b). Effects of gibberellin, kinetin, thiourea, and photomorphogenic radiation on mitotic activity in dormant lettuce seed. *Plant Physiol.*, **35**, 486–94.

40 Hageman, R. H., and Hanson, J. B. (1955). Carbohydrase activity of cytoplasmic particles prepared from corn scutellum. *Plant Physiol.*, **30**, suppl. iv.

41 Harrington, G. T. (1923). Use of alternating temperatures in the germination of seeds. *J. Agric. Res.*, **23**, 295–333.

42 Harrington, G. T., and Crocker, W. (1923). Structure, physical characteristics and composition of the pericarp and integument of Johnson grass seed in relation to its physiology. *J. Agric. Res.*, **23**, 193–222.

43 Harrington, J. F. (1959). Drying, storing, and packaging seeds to maintain germination and vigor. *Proc. 1959 Mississippi short course for Seedsmen*, 89–107.

44 Hayashi, T. (1940). Biochemical studies on 'Bakanae' fungus of rice. VI. Effect of gibberellin on the activity of amylase in germinated cereal grain. *Bull. Agr. Chem. Soc. Japan*, **16**, 531–8.

45 Horning, E. S., and Petrie, A. H. K. (1927). The enzymatic function of mitochondria in the germination of cereals. *Proc. Roy. Soc. B.*, **102**, 188–206.

46 Humphreys, L. R. (1958). Studies in the germination, early growth, drought survival, and field establishment of buffel grass (*Cenchrus ciliaris* L.) and of Birdwood grass (*C. setigerus* Vahl), with particular reference to the Yalleroi district of Queensland. M.Sc.Agric. Thesis. University of Sydney.

[47] Hylton, L. O., and Bass, L. N. (1961). Germination of Sixweeks Fescue. *Proc. Assoc. Off. Seed Anal.*, **51**, 118–21.

[48] Isely, D., and Bass, L. N. (1959). Seeds and packaging materials. *Proc. 14th Hybrid Corn Industry-Research Conferences*, 101–10.

[49] James, W. O. (1953). *Plant Respiration*. Clarendon Press, Oxford.

[50] Kirsop, B., and Pollack, J. (1958). Studies in barley and malt. XII. Interaction between the embryo and the endosperm during malting. *Jour. Inst. Brewing*, **64**, 227–33.

[51] Koller, D. (1961). Ecological problems of seed dormancy. In *Cryptobiotic stages in Biological systems* ed. N. Grossowicz. Elsevier Publishing Co., Amsterdam.

[52] Koller, D., Mayer, A. M., Poljakoff-Mayber, A., and Klein, S. (1962). Seed Germination. *Annu. Rev. Plant Physiol.*, **13**, 437–64.

[53] La Rue, C. D. (1936). Growth of plant embryos in culture. *Bull. Torrey Bot. Club*, **63**, 365–82.

[54] Lehmann, R., and Aichele, F. (1931). *Keimungsphysiologie der Gräser (Gramineen). Eine Lebensgeschichte des reifenden, ruhenden und keimenden Grassamens.* Ferdinand Enke, Stuttgart.

[55] Leizorowitz, R., and Poljakoff-Mayber, A. (1960). The effect of gibberellin and kinetin on the germination of some photosensitive desert seeds as compared with that of light. *Opton*, **15**, 103–7.

[56] Linstrom, E. W. (1923). Heritable characters of maize: XIII. Endosperm defects – sweet defective and flint defective. *J. Heredity*, **14**, 125–35.

[57] Mangelsdorf, P. C. (1923). The inheritance of defective seeds in maize. *J. Heredity*, **14**, 119–25.

[58] Mangelsdorf, P. C. (1930). The inheritance of dormancy and premature germination in maize. *Genetics*, **15**, 462–94.

[59] Mauldin, M. P. (1951). Grass seed testing is tricky. *Southern Seedsman*, **14**, 66–7.

[60] Meadow, M. V. (1953). Problems in Bahia grass analysis. *Proc. Assoc. Off. Seed Anal.*, 43rd Annual Meeting, 82–3.

[61] Merry, J. (1942). Studies on the embryo of *Hordeum sativum*. II. The growth of the embryo in culture. *Bull. Torrey Bot. Club*, **69**, 360–72.

[62] Miyamoto, R., Tolbert, N. E., and Everson, E. H. (1961). Germination inhibitors related to dormancy in wheat seeds. *Plant Physiol.*, **36**, 739–46.

[63] Morinaga, T. (1926). The favourable effect of reduced oxygen supply upon the germination of certain seeds. *Amer. J. Bot.*, **13**, 159–66.

[64] Munekata, H., and Kato, S. (1957). Studies on 'Bakanae' fungus of rice. XXXX. Application of gibberellin to the malting industry. *Bull. Brewing Soc. Japan*, **3**, 1–10.

[65] Naylor, J. M., and Simpson, G. M. (1961). Dormancy studies in seed of *Avena fatua*. 2. A gibberellin-sensitive inhibitory mechanism in the embryo. *Can. J. Bot.*, **39**, 281–95.

[66] Owen, E. B. (1956). The storage of seeds for maintenance of viability. *Bulletin* 43, *Commonwealth Bureau of Pastures and Field Crops* (Commonwealth Agricultural Bureaux: Farnham Royal, Bucks.).

[67] Owen, P. C. (1952a). The relation of germination of wheat to water potential. *J. Exp. Bot.*, **3**, 188–203.

[68] Owen, P. C. (1952b). The relation of water absorption by wheat seeds to water potential. *J. Exp. Bot.*, **3**, 276–90.

[69] Paleg, L. (1960a). Physiological effects of gibberellic acid. I. On carbohydrate metabolism and amylase activity of barley endosperm. *Plant Physiol.*, **35**, 293–9.

[70] Paleg, L. (1960b). Physiological effects of gibberellic acid. II. On starch hydrolysing enzymes of barley endosperms. *Plant Physiol.*, **35**, 902–6.

[71] Paleg, L. (1961). Physiological effects of gibberellic acid. III. Observations on its mode of action on barley endosperms. *Plant Physiol.*, **36**, 829–37.

[72] Pope, M. N. (1941). Artificially induced vivipary in barley. *J. Amer. Soc. Agron.*, **33**, 850–1.

[73] Pope, M. N., and Brown, E. (1943). Induced vivipary in three varieties of barley possessing extreme dormancy. *J. Amer. Soc. Agron.*, **35**, 161–3.

[74] Prat, H. (1952). Micro calorimetric studies on germination of cereals. *Can. J. Bot.*, **30**, 379–94.

[75] Prat, H. (1960). Vers une classification naturelle des Graminées. *Bull. Soc. Bot. de France*, **107**, 32–79.

G

[76] Robertson, D. S. (1955). The genetics of vivipary in maize. *Genetics*, **40**, 745–60.

[77] Schwartz, D., and Bay, C. E. (1956). Further studies on the reversal in the seedling height dose curve at very high levels of ionizing radiations. *Am. Naturalist*, **90**, 323–7.

[78] Sprague, C. F. (1936). The relation of moisture content and time of harvest to germination of immature corn. *J. Amer. Soc. Agron.*, **28**, 472–8.

[79] Sprague, V. G. (1940). Germination of freshly harvested seeds of several *Poa* species and of *Dactylis glomerata*. *J. Am. Soc. Agron.*, **32**, 715–21.

[80] Toole, E. H. (1924). The transformations and course of development of germinating maize. *Amer. J. Bot.*, **11**, 325–50.

[81] Toole, E. H., Toole, V. K., Borthwick, H. A., and Hendricks, S. B. (1955). Interaction of temperature and light in germination of seeds. *Plant Physiol.*, **30**, 473–8.

[82] Toole, E. H., Hendricks, S. B., Borthwick, H. A., and Toole, V. K. (1956). Physiology of seed germination. *Annu. Rev. Plant Physiol.*, **7**, 299–324.

[83] Wareing, P. F. (1957). Growth inhibitors and dormancy in *Xanthium* seed. *Physiol. Plantarum*, **10**, 266–80.

[84] Wareing, P. F., and Foda, H. A. (1956). The possible role of growth inhibitors in the dormancy of seed of *Xanthium* and lettuce. *Nature*, **178**, 908.

[85] Wellington, P. S. (1956a). Studies on the germination of cereals. I. The germination of wheat grains in the ear during development, ripening, and after-ripening. *Ann. Bot. N.S.*, **20**, 105–20.

[86] Wellington, P. S. (1956b). Studies on the germination of cereals. 2. Factors determining the germination behaviour of wheat grains during maturation. *Ann. Bot. N.S.*, **20**, 481–500.

[87] Wellington, P. S., and Durham, V. M. (1961). Studies on the germination of cereals. 3. The effect of the covering layers on the uptake of water by the embryro of the wheat grain. *Ann. Bot. N.S.*, **25**, 185–96.

[88] Went, F. W. (1957). *Experimental Control of Plant Growth*. Chronica Botanica, Waltham, Mass.

6

The Quantitative Description of Growth

By R. F. Williams

THIS chapter is concerned with some quantitative aspects of growth in higher plants, the general thesis being built upon data for the wheat plant. A more specific treatment of the subject of growth in grasses would not be profitable because the detailed information necessary to characterize the wide range of growth form found in the family (see Chapter 4) does not exist. However, the general pattern which emerges may well be relevant to all grasses. The first part of the chapter deals with growth curves and curve fitting, and the second with the pattern of growth within the main shoot.

In his *Principles of Embryology*, Waddington[7] looks briefly at the main varieties of growth function which have been used as mathematical models for growth. These are the 'monomolecular' formula, the logistic or autocatalytic formula, the Gompertz equation, and the parabolic or double-log curve. In varying degrees, these have all been shown to fit sets of experimental data, but it has never been possible to show that any one of them fits the facts so exactly that the others can be excluded. If we can use these formulae 'merely as convenient means of summarizing the empirical observations', the theoretical gain has not been great.

Perhaps the trouble is in our fascination with the well-nigh universal sigmoid form of growth curves; a universality which seems to imply a unitary explanation where it is now safe to say that no such implication is justified.

In an earlier statement, Medawar[5] put forward the view that only one fundamental generalization can be made about the relationship between the size of an organism and its age: that which is represented by the equation

$$\frac{d \log W}{dt} = R$$

where W is the weight of the system, and R is positive, decreasing with time at a diminishing rate towards a zero bound. R, the relative growth rate, is the *specific growth rate* of Minot,[6] the *percentage rate of growth* of Brody,[3] and the *efficiency index* of Blackman.[2] Only for special cases is R a constant, such that growth proceeds by continuous compound interest. Medawar prefers to work with the curve of specific growth (log W) and with R because they record the *multiplication* of living substance, and because they give up their information more easily than does the curve of growth (W) and its simple derivatives. Those who disagree with this preference, particularly among plant scientists, do so because R is seldom constant in higher plants, or because not all parts of the plant are involved in growth.[8] That Medawar's preference is justified for plants as well as animals will emerge from the sequel.

The value of R at any instant is

$$\frac{1}{W}\frac{dW}{dt} = \frac{d \log W}{dt}$$

89

and its average value over the time interval $t_2 - t_1$ is given by

$$\frac{\log_e W_2 - \log_e W_1}{t_2 - t_1}$$

There is little doubt at all that Medawar is right in pointing the need for rehabilitation and new development in the study of growth. We will first look at the growth curve as a whole, and see if the limited and seemingly pessimistic conclusions reached by Medawar and Waddington are equally applicable to plants, and to grasses in particular.

Text figures 6.1–6.6 are based on hitherto unpublished data for the wheat plant, and are from field-grown material for two sowing dates 5 weeks apart. The data are not ideal for our purpose, for only shoot growth was recorded, and the environment was one of steadily increasing temperature and lengthening days. These shortcomings are offset considerably by the unusually large number of sampling occasions and the high precision of the experimental means.*

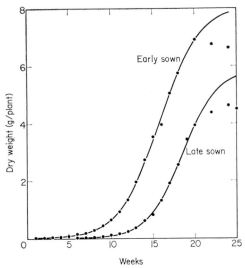

FIG. 6.1. Dry weights of the shoots of field-grown wheat for two sowing dates. The fitted logistic curves are discussed in the text.

The raw data were plotted both on arithmetic and logarithmic scales and a number of attempts were made to provide algebraic descriptions of the time dependence of growth. The more successful descriptions reported below are the logistic curve (applied to W), a third degree polynomial (applied to log W), and a sequence of exponential curves (applied as straight lines to log W).

The arithmetic data (Fig. 6.1) clearly invite the fitting of logistic curves, the general equation for which is

$$W = \frac{K}{1 + e^{a - bt}}$$

where K is the upper asymptote of the curve, and a and b are constants.

* Each point in Figures 6.1–6.4 represents 16 random sampling areas carrying, on average, 25 plants each.

The two curves of Figure 6.1 are for the specific equations:

EARLY SOWN
$$W = \frac{8 \cdot 10}{1 + e^{6 \cdot 636 - 0 \cdot 421\,t}}$$

and

LATE SOWN
$$W = \frac{5 \cdot 90}{1 + e^{8 \cdot 896 - 0 \cdot 481\,t}},$$

which were computed in the usual way from the linear form of the general equation, and from estimates of the upper asymptote K. It was found, however, that the linear form would not accommodate the last two points for the early-sown or the last three points for the late-sown crop. To that extent the equations fail to give a full description of the data, and, as will be shown later, the curves also do some violence to the early experimental values for each crop. Even apart from these defects, no realistic biological meaning can be attached to the K values, or to the constants a and b.

The fitting of third degree polynomial curves to the logarithms of the original data yielded surprisingly good results, as will be seen in Figure 6.2.

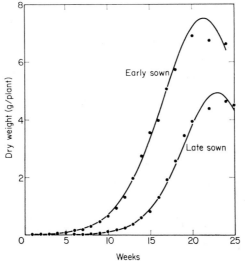

FIG. 6.2. Dry weights as in Fig. 6.1. The curves are based on third degree polynomials fitted to the logarithms of the data (see text).

The smooth curves are plotted on an arithmetic scale to facilitate comparison with Figure 6.1.

The original polynomials are as follows:

EARLY SOWN
$$\log_{10} W = -2 \cdot 047 + 0 \cdot 2031t + 0 \cdot 00021t_2 - 0 \cdot 000155t_3$$

LATE SOWN
$$\log_{10} W = -2 \cdot 072 + 0 \cdot 2110t + 0 \cdot 00226t_2 - 0 \cdot 000302t_3$$

the time being measured in weeks, and the first sampling occasion being called week 1 in each case.

The curves of Figure 6.2 give superficially satisfying descriptions of the data, and this without the need to discard any terminal values. It may also be said in advance that these curves do more justice than do the logistic curves to

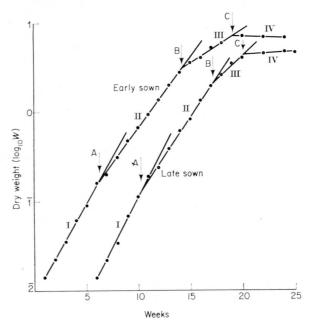

FIG. 6.3. Logarithms of the dry weights as in Fig. 6.1, fitted with sequences of linear regressions (see text).

the early experimental values for each crop. For all that, close inspection shows that the descriptions are not accurate in detail, especially for the late sown crop. There is a strong tendency for sequences of points to be found either above or below the fitted curves.

Yet another approach to the analysis of growth curves departs from the notion that growth is a continuous function of time. Thus Hammond and Kirkham[4] find growth in dry weight for soybeans and corn to be best described as sequences of three and four exponential segments respectively.* Sometimes their evidence for these segments rests precariously on straight lines drawn through as few as two experimental points, but their case is sufficient to justify the application of their methods to the present sets of data. This is done in Figures 6.3 and 6.4. Clearly, there are many pitfalls in the procedure, for subjective judgements must be made as to which experimental values belong to the successive straight-line segments of Figure 6.3. These judgements are not difficult for the early-sown crop, though very uneven numbers of values contribute to the successive segments. Segment III is

* See Brody[3] for similar analyses of growth in animals, and to a limited extent in plants.

defined by only four points and segment IV by three. Segments I and II for the late-sown crop can also be regarded as satisfactory, but segments III and IV are open to question. The last five or six values do not readily fall on straight lines at all, and the compromise solution is based too obviously on a desire for conformity with the pattern set by the early sown crop.

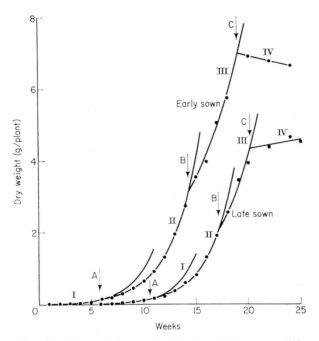

FIG. 6.4. Dry weights as in Fig. 6.1. The exponential curves are based on the linear regressions of Fig. 6.3.

The equations for the two sets of straight lines of Figure 6.3 are

EARLY SOWN

$$
\begin{aligned}
\text{Equation I} \quad \log_{10} W &= -2\cdot044 + 0\cdot2025t \\
\text{,, \quad II \quad ,,} \quad &= -1\cdot774 + 0\cdot1585t \\
\text{,, \quad III \quad ,,} \quad &= -0\cdot572 + 0\cdot0742t \\
\text{,, \quad IV \quad ,,} \quad &= 0\cdot927 - 0\cdot0044t
\end{aligned}
$$

LATE SOWN

$$
\begin{aligned}
\text{Equation I} \quad \log_{10} W &= -3\cdot203 + 0\cdot2232t \\
\text{,, \quad II \quad ,,} \quad &= -2\cdot692 + 0\cdot1750t \\
\text{,, \quad III \quad ,,} \quad &= -1\cdot524 + 0\cdot1071t \\
\text{,, \quad IV \quad ,,} \quad &= 0\cdot534 + 0\cdot0051t
\end{aligned}
$$

When reduced to the arithmetic scale of Figure 6.4, these equations appear as series of exponential curves, and the descriptive power of the procedure is clearly superior to those of Figures 6.1 and 6.2. However, this superiority rests in some measure on the fact that the equations for Figures 6.1, 6.2, and 6.3 use 3, 4, and 8 constants respectively, so it would be wrong to infer that this form of analysis must therefore have biological significance. It seems possible that Hammond and Kirkham[4] were too ready to reach this conclusion, for their interpretations make heavy demands on the goodwill of the reader.

The analysis of the wheat data can be carried a little further in terms of the growth of the major plant parts. Figure 6.5 presents curves for leaves (blades only), stems plus leaf sheaths, and for the inflorescences in both the early- and late-sown crops. The points A, B, and C, marking the change from one exponential curve to the next (Figures 6.3 and 6.4), are also shown on Figure

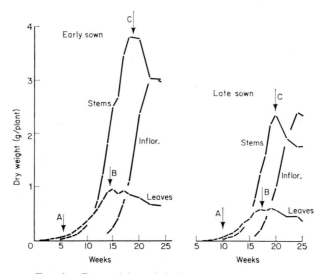

FIG. 6.5. Dry weights of the leaves, stems and inflorescences of field-grown wheat for two sowing dates. Points A, B and C are as in Figs. 6.1 and 6.4.

6.5, and it will be noted that B and C mark the rather sudden cessation of growth of the leaf and stem fractions respectively. No such obvious descriptive explanation is available for point A, though independent evidence suggests that this might be the point at which dry matter production is diverted for the establishment of the secondary root system. If this is so, point A could disappear in curves based on the whole plant. Indeed, the extrapolations from equation I (Fig. 6.4) are consistent with root growth of an appropriate order of magnitude. However, all this is too speculative to be carried by the evidence.

The first harvests of the above field experiment were made 22 days after sowing, and the data exclude the period of early seedling establishment. This period has since been studied in detail[10] in a controlled environment. The results show that growth is then best described as a sequence of two exponential phases linked by a period of transition. The first phase is clearly that of dependence on grain reserves, and the relative growth rate of the seedling axis is 0·86 g/g/day for days 1–4. In the second phase, the seedling is entirely dependent on photosynthesis, and the relative growth rate falls to the comparatively low figure of 0·15 g/g/day for days 8–18. The transition from the higher to the lower value takes about 4 days, and establishes the rather obvious point that all growth stages such as those postulated in Figure 6.4, are likely to be linked by smooth transitions rather than by discontinuous change.

What, then, are the relative merits of the three forms of mathematical description which have been used here? Visual comparison of Figures 6.1, 6.2, and 6.4 suggests that the growth stage approach has superior descriptive power to the other two, and the independent evidence from the study of the seedling establishment phase suggests that this has biological meaning. Nevertheless, the method is subjective, and therefore liable to abuse. It should

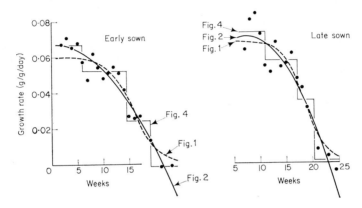

FIG. 6.6. Relative growth rates for the shoots of field-grown wheat for two sowing dates. The points are experimental values for two-week intervals. The curves are appropriate to the logistic curves of Fig. 6.1, the polynomials of Fig. 6.2 and the exponential sequences of Fig. 6.4.

be applied only to data of high precision, and with the use of controlled environments. Concerning the other two descriptions, it is worthy of note that the one which is less exacting in the assumptions it makes (the third-degree polynomial) gives the more satisfying description. However, neither description has any demonstrable explanatory value. The growth stage approach does at least offer a testable hypothesis, together with a reminder that explanation must be in terms of smaller units than the phenomenon to be explained.

If it is not already clear that no firm conclusions can be based on the present exercise in curve fitting, this will become evident from an examination of Figure 6.6. This expresses the wheat data in terms of the concept of relative growth rate. The experimental values (the points on the graph) are for two-week intervals and they suggest only a general fall with time, the rate of fall tending to increase with time. Super-imposed on the experimental values are the relative growth rates appropriate to the three descriptive analyses of the growth curves (Figs. 6.1, 6.2, 6.4). Of the two pairs of continuous curves in Figure 6.6, those based on the third-degree polynomials are again the more satisfying (Fig. 6.2). Those for the logistic curves fail both at the beginnings and endings of the growth periods. On the other hand, one can scarcely claim that the experimental values uphold the stepwise fall in relative growth rate which follows from a rigid acceptance of growth as a sequence of discrete exponential segments.

An incidental point of some importance to the study of growth is well brought out by Figure 6.6. This is that growth rates are at their highest during the first half of the growth period. This may seem a trivial point to make, but many otherwise excellent sets of data have been reduced in value because sampling did not commence early enough. Presumably, growth – that is, incremental growth – was thought to be too slow to be worth measuring.

So far we have been concerned primarily with the growth of the whole organism (without roots in the example), though Figure 6.5 does provide a breakdown in terms of major organ types. Whether or not this provides an explanation of the curve of growth for the whole plant, it is clearly important to know something of the timing and the growth characteristics of such organ types. This has been done in some detail by Ballard and Petrie[1] for wheat (*Triticum aestivum*) and Sudan grass (*Andropogon sudanensis*), by Williams[9] for oats (*Avena sativa*), by Williams and Shapter[11] for barley (*Hordeum vulgare*) and rye (*Secale cereale*), and by Williams[10] for the wheat seedling.

The growth of the seminal root system is dominant during early establishment, and in wheat it receives more than half of the reserves exported from the grain during the first few days of growth.[10] The leaves get an increasing share of these reserves, and they are well placed to get their share of the early products of photosynthesis. As a result, from 40 to 60 per cent of the dry matter may be localized in the leaf blades during vegetative growth. The adventitious root system is established during this period, and total root growth roughly parallels that of the leaves. The growth of leaf sheaths closely follows that of the blades, with a delay of some days for each individual sheath. In wheat, and presumably in all tufted or tussock grasses, stem growth is at a minimum until after floral induction. When, as in spring wheat, all apices are induced at the same time, no further leaves are formed and leaf growth comes to an abrupt end some time later (see Fig. 6.5). Evidence from other cereals suggests that root growth stops at about the same time, and all growth is then channelled into the production of the stem and inflorescence fractions. It is often claimed, perhaps on inadequate evidence, that the annual habit in cereals and many grasses is due to self starvation resulting from the production of these excessively large stem, inflorescence and grain fractions.

There is little quantitative information on the growth of grasses with creeping or straggling growth forms. Clearly, stem growth is not restricted during vegetative growth, and they differ in other important ways. Most of them are perennials.

As pointed out earlier, explanation must be in terms of smaller units than the phenomenon to be explained, and the growth of higher plants receives descriptive explanation in terms of the major organ assemblages which we have been considering. However, the mere admission that they are assemblages of organs suggests that a much clearer understanding of growth is likely to follow the detailed study of the growth of individual organs. Such a study of successive organs of the primary shoot in wheat has now been made by Williams.[10]

The central feature of this work is the quantitative description of the growth of each leaf from its initiation through to maturity. The technique of serial reconstruction was adopted for the measurement of volume change

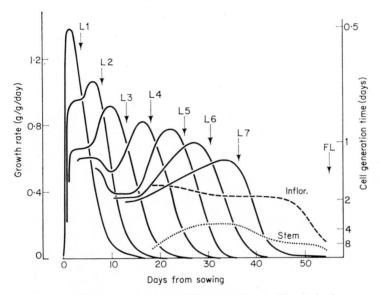

FIG. 6.7. Relative growth rates for seven leaves (L1–L7), the stem, and the inflorescence of the primary shoot of wheat plants grown in continuous light. The arrows indicate the times of emergence of the successive leaves, and the time of flowering. The curves can be read in R units or dry-weight doubling times (mean cell generation times where applicable).

within the shoot apex and for young leaf primordia, but dry weight determinations were substituted as soon as the parts could be separated with reasonable precision.

As Barnard points out in Chapter 4, the leaf primordia in wheat and other grasses arise by the periclinal division of cells of the two-layered tunica (see Plate 3), the corpus contributing nothing to their development. These facts made it possible to estimate volumes for very early stages of primordium development: far earlier than would have been possible by procedures of dissection and weighing. The range of size through which leaf primordia develop into mature leaves is tremendous, being of the order of 10^5 times the size when first measurable by these procedures. This size has a dry-weight equivalent of the order of 3×10^{-4} mg. The presentation of such data on a linear scale is of very limited value, for it does justice only to the closing phases of growth. A logarithmic scale has excellent descriptive value, and one usually adopts this when having a preliminary look at a set of data. However, quite the most sensitive index of growth is the relative growth rate, R, and this is the one used in Figure 6.7.

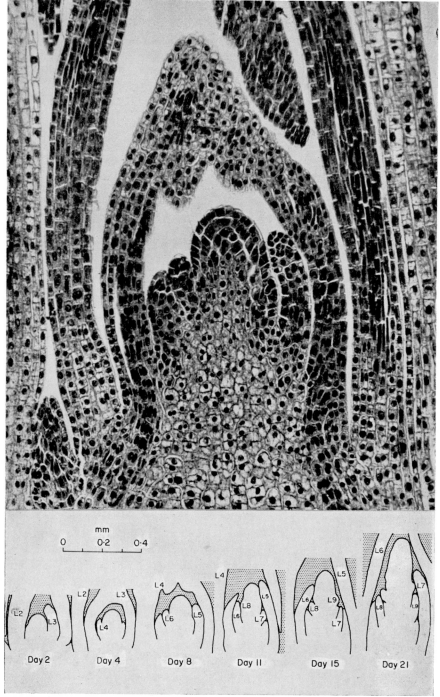

PLATE 3. Longitudinal section of an 8-day wheat seedling, showing the two-layered tunica of the growing point and outline drawings of longitudinal sections covering the transition from the vegetative to the reproductive state. (From Williams, 1960, *Aust. J. Biol. Sci.*, **13**, 401–28, Fig. 3.)

This figure is a synthesis of the results of several experiments, and portrays the pattern of growth for seven foliage leaves, the stem and the inflorescence of the primary shoot of wheat grown under long days. Most plants produced only seven leaves under these conditions. The arrows mark the times of emergence of the leaves, and flowering took place on day 55. The weights of the leaves at emergence and at maturity are shown in Table 6.4.

TABLE 6.1

Dry Weights of Successive Leaves in mg per Plant

	L1	L2	L3	L4	L5	L6	L7
At emergence	1·4	1·5	2·0	2·7	5·1	7·3	12·4
At maturity	12	18	36	62	76	89	109

The weights of the inflorescence and stem at flowering were 191 and 637 mg respectively, and their weights at day 16 were $2·5 \times 10^{-4}$ and 2·25 mg respectively. The stem had, of course, been growing for some time, and would undoubtedly have shown a peak in the first ten days if precise measurements had been made.

A valuable property of the relative growth rate scale is that it can be transformed into a scale which shows the time taken for the organ or organism to double its size. In the special case where size increase is due solely to cell division and mean cell size does not change, this is the mean cell generation time, and the scale to the right of Figure 6.7 is so labelled. This is another way of saying that R measures the rate of multiplication.

The first leaf primordium, L1, attains the very high maximum value of 1·4 for R. This implies a mean cell generation time of half a day, and a four-fold increase in size in one day ($\log_e 4 = 1·4$). The R maxima fall rather sharply for successive leaf primordia, but even L6 attains a doubling time of one day. Then, too, the inflorescence has a mean cell generation time of two days or less for more than three weeks. All these points, and many others, can be derived from Figure 6.7, and the whole provides a sensitive picture of the pattern of growth. Periods of relative constancy in R for individual organs are the exception rather than the rule.

The most regular feature of the diagram is that R for each leaf rises to a maximum a few days prior to leaf emergence and then falls asymptotically to zero. The curves for postmaximal growth are those to be expected for organs undergoing the normal processes of maturation, though it is curious that R starts to fall so early. Thus, 90–95 per cent of the dry matter of the leaf is laid down after emergence (Table 6.1), when R is already falling.

Special interest attaches to the great variety of trends in R prior to leaf emergence, for it is then that one might expect growth to be strictly exponential. Each leaf primordium follows a different course, though there are similarities in the trends for successive members. It is reasonably certain that these early changes in R reflect changes in rates of cell division and hence of protein synthesis. The rates also seem to be correlated with the stainability of the cytoplasm of the cells, increased staining being thought to be due to high ribonucleic acid content, and to imply an increase in the potential for protein synthesis.

What, then, are the factors which govern these pre-emergence trends in R? Intra-plant competition for metabolites and nutrients are probably important; and energy substrates are thought to be the most likely substances competed for in the present case. One obvious pointer to competition is the marked drop in the successive initial values of R at the time of the exhaustion of seed reserves, about eight days after sowing (Fig. 6.7). The timing of effective vascular connection of the successive primordia with the sources of substrate for growth may also be important. Examination of Plate 1 (see p. 66) will show that all such substrate must get to the apex and to L5 and L6 by active transport across a region of small, undifferentiated cells. L4, which has a slightly higher R value at this time, is closer to the source of substrate and its provascular strands are well developed. The fastest growing leaf, however, is L3 (base only showing in Plate 1), in which vascular differentiation has already begun. It will be noted, too, that the cytoplasm of the cells of this leaf is more heavily stained than is that of L4.

Finally, there are the changes which accompany the transformation from the vegetative to the reproductive condition. There is a progressive increase in the rate of growth of the apex itself (Plate 1(b)), an almost explosive growth of corpus-derived tissue, and a remarkably sustained increase in the R value for the stem as a whole (Fig. 6.7). The analysis of stem growth in terms of R for successive internodes should be a rewarding exercise in itself, for this will yield a pattern rather different from that for the successive leaves. However, further speculation at this stage is scarcely profitable; only comparative studies of plants grown in selected controlled environments are likely to provide a sound quantitative description of the change to the reproductive state. There is also a need for detailed anatomical and biochemical studies of some of the developmental phenomena revealed by this work.

In the light of the above analysis of the growth of the wheat plant, it will be apparent that further studies of the kind could contribute much to an understanding of the internal factors and mechanisms which integrate the parts of a plant into the whole organism. The basic importance of the concept of relative growth rate is also clear, and its role as a yardstick rather than a restrictive principle will be recognized. By this I mean that, too often, there has been a tendency to *expect* plant growth to conform to a rigid compound interest law – an expectation which, incidentally, was not shared by Blackman (1919) when he proposed the use of his 'efficiency index'.

REFERENCES

[1] Ballard, L. A. T., and Petrie, A. H. K. (1936). Physiological ontogeny in plants and its relation to nutrition. 1. The effect of nitrogen supply on the growth of the plant and its parts. *Aust. J. Exp. Biol. Med. Sci.*, **14**, 135–63.

[2] Blackman, V. H. (1919). The compound interest law and plant growth. *Ann. Bot.*, **33**, 353–60.

[3] Brody, S. (1927). Growth and development with special reference to domestic animals. 4. Growth rates during the self-accelerating phase of growth. *Univ. Missouri Agric. Exp. Sta. Res. Bull.* No. 98.

[4] Hammond, L. C., and Kirkham, D. (1949). Growth curves of soybeans and corn. *Agron. J.*, **41**, 23–9.

[5] Medawar, P. B. (1945). Size, shape, and age. *Essays on Growth and Form.* Oxford University Press, pp. 157–87.

[6] Minot, C. (1908). *The Problem of Age, Growth and Death.* Putnam, New York.

[7] Waddington, C. H. (1956). *Principles of Embryology.* George Allen and Unwin, London.

[8] Whaley, W. G. (1961). Growth as a general process. *Encyclopedia of Plant Physiology.* 14. *Growth and growth substances.* Springer-Verlag, Berlin, pp. 71–112.

[9] Williams, R. F. (1936). Physiological ontogeny in plants and its relation to nutrition. 2. The effect of phosphorus supply on the growth of the plant and its parts. *Aust. J. Exp. Biol. Med. Sci.*, **14**, 165–85.

[10] Williams, R. F. (1960). The physiology of growth in the wheat plant. 1. Seedling growth and the pattern of growth at the shoot apex. *Aust. J. Biol. Sci.*, **13**, 401–28.

[11] Williams, R. F., and Shapter, R. E. (1955). A comparative study of growth and nutrition in barley and rye as affected by low-water treatment. *Aust. J. Biol. Sci.*, **8**, 435–66.

7

Environmental Control of Growth

By L. T. Evans, I. F. Wardlaw, C. N. Williams

THE growth of grasses, both as single plants and in swards, has been measured at different seasons, and under a range of temperatures, daylengths, light intensities, water and nitrogen supplies, and cutting frequencies, for many species. Far less frequently, and only recently, have the effects of such conditions on the pattern of vegetative growth been examined, although such analysis throws far greater light on the way environment influences growth, and may more closely define the objectives of breeding programmes for pasture grasses.

In leys and in the establishment of perennial pastures, a high rate of tillering is often an advantage. Once a perennial pasture is established, however, differences between genotypes in their rate of tillering may be suppressed, growth rate per tiller becoming the main determinant of yield, as Knight[77] has shown with nine genotypes of *Dactylis glomerata*. Grown as single plants, the ranking of the nine clones for yield was largely determined by their rate of tillering, whereas in swards high tillering could decrease yield, which was more closely related to individual tiller weight. Similarly, Vose[174] found that the marked yield differences between three genotypes of *Lolium perenne* when grown as single plants, which were associated with parallel differences in their root systems, were not apparent in swards, where differences in root growth were suppressed, or in nutrient culture, where they were not important.

Growth rate per tiller can be resolved into leaf area growth rate and photosynthetic rate per unit leaf area, and the relative importance of these in determining sward productivity has yet to be established. Marked genotypic differences in net assimilation rate have been found,[28, 70] but could be due to differences in either the photosynthetic rate of individual leaves or in the penetration of light into the sward.

It should be clear from these few examples that a further understanding of the effects of environmental conditions on both swards and single plants will involve an increasing degree of resolution of these effects on the components of grass growth. In this chapter we will deal with a few aspects of growth in swards, briefly summarize the large volume of work on the effect of such factors as temperature, light intensity, and photoperiod on the total growth of individual plants, and then concentrate on the relatively few investigations where growth analysis permits us to begin to derive some general principles for the effect of climatic conditions on the rate and pattern of grass growth.

Seasonal Growth in Swards

Pattern of Growth

The pattern and rate of seasonal growth in grass swards varies profoundly, being determined by climatic factors and by the grass species. Data for warm season grass pastures are sparse. Among temperate Festucoid* perennial grasses one fairly general pattern [9, 15, 47, 50, 69, 86, 87, 88, 141] is as follows. In winter leaf growth is slow, but some tillering and strong root growth may occur, these increasing in tempo into spring. In early spring there is an acceleration of leaf growth and stem elongation following flower initiation and a decline in tillering and root initiation, although there may be depth increase in established roots.[68] After flowering in summer there is often a decline in leaf growth, some renewal of tillering and root growth, and, in rhizomatous species such as *Poa pratensis* and *P. angustifolia*, rapid development of rhizomes. In autumn rhizome growth declines, and there is a marked increase in tillering and the initiation and growth of roots.

As a result of these cycles of growth of the various organs, not only the number of leaves, but also the numbers of tillers, roots, and rhizomes in established perennial swards are extremely dynamic. Tiller numbers frequently reach a peak in mid-winter, and mid-summer numbers may be only half as great.[50, 77, 87] By contrast, rhizome numbers often reach a peak in late summer.[51]

The initiation of new roots in swards, like that of tillers, often shows a negative correlation with leaf yields.[69, 96, 97, 139] In a number of mountain forage grasses root growth was confined to early spring and autumn, root weights decreasing in winter when the ground was snow covered.[97] However, root growth may continue in some Festucoid grasses at temperatures near to freezing.[74, 156]

Active root growth through the summer has not often been recorded, although Stapledon and Milton[154] found a continuous increase in the root weight of *Dactylis glomerata* swards from April to September. More usually, root weights decline in summer,[59, 81, 152, 156, 168] the roots initiated in the previous year becoming darker, thinner, and disintegrating.[26, 68] Reduced root growth is frequently associated with flowering,[8, 169, 171] and removal of inflorescences may increase root yields.[154] Roots often lose cortical tissue at flowering, but this may not prevent their continued functioning in water and nutrient conduction.[68, 150]

The fact that tillering and root and rhizome growth in many temperate grasses is out of phase with leaf growth means that herbage yields will give an extremely biased picture of the effect of seasonal conditions on the growth of grasses in swards, particularly underestimating the growth during autumn and winter. This point should be borne in mind in the next section where we consider the influence of seasonal conditions on herbage growth. It may, for example, account for the increasing difference between potential and actual photosynthesis in autumn in the sward examined by Alberda and de Wit.[2] It should also be clear that any treatment affecting one phase of the growth cycle may indirectly affect subsequent phases to a great extent.

Rate of Growth

Seasonal trends in herbage yields depend on both species and climate for their form. They are of the greatest importance in determining pasture

---

* Wherever grasses are referred to in this chapter as either Festucoid or non-Festucoid, the classification being followed is that of Prat.[132]

H

management in any area, but here we will consider only some more general aspects of the rate of herbage production by swards.

When swards are closely grazed or mown the curve of regrowth is broadly sigmoid in form.[16] The duration of the initial exponential phase depends on the closeness of defoliation. Brougham[17] found it to last about 20 days following defoliation to 1 inch height in spring, and about 12 days following defoliation to 3 inches, while swards defoliated to 5 inches had passed out of the exponential phase of regrowth within 4 days. The length of this phase was greatly extended under late autumn and winter conditions.[18]

Following the exponential phase of regrowth, swards enter a phase characterized by an approximately constant rate of increase in herbage dry matter. Brougham[17] associated entry into this phase with absorption by the leaf canopy of about 95 per cent of the incident light, so that growth rate is largely light-limited and highly correlated with seasonal trends in solar radiation. Brougham[20] and Glenday[63] attempted to assess the relative importance of the long term seasonal changes and the short term weather fluctuations on the rate of sward growth in this linear phase. The magnitude of the correlation coefficients for weather parameters indicates that short term fluctuations in solar radiation and air temperatures have quite a marked effect on sward growth rates. However, the correlation coefficients for the climate parameters are far higher, particularly for total radiation.

Eventually, growth rate falls and ceiling herbage yields are obtained, where senescence and death of the older, lower leaves in the sward balance the appearance of new leaves above. It is quite possible that there is active growth of below ground organs at this stage. The ceiling herbage yields are determined by seasonal light conditions and by the botanical composition of the sward, particularly as it affects light penetration into the herbage canopy, photosynthetic efficiency, and the rate of senescence of the lower shaded leaves.

In a particular environment, pasture productivity will depend on the maximum sward growth rate, on how soon it is reached and how long maintained. According to Brougham[17] the maximum growth rate is attained when about 95 per cent of the incident light at noon is intercepted by the leaf canopy. He termed the total leaf area per unit ground area at this stage the critical leaf area index (LAI). In subsequent work it appears that the critical LAI may be attained near, or even slightly after, the inflexion in the growth curve.[19] The critical LAI found in these experiments varied greatly with species, being about 7·1 for *Lolium perenne*, 6·5 for *Phleum pratense*, and 3·5 for *Trifolium repens*. Brougham[21] has since shown that the critical LAI of various pastures and crops bears a close relation to the amount of chlorophyll per unit ground area at the critical LAI, and to the maximum growth rate. This latter is thus largely determined by the profile of light penetration into crops and swards, as reflected by the critical LAI, which is in turn determined by the size and shape of leaves, the angle at which they are held to the vertical, the distances between them, and their arrangement in the horizontal plane. Ways of measuring these properties in swards have been given by Warren-Wilson.[176] The long, slender leaves of grasses, many of which are held relatively erect, favour the penetration of light well into the sward, resulting in active photosynthesis by the lower leaf layers. Light profiles in plant communities can be described by Beer's Law,[110] and Stern[155] has reviewed data which indicates that whereas the extinction coefficient for light in communities of plants with horizontal leaves, such as clover, ranges from 0·5–1·0, that in grass communities is often 0·3–0·5. Light profiles do not always follow Beer's Law,[107] but penetration of light into grass swards is always much greater than that into clover swards, except when severe leaf flagging occurs. Nichiporovitch,[115] reasoning that the maximum use of light by a plant community will occur when the range of leaf angles is such that their projection covers the surface of a sphere, has derived an ideal distribution in which 13 per cent of the leaf area lies at angles between 0° and 30° to the horizontal, 37 per cent at 30–60°, and 50 per cent at 60–90°. All three

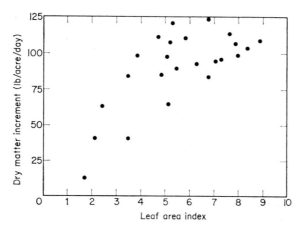

FIG. 7.1. Relation between leaf area index and sward growth rate. (Data from Brougham, 1956, *Aust. J. Agric. Res.*, **7**; 377–87.)

gramineae examined by him came very close to this ideal, *Phleum pratense* having 10 per cent at 0–30°, 43 per cent at 30–60°, and 47 per cent at 60–90°. At the other extreme were clovers with 70 per cent of their leaf area at 0–30°, 20 per cent at 30–60° and only 10 per cent at 60–90° to the horizontal.

Maximum sward growth rates are unlikely to be maintained for long under constant conditions. Brougham[17] found no decline in growth rate while the LAI of the sward increased from 5 to 9 (see Fig. 7.1). However, this was for growth in spring, when radiation and temperature were increasing progressively. In midsummer the maximum growth rate was sustained for only a brief period before growth rate declined.[19] This is to be expected since new leaves added to the top of the canopy will progressively shade the lower leaves. However, in favourable light conditions the decline in growth rate beyond the optimum LAI may be gradual because, in the relatively cool, shaded environment at the base of a dense sward, the respiration rate of older leaves may be reduced to very low levels,[117] and the light intensity at their compensation point correspondingly reduced. This may account for the extremely high LAI values attained in some grass swards.[3] However, periodic reductions in light intensity will greatly reduce growth rates when the LAI exceeds the optimum.[162]

Moreover, the optimum LAI may rise with the approach of flowering, because of the greater vertical spacing between the upper leaves on the flowering stems, leading to greater light penetration into the sward. This may partly account for the maximum growth rates found by Langer[87] in swards of timothy and meadow fescue as flowering approached, despite the fact that this occurred at different times in the two swards.

Single Plant Studies

Published work on the effect of temperature, light intensity, daylength, and other environmental factors on the growth of single grass plants is voluminous. Data on root and shoot growth in the various conditions are often given, but only rarely are there data on tiller number, so the effects on root and shoot growth per tiller cannot be ascertained. Moreover, the occurrence of flowering in some conditions and not in others may mask differences in the rate of vegetative growth. One further point to be borne in mind is that the effects of one environmental factor may depend markedly on others, and on the previous history of the plants. For example, low light intensities, or frequent defoliation, have been found largely to mask the effects of temperature on the growth of *Lolium perenne*.[104] Thus, differences in the responses reported below for species which have frequently been examined may reflect differences in other experimental conditions, or differences in the genotypes used.

Effects of Temperature

All the Festucoid grasses examined to date grow relatively well at low temperatures (e.g. 10°C), have an optimum temperature for growth below 27°C, and grow poorly at temperatures around 35°C. This has been found with *Lolium perenne, Dactylis glomerata, Agrostis tenuis*, and *Holcus lanatus*,[106] *Poa pratensis* and *P. compressa*[22, 65] and *Agrostis palustris*.[10] The optimum temperature for the growth of roots and rhizomes is usually lower than that for top growth,[22] although the optimum for extension growth of roots may be higher.[10,138]

The non-Festucoid grasses, on the other hand, have a high optimum temperature for growth, grow vigorously at 35°C, and extremely slowly at temperatures below 15°C, as has been shown with *Paspalum dilatatum*,[93,106] *Cynodon dactylon*,[22, 184] *Zoysia japonica*,[185] *Sorghum sudanense*,[159] *S. halepense*,[67] and *Axonopus affinis*[93] (see Fig. 7.2).

When grown at fluctuating day and night temperatures these two groups remain consistently different. Sprague[153] found considerable growth at 12°/4°C, optimal growth at 21°/12°C, and none at 38°/30°C in *Dactylis glomerata, Festuca elatior, Phleum pratense, Poa pratensis*, and *Agrostis tenuis*, whereas there was no growth at 12°/4°C, and optimal growth between 30°/21°C and 38°/30°C in the non-Festucoid *Sorghum sudanense*. At a day temperature of 24°C, a decrease in night temperature to 15°C increased both top and root growth in the Festucoid *Agropyron smithii*, but decreased them in the non-Festucoid grasses *Bouteloua gracilis* and *Panicum virgatum*.[12] Similar reductions in growth with lower night temperatures have been observed in *Sorghum halepense*,[67] *Cynodon dactylon*,[184] and *Acroceras macrum*.[99] With the Festucoid grasses, on the other hand, lower night temperatures often increase growth, as in several species of *Poa*[66, 71] and *Bromus* and *Melica imperfecta*.[6]

The differences in temperature response between Festucoid and non-Festucoid grasses are particularly striking for root growth and for differences in soil temperature. In fact, soil temperatures frequently have a more marked effect on growth than air temperatures, possibly because the shoot apices and tiller buds often lie close to the soil surface.[22, 75, 151, 158] In *Poa pratensis*, *P.*

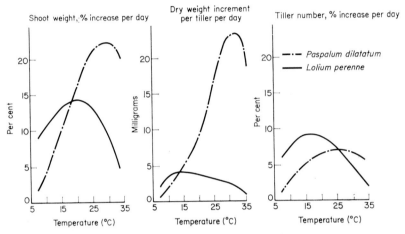

FIG. 7.2. Growth of *Lolium perenne* and *Paspalum dilatatum* over a range of constant temperatures. (From Mitchell, 1956, *N.Z. J. of Sci. & Tech.*, Sect. A., vol. **38**, 203–215).

compressa, *Dactylis glomerata*,[22] and *Phalaris tuberosa*[75] top growth could continue actively at above optimal air temperatures when soil temperatures were held near the optimum. In *Bromus inermis* both top and root growth were greatest when soil temperature was 20–26°C, and both fell sharply at soil temperatures above this.[39] Similarly, in *Lolium multiflorum* top growth was highest when the soil temperature was 20°C.[126]

In the Festucoid grasses the optimum temperature for root growth is quite low, and often lower than that for shoot growth. This last effect could be due to roots having a generally lower optimum temperature for their growth, or merely to there being more assimilates available for root growth at temperatures suboptimal for shoot growth, although this implies that roots are at least able to grow actively at lower temperatures than can shoots. By varying the soil temperature independently of air temperature some light might be thrown on these alternatives. In *Poa pratensis* grown at a root temperature of 21°C, top growth increased with increase in air temperature from 21° to 30°C, or with increase in the amplitude of diurnal change in air temperature, while root and rhizome growth decreased proportionately.[22] This could suggest that root growth is being indirectly determined by the substrates available for growth. Also with *Poa pratensis*, Darrow[37] found a soil temperature of 25°C to be optimal for root growth, whereas greatest top growth occurred when the soil temperature was 15°C. The roots formed at 15°C were large, succulent, white, and with few laterals, while those formed at a soil temperature of 35°C were small, brown, and finely branched. However, Naylor[113] obtained greater root growth in *Poa pratensis* at a soil temperature of 15°C than at 25°C, while top growth was unaffected.

Only one non-Festucoid grass, *Cynodon dactylon*, has been grown at differential soil and air temperatures, and behaved in opposite fashion to the Festucoid grasses, in that a lowering of the soil temperature (to 21°C) very greatly reduced growth at high air temperatures, and led to severe wilting.[22]

Effects of Light Intensity

Increased growth with increased light intensity has been found with many species[13,14,39,183] but the magnitude of the effect on the growth of single plants will depend, as it does for swards also, on the stage of growth or re-growth and on concurrent temperature, soil fertility, and other conditions. Individual grass leaves show light saturation for photosynthesis at values well below full daylight. Leaves of *Cynodon dactylon*, for example, reached light saturation at 3000 ft candles. Similarly, swards of *Cynodon* which were severely or frequently cut showed light saturation for photosynthesis at low intensities, whereas those allowed to grow to greater height (and LAI) were not light saturated even at 6000 ft candles.[4] Burton *et al.*[25] examined the effect of shading on growth of *Cynodon dactylon* at various seasons and nitrogen levels, and found growth of both tops and roots increased with light intensity at all seasons and nitrogen levels, but particularly in summer at high nitrogen levels.

In several species increased light intensity particularly increases root and rhizome growth. In *Bromus inermis*, for example, top weight increased five-fold and root weight thirty-fold with increase in average daily light intensity from 157 to 2833 ft candles.[133] Shading to 30 per cent daylight reduced root growth more than shoot growth in *Lolium perenne*, *Dactylis glomerata*, and *Paspalum dilatatum*,[105] the effect being particularly striking in the last species, as also in *Agropyron smithii*.[13]

Effect of Daylength

No clear pattern is discernible from the reports of the effect of daylength on the growth of single plants. In some cases this is due to the occurrence of flowering in some daylengths, and not (or later) in others. In other cases differences in light quantity are confounded with daylength, and may explain the effects, particularly the very great increases in the growth of many forage grasses with increase in photoperiod found by Pohjakallio.[130,131] Sprague[153] also found marked increases in the growth of 7 pasture grasses with increase in daylength from 9 to 16 hours; however, since the natural daylength was extended by light of 550 ft candles intensity, light quantity effects on growth might well have been involved. This suggestion is supported by Sprague's finding that the growth of roots relative to tops was increased in long days.

A further factor complicating the relation between daylength and growth of single plants is that daylength may have differential effects on top and root growth, and on leaf growth and tillering. These effects will be examined further below. It may be noted here that Gall[57] found no difference in the total growth of *Bromus inermis* in 13 and 18 hour daylengths, but top growth exceeded root growth in long days, while it was less than root growth in short days. Watkins,[178] on the other hand, found that top, root, and rhizome growth in *Bromus inermis* all increased with daylength. In *Festuca arundinacea* daylength had no net effect on growth, due to the greater tillering and root growth in short days offsetting greater leaf growth in long days.[165]

Concurrent temperature, light, and fertility conditions may also affect the growth response to daylength. Thus Lovvorn[93] found no effect of daylength on either top or root growth of 4 grasses when grown at 27–32°C, but increase in both top and root growth of all four with increase in daylength at 16–21°C. In *Sorghum halepense*, on the other hand, the increase in growth with increase in daylength was more marked the higher the temperature.[67] In *Zoysia japonica*, too, the effect of daylength in increasing the growth of tops, roots, and rhizomes increased as the temperature rose to 27°C.[185]

Winter Dormancy

An extreme response of growth to daylength is found in temperate grasses which become dormant in winter. In *Bouteloua curtipendula* in U.S.A. southern strains grew actively over a wide range of daylengths, whereas the northern strains showed sharply reduced growth at daylengths below 13 hours.[121, 122] That this short-day-induced dormancy in the northern strains is associated with greater winter survival was shown by Rogler[137] for *Bouteloua curtipendula*, *B. gracilis*, *Panicum virgatum*, and *Andropogon furcatus*. A close relation between winter dormancy and winter survival has also been shown among races of *Lolium perenne*.[32] That such dormancy is induced by short days has also been found in *Poa bulbosa* and *Sorghastrum nutans*[5] and in *Andropogon furcatus* and *Panicum virgatum*.[12]

Heat Resistance and Summer Dormancy

Seedlings of grasses appear to be highly tolerant of heat just after sowing, pass through a stage of great sensitivity to heat injury, and then become increasingly heat tolerant as they become older.[91,95,142] Species differ greatly in heat tolerance in the later stages of seedling growth, and the heat tolerance of any one species is greatly affected by prior temperature and light conditions. Brief exposures to high temperatures greatly increased subsequent survival of high temperatures in several species of *Bromus*, as did high light intensities prior to the high temperatures.[91] Julander[72] examined the effect of exposures to 48°C, for periods varying from $\frac{1}{2}$ to 16 hours, on survival of mature plants of several grasses. There were marked differences between species, but for all species prior droughting greatly increased survival, while defoliation decreased it. Julander associated greater survival with the accumulation of carbohydrate reserves, which was increased by droughting and decreased by cutting. With *Lolium perenne*, summer survival was greatly reduced by shading;[94] however, it was also reduced by soil moisture stress, high temperatures, and high nitrogen levels.

In many temperate grasses survival of extreme summer conditions is aided by the induction of dormancy or by the formation of corms and other organs of survival (see below). Cessation of growth occurs in many grass species when the water supply becomes limiting, but rewatering at any time during summer leads to immediate growth. Some species, such as *Phalaris tuberosa*, may begin autumn growth prior to the rains, but Laude[90] showed that this depended on water secured by deep roots, and could be prevented if these were severed. Many grasses ceased growth in summer even when continuously watered. Some of these, such as *Melica californica* and *Poa nevadensis*, stayed green, others, such as *Poa scabrella* and *P. secunda*, dried off. With *Poa scabrella* he found that plants could be kept growing throughout the summer at a temperature of 25°C. Three exposures, of 4 hours duration, to 55°C failed to induce dormancy in plants growing in winter, short-day conditions, but did so in greenhouse plants growing under long-days, although such plants grew well without heat shocks. Summer dormancy in *Poa scabrella* would therefore seem to be induced by a combination of long-days and high temperatures. It could only be induced, however, in plants more than 15 weeks old. Plants could be held dormant for up to 20 months, dormancy being broken by watering combined with temperatures below 25°C. With two races of *Poa scabrella*, Hiesey[66] obtained growth at a day temperature of 30°C in 12 hour photoperiods provided the night temperatures were low.

Growth Analysis in Single Plants

In established perennial swards, with fairly stable tiller densities, the rate of growth per tiller largely determines productivity, and the effect of environmental conditions on growth per tiller is far more important than effects on tillering. During establishment, on the other hand, and in ley pastures, the effect of environment on tillering may be of great importance.

In most of the work done to date on the growth of grasses, effects on growth per tiller and those on tillering cannot be differentiated. For example, many have shown that any reduction in natural light intensity leads to reduced total growth; the importance of this effect in swards will depend on whether it is tillering or growth per tiller which is mainly affected. In *Lolium perenne* it is mainly the former,[1] but species and strains may differ markedly in this respect, depending on how they partition the substrates available for growth. Cooper and Edwards[33, 34, 35] selected within *Lolium perenne* and *L. multiflorum* for what were essentially high and low rates of growth per tiller, and found that selection did not lead to any marked change in dry matter production, but only to a change in growth pattern, the progeny with high growth rates per tiller having a far lower rate of tillering.

Some adverse environmental conditions such as low light intensity and frequent defoliation, which are both associated with low carbohydrate status, particularly affect tillering. Others reduce leaf growth more than photo-synthesis, such as low temperature[140,160] and drought,[72] and affect growth per tiller more than they affect tillering.

One further point should be made before we consider the components of grass growth. Tillering is usually measured as the rate at which tillers emerge from the subtending leaf sheaths. At this stage the tiller has undergone con-siderable growth, and environmental effects on growth per tiller therefore have some influence on what is called tillering. Therefore no absolute separation between the two components can be made.

Growth per Tiller

(i) *Leaf growth*—Leaf primordia are initiated at the shoot apex in the manner described in Chapter 4. There is little data on the effect of environ-mental conditions on the rate of leaf initiation in the grasses. In wheat, daylength had little effect, but leaf initiation increased to a small extent with increasing light intensity (up to 1500 f.c.) and temperature (up to 25°C).[56]

Many temperate grasses accumulate leaf primordia at the shoot apex, indicating that the rate of leaf initiation is greater than the rate at which they begin to expand. In many non-Festucoid grasses, on the other hand, the shoot apex bears only one leaf primordium, and the interval between initiation and expansion is therefore much shorter.[149]

Each new leaf blade begins expansion inside the folded sheaths of the older leaves. The blade grows until its tip appears above the sheath of the preceding leaf. Unrolling of the blade – mediated by phytochrome[173] – then occurs, the ligule is differentiated, and meristematic activity in the blade ceases.[11,46,145,146] The leaf sheath then grows until the ligule is exposed when, according to Dobrynin,[43] further growth of the sheath is inhibited. The blades and sheaths of successive grass leaves formed prior to flower initiation tend to become progressively longer, but continue to appear at a constant rate characteristic of the conditions.[31,106] This rate of leaf appearance depends on the rate of expansion of the enclosed leaf blades. In *Lolium perenne*, *Agrostis tenuis*, and *Dactylis glomerata*, 25°C is optimal for the rate of leaf appearance, while in *Holcus lanatus* and *Paspalum dilatatum* 30°C is optimal.[106] In *Phleum pratense*[85] and in four species of *Lolium*[31] leaf appearance rate increases with temperature. Light intensity[56,101,105] and daylength[31,56,153,165] appear to have only slight effects on the rate of leaf appearance.

Mature leaf size is markedly affected by environmental conditions. Since cell division in the intercalary meristems ceases when the leaf tip is first exposed to light, differences in mature leaf size must be largely due to differ-ences in cell size rather than in cell number, as Stuckey[157] has shown to be the case.

Leaf length increases with increase in temperature in *Zoysia* (up to 27°C),[185] *Phleum pratense*,[85] *Phalaris tuberosa* (up to 24°/19°C),[144] and many cereals[42] and grasses (up to 30°/21°C).[153] In *Lolium perenne*, leaf length was greater at 22°C, leaf width at 14°C,[104] and in wheat leaf length was greatest at 25°C, width and thickness at 15°C, and leaf area at 20°C.[56]

The effect of light intensity on leaf size is more complex, since a degree of shading may increase leaf area.[104,105] In wheat, leaf length was greatest at an intensity of 500 f.c., leaf width and thickness at 2500 f.c., and leaf area at 1000–1750 f.c.[56]

Increasing daylength markedly increases leaf length and leaf size.[85,153,157,165,185] In *Bouteloua curtipendula* periodic droughting had its greatest effect on leaf size, and had far less effect on leaf, root, and tiller numbers.[120]

(ii) *Root growth*—In the single plant studies with Festucoid grasses where root growth has been measured, it has nearly always been found to be greater under higher light intensities, shorter days, and lower temperatures. As will be seen, however, these are also the conditions which favour tillering, and it is therefore difficult to determine whether these conditions favour root growth directly, or only indirectly through increased tillering. There are remarkably few studies of root growth on a per tiller basis, but these tend to give a different picture from that yielded by the single plant work. In *Lolium perenne*, Alberda[1] found total root growth to increase with increased light intensity and with decrease in day or night temperature – the usual pattern. Root growth per tiller, however, was scarcely affected by light intensity and was, if anything, higher with higher temperatures. Similarly, in *Phalaris tuberosa*, whereas total root and shoot weights were greatly affected by day and night temperature and by root temperature, root weights per tiller were only slightly affected.[144] In *Bouteloua gracilis*[121] all strains had more roots per tiller in longer days.

Individual roots may be as long lived as the tillers they support; Langer[86] and Evans and Ely[52] have shown that individual tillers do not usually survive in swards for more than one year; roots of several perennial grasses in swards have been shown to live for a year or more.[48,50,156]

Tillering

Tiller primordia appear to be initiated at the shoot apex almost as soon as the primordia of the subtending leaves.[64,145,146] Environmental conditions have little effect on the initiation of tillers,[118,151] and tiller buds may be found in the axils of all leaves, except in the prophylls of some species.[49,119]

Whether the tiller buds develop beyond this early stage (beyond about 1 mm length according to Mitchell[102]) is highly dependent on environmental conditions. An upper limit to the rate of tillering is imposed by the rate of leaf expansion and appearance, and in certain conditions there is a high correlation between tiller and leaf appearance rates.[34] For this reason Mitchell[101] suggested the use of leaf appearance age as a physiological time scale in studies on tillering, in order to eliminate the effects of genotype and environment on leaf appearance rates from estimates of tillering rate. When this is done, tiller number at a given leaf appearance age is still markedly dependent on environment. In *Lolium perenne* at a leaf appearance age of 7·9, tillers had appeared in the axils of the second, third, and fourth leaves of all plants under favourable conditions, while they failed to appear in many of the plants under low light intensities and high temperatures.[101] Thus, under adverse conditions, either the tiller buds do not develop further, or they begin development but die before the tiller appears. A delay in bud development has been found in *Lolium perenne* at high temperatures[151] and in barley under conditions of nutrient shortage.[7]

Unfortunately, most work on tillering deals only with the appearance of tillers at a fairly advanced stage, and cannot distinguish between the possibilities of differential development and differential death. The former may be of particular importance under conditions of marked apical dominance, the latter under conditions of carbohydrate, nutrient, or water shortage. Certain environmental conditions, such as short days, may effect tillering through both of these processes, and in opposite ways, their net effect being highly dependent on other conditions, and on the age of the plants.

The number of tillers at a given leaf appearance age is determined by the axillary position at which tillering begins, and by the rate of tiller appearance. Both genotype and environment determine the position of the first tiller. In *Lolium perenne*, the coleoptile node frequently bears tillers, particularly when plants are summer sown; in *Phleum pratense*, on the other hand, there are no coleoptile tillers. Patel and Cooper[127] found more tillers in *L. perenne* plants of given leaf appearance age under long days, an effect due almost entirely to the lower node of first tillering in long days. This may also account for the fact that in *Paspalum dilatatum* young plants in daylengths of 12–14 hours had more tillers than those in 8 hour days, whereas older plants had far more tillers when grown under short days.[78]

Once tillering starts tiller numbers frequently increase exponentially at a rate characteristic of the prevailing environmental conditions, until nutrient exhaustion[30,170] or flower initiation[7] sets in. The effects of environmental conditions on this rate will now be considered, although most of the data available refer only to a final tiller count rather than to the rate of increase in tiller numbers.

(i) *Effect of Light Intensity*—Tiller buds are in competition with other parts of the plant for carbohydrates, and their development is particularly influenced by light intensity. High light intensities are associated with high tillering in sugar cane,[41] oats,[181] wheat,[76] and *Lolium perenne*.[1,101,103,104,105] In *L. perenne* the growth component most affected by reduced light intensities is tillering, and Mitchell[101] has shown that periodic reductions in light intensity affect only the tiller buds which would normally develop during the low intensity periods. Shading only the leaf sheaths also leads to a reduction in tillering.[108]

(ii) *Effect of Daylength*—The effect of daylength on tillering is frequently confused by its effect on the earliness of flowering in many grasses. Thus long days, leading to earlier flowering in some grasses and later flowering in others, might depress tillering in the former and increase it in the latter regardless of any direct effect of daylength on tillering. In fact, increased tillering with decrease in daylength has been found in many gramineae whose flowering is hastened by long days.[15,53,57,58,76,82,92,114,128,134,165,178] Work with unvernalized grasses, which would not initiate flowers whatever the daylength, would eliminate possible effects on tillering due to flower initiation. Unfortunately, in the work with *Lolium perenne* either daylength differences were confounded with light quantity differences[102] or they were applied at temperatures where growth was severely limited.[31] Confounding of daylength and light quantity differences also applies to some work on wheat.[29]

In strains of *Andropogon scoparius* flowering was hastened and tillering reduced as the daylength increased from 13 to 15 hours,[89] and in older plants of *Paspalum dilatatum* and *P. notatum* as it increased from 8 to 14 hours.[78, 79] Further increase in daylength to 16 hours, however, delayed flowering and reduced tiller number markedly. In this case, then, increased daylength has depressed tillering regardless of later flowering. This is true also in work on the southern strains of *Bouteloua curtipendula*.[121] In work on rice[125] short days reduced tillering, but only in strains where short days led to very early flowering. Oda and Honda[118] also conclude that the decrease in tiller emergence in rice under short days was associated with a hastening of heading.

Taken as a whole, the evidence suggests that short days hasten tillering in most grasses, although much of the data is confused by effects of daylength on flowering.

Daylength may also affect the pattern of tillering. In *Panicum miliaceum* the total number of tillers was not greatly affected by daylength, but in long days tillers appeared in acropetal succession, while in short days they appeared in basipetal succession.[112] In *Phalaris tuberosa* tillers appear in the axils of higher leaves on the primary shoot in short days, while in long days bud development is shifted to the secondary and tertiary tillers (C. N. Williams, unpublished data).

(iii) *Effect of Temperature*—Tillering in many Festucoid grasses appears to have a fairly low optimum temperature.[1, 64, 76, 101, 106, 114, 128, 165] Mitchell[106] found the greatest rate of tillering at about 15°C in *L. perenne*, but at 20°C in *Agrostis tenuis* and *Holcus lanatus*, and at 25°C in *Dactylis glomerata*. However, these rates may largely reflect the effect of temperature on the rate of leaf appearance and tiller leaf expansion. Thus, whereas a rise in temperature from 15° to 28°C had little effect on the number of tillers appearing on *L. perenne* plants in a given time, if allowance for the effect of temperature on leaf appearance rate was made by counting tillers when there were 9·5 leaves on the main stem, the rise in temperature decreased tillering considerably.[105] With *L. perenne*, *Holcus lanatus*, *Dactylis glomerata*, and *Agrostis tenuis*, tillering increased slightly with a rise in day temperature from 7° to 15°C, and markedly with a fall in night temperature from 7° to 2°C.[109] With *L. perenne* Alberda[1] found tillering increased markedly with lowering of either day or night temperature. Cooper,[31] on the other hand, found it to increase with increase in night temperature; since leaf appearance rate increased in a parallel way, the net effect on tillering is not clear. In *Phalaris tuberosa* tiller number increased as day temperature increased from 10° to 29°C and night temperature from 7° to 24°C.[144] The optimum soil temperature for tillering was 20°C. Here again, as also in the work of Bommer[15] with *Arrhenatherum elatius*, effects on tillering may be confounded with effects on leaf appearance.

In the Festucoideae, then, the evidence suggests that there is generally a fairly low optimum temperature for the rate of tiller appearance. In the non-Festucoid grasses optimum temperatures for tillering are much higher, though they may still be lower than those for growth per tiller. In *Paspalum dilatatum* the optimum temperature for tillering is about 27°C, whereas that for growth per tiller is 30°C[106] (see Fig. 7.2). Knight[78] found far more tillers at a night temperature of 21°C than at 10°C in the same species. Tillering increased with temperature up to 27°C in *Sorghum halepense*,[67] and up to 30°C in sugar cane.[41]

(iv) *Effect of other conditions*—Nutrient supply has a marked effect on the tillering of grasses. Aspinall,[7] for example, has shown that the rate of tillering in barley depends on the rate of nutrient supply, in situations where tillering is not limited by the number of tiller buds. Nitrogen,[30,41,60,61,179] phosphorus,[41,161] potassium, magnesium, and calcium[58] status may all affect tillering.

The influence of water supply on tillering is not clear. In *Bouteloua curtipendula*, longer intervals between waterings led to fewer tillers developing, the effect being particularly marked on the higher order tillers.[119] In *Agropyron smithii*, on the other hand, more tillers were produced when soil moisture levels were maintained near the wilting point than at higher moisture contents.[58] In this case the higher tiller numbers on the drier soil were associated with a reduced number of rhizomes. Gardner also found that grasses growing in swards containing several species formed fewer tillers than those growing in pure swards. The effect of competition between species was also examined by Donald[44] with *Phalaris tuberosa* and *Lolium perenne*, in experiments where competition was for light alone, nutrients alone, or both light and nutrients. In *L. perenne*, the aggressor species, tiller number was reduced to some extent by competition for either light or nutrients, while in *Phalaris* competition for nutrients greatly reduced both tiller number and weight.

Defoliation also has a particularly marked adverse effect on tillering, as in *Lolium perenne*[1,103,104] and *Bromus inermis*.[164]

Rhizome and Stolon Growth

The growth of rhizomes and stolons is most prominent in the summer,[9,23,47,51,55,178] which appears to be largely a response to long days in both Festucoid[5,22,53,178] and non-Festucoid[67,121,185] grasses. In these grasses daylength has a profound effect on the relative numbers of tillers and rhizomes; for every 100 tillers in *Poa pratensis* there were 67 rhizomes in short days, 190 in long days.[53]

Some of the increased rhizome growth in long days may be due to the plants receiving significantly more total light energy, as Watkins[178] found shading to reduce rhizome production in *Bromus inermis*. With the same species Gall[57] found no effect of daylength over the range 13 to 17 hours, but reduction in rhizome production with shading.

Poa compressa differs from other species in producing rhizomes in the autumn and early spring. Brown[22] attributed this to a short day requirement for rhizome growth in this species, but Evans and Watkins[53] obtained greater rhizome production at a daylength of 14 hours than at either 8 or 18 hours.

Temperature also influences rhizome growth. For *Poa pratensis* and *P. compressa* the optimum temperature for rhizome production, like that for roots, was much lower than the optimum temperature for shoot growth.[22] In

Zoysia, however, rhizome, root, and shoot growth all increased as the temperature rose to 27°C.[185]

Soil moisture and nutritional status also affect rhizome growth. High soil moisture status favoured rhizome production in *Agropyron smithii*, the buds forming tillers under dry conditions.[58] Several workers have noted that rhizomes tend to grow away from competition and crowding,[52, 129] which may be due to depletion of nutrients in the areas of compact growth. Nitrogen fertilization, however, has been reported to reduce rhizome growth and to promote the emergence of aerial shoots in *Agropyron repens*,[38] *Poa* species,[182] and *Bromus inermis*.[65,178]

What influences a rhizome tip to begin to grow upwards to form an aerial tiller is not clear. Changes in both phototropic and geotropic responses of the rhizome through a change in the environment of the parent plant have been proposed.[124] Low light intensities[124] and high temperatures[22, 65] both seem to hasten the emergence of rhizomes.

Corms and Bulbs

In the temperate grasses, corms and bulbs are generally formed in summer. Burns[24] studied many species of corm and bulb forming grasses, which are particularly evident in Mediterranean areas. The main function of these organs appears to be survival of the hot dry summer, occasionally survival of a cold season. Morphologically, the corms of grasses are the swollen basal internodes of the flowering culm, usually formed during flowering, and possibly in response to the same environmental stimuli. In *Phalaris tuberosa* corms were formed at the time of inflorescence initiation, in response to long days (C. N. Williams, unpublished data). In *Phleum pratense* the corms enlarge as the culm grows, reaching full development at the time of seed ripening.[177]

The corms of grasses store organic materials which are probably used for subsequent growth of the buds associated with them. In *Phleum pratense* corms, the carbohydrate content reached a maximum at heading, and declined only when the new shoots developed.[167] In general, new shoots arise from the corms following flowering and seed maturity, or when moisture and temperature levels are favourable.[177] The corms wither and die after producing shoots, but in favourable conditions secondary corms may be produced in autumn and winter which may feed the flowering heads of the following spring.[80] Roberts and Hunt[136] claim that the reduction in the root system often associated with flowering does not occur in some corm-producing species, such as *Phleum pratense*.

Growth Correlations

In many of the Festucoid grasses there is a noticeable inverse relation between environmental conditions favouring leaf and stem growth on established tillers (long days and moderately high temperatures) and those favouring root growth and abundant tillering (short days and low temperatures). All components of growth are depressed by low light intensities, frequent defoliation and nutrient shortage, but root growth and tillering are the most affected. These latter flourish under conditions where photosynthesis is still active but where the substrate demands for leaf and stem growth are limited. Carbohydrates accumulate in the roots and stems under these conditions[22, 72, 160, 180] and are available for root and tiller growth.

The growth pattern in these grasses is therefore envisaged as being primarily determined by the effect of environmental conditions on leaf growth on established tillers, and by photosynthetic rate, as these affect the supply of carbohydrates for root and tiller growth. The early stages of tiller development seem to be particularly dependent on carbohydrate supplies from the parent shoot. Work with rice[147, 163] and wheat[135] suggests that tillers continue to be dependent on the parent shoot for some time after their appearance, but eventually a stage is reached where they become independent, and in turn supply carbohydrates to tillers developing in the axils of their lower leaves.

Seasonal changes in carbohydrate levels in grass plants suggest that tillers developing in the early spring are dependent for growth on reserve carbohydrates in the roots, while those developing after a period of summer dormancy depend on carbohydrates in the stem bases and rhizomes. The importance of reserve carbohydrates in such regrowth has been queried,[98] but in *Dactylis glomerata* regrowth has been clearly shown to be dependent on reserves.[175]

Once a tiller has reached the stage of assimilate independence and has a functional root system, it may act as an independent unit capable of competition for nutrients with other tillers.[36, 45, 83, 148, 166] The tiller then becomes the ecological unit of growth in the sward. Such independent tillers may still possess the ability to act as an integrated unit under adverse conditions, with transfer between tillers of assimilates[84, 148] and mineral nutrients.[62, 111, 123, 172]

If the growth pattern of these grasses is determined by a hierarchy of sinks for translocated assimilates and nutrients, in what way are the priorities in this hierarchy determined? Certainly, they are under ultimate genetic control, as the work of Cooper and Edwards[35] shows. Probably, they are largely mediated through the effects of environmental conditions on endogenous growth substance levels.

The tiller buds of grasses are, as in other plants, subject to auxin-mediated apical dominance, as shown by Dillewijn[40] in *Andropogon sorghum* and by Leopold[92] in barley and teosinte. In a number of grasses gibberellic acid inhibits tillering and root growth while promoting leaf and stem growth on established tillers,[27, 54, 73, 143] as happens in long days. It seems possible, then, that the higher levels of endogenous gibberellins and auxins found under long day conditions in many plants[116] play a major role in determining the growth pattern of Festucoid grasses in summer conditions.

In the non-Festucoid grasses the complementary pattern of growth of leaves and stems on the one hand, and of roots and tillers on the other, is not so clear. All growth components increase as the temperature rises to quite high levels although, at least in *Paspalum dilatatum*,[106] the optimum temperature for tillering is below that for growth per tiller. Moreover, photo-synthesis, which may be quite active in Festucoid grasses at low temperatures, is inactive at low temperatures in non-Festucoid grasses, and may have a high optimum temperature. While net photosynthesis was greatest at 20–25°C in *Agrostis palustris*, it was maximal in *Cynodon dactylon* at 35°C.[100] Thus accumulation of assimilates at low temperatures is unlikely to occur in the tropical grasses. Mitchell's work,[106] which is admittedly confined to five Festucoid grasses and one non-Festucoid, suggests a major difference between these groups in the way temperature affects their growth. In the Festucoid grasses, which grow well at low temperatures (e.g. 7°C) and very poorly above 30°C, the growth rate per tiller is uniformly low and not greatly affected by temperature, the main differences in growth at the various temperatures being due to effects on tillering. In *Paspalum dilatatum*, on the other hand, effects on tillering are less marked, and definitely subordinate to the very marked effects on the rate of growth per tiller, which rises to far higher levels than in the Festucoid grasses. Extension, and further analysis, of these differences between the two main taxonomic groups of grasses is an urgent task.

REFERENCES

[1] Alberda, T. (1957). The effects of cutting, light intensity and night temperature on growth and soluble carbohydrate content of *Lolium perenne* L. *Plant and Soil*, **8**, 199–230.

[2] Alberda, T., and de Wit, C. T. (1961). Dry matter production and light interception of crop surfaces. Uninterrupted growth of a grass sward. *Jaarb. Inst. Biol. Scheik. Onderz. Landb. Meded.*, **153**, 37–44.

[3] Alekseenko, L. N. (1958). The structure of a perennial herbage sward in relation to yield. *Dokl. Vsesojuz Akad. S-H. Nauk.*, **23** (6), 14–18.

[4] Alexander, C. W., and McCloud, D. E. (1962). CO₂ uptake (net photosynthesis) as influenced by light intensity of isolated Bermuda grass leaves contrasted to that of swards under various clipping regimes. *Crop Sci.*, **2** (2) 132–5.

[5] Allard, H. A., and Evans, M. W. (1941). Growth and flowering of some tame and wild grasses in response to different photoperiods. *J. Agr. Res.*, **62** (4), 193–228.

[6] Ashby, W. C., and Hellmers, H. (1959). Flowering and growth responses to photoperiod and temperature for six southern California grasses. *Bot. Gaz.*, **120** (3), 151–7.

[7] Aspinall, D. (1961). The control of tillering in the barley plant. I. The pattern of tillering and its relation to nutrient supply. *Aust. J. Biol. Sci.*, **14** (4), 493–505.

[8] Baker, H. K. (1957). Studies on the root development of herbage plants. 3. The influence of cutting treatments on the root, stubble and herbage production of a perennial ryegrass sward. *J. Brit. Grassl. Soc.*, **12**, 197–208.

[9] Barling, D. M. (1959). Biological studies in *Poa angustifolia*. *Watsonia*, **4** (4), 147–68.

[10] Beard, J. B. (1959). Growth of bent grass roots as influenced by temperature and management. *U.S. Golf Ass. J.*, **12** (3), 30–1.

[11] Begg, J. E., and Wright, M. J. (1962). Growth and development of leaves from intercalary meristems in *Phalaris arundinacea* L. *Nature*, **194**, 1097.

[12] Benedict, H. M. (1940). Effect of daylength and temperature on the flowering and growth of four species of grasses. *J. Agr. Res.*, **61** (9), 661–71.

[13] Benedict, H. M. (1940). Growth of some range grasses in reduced light intensities at Cheyenne, Wyoming. *Bot. Gaz.*, **102**, 582–9.

[14] Blackman, G., and Templeman, W. G. (1938). The interaction of light intensity and nitrogen supply in the growth and metabolism of grasses and clover (*Trifolium repens*). *Ann. Bot. N.S.*, **2**, 765–91.

[15] Bommer, D. (1960). Entwicklung und Substanzbildung von Glatthaferpflanzen unter der Wirkung wechselnder Temperatur und Tageslange. *Proc. 8th Int. Grassl. Congr.*, 1960, 409–13.

[16] Brougham, R. W. (1955). A study in rate of pasture growth. *Aust. J. Agr. Res.*, **6**, 804–12.

[17] Brougham, R. W. (1956). Effect of intensity of defoliation on regrowth of pasture. *Aust. J. Agr. Res.*, **7**, 377–87.

[18] Brougham, R. W. (1956). The rate of growth of short rotation ryegrass pastures in the late autumn, winter, and early spring. *N.Z. J. Sci. Tech.*, **38A**, 78–87.

[19] Brougham, R. W. (1958). Interception of light by the foliage of pure and mixed stands of pasture plants. *Aust. J. Agr. Res.*, **9** (1), 39–52.

[20] Brougham, R. W. (1959). The effects of season and weather on the growth rate of a ryegrass and clover pasture. *N.Z. J. Agric. Res.*, **2** (2), 283–96.

[21] Brougham, R. W. (1960). The relationship between the critical leaf area, total chlorophyll content, and maximum growth rate of some pasture and crop plants. *Ann. Bot. N.S.*, **24** (96), 463–74.

[22] Brown, E. M. (1939). Some effects of temperature on the growth and chemical composition of certain pasture grasses. *Mo. Agric. Exp. Sta. Res. Bull.*, **299**, 1–76.

[23] Brown, E. M. (1943). Seasonal variations in the growth and chemical composition of Kentucky bluegrass. *Mo. Agric. Exp. Sta. Res. Bull.*, **360**, 1–56.

[24] Burns, W. (1946). Corm and bulb formation in plants, with special reference to the Gramineae. *Trans. Proc. Bot. Soc. Edinb.*, **34**, 316–47.

[25] Burton, G. W., Jackson, J. E., and Knox, F. E. (1959). The influence of light reduction upon the production, persistence, and chemical composition of coastal Bermuda grass, *Cynodon dactylon*. *Agron. J.*, **51** (9), 537–42.

[26] Cepikova, A. (1942). Root systems of perennial herbage plants and when they die out. (A preliminary communication) (Russian). Dokl. Vsesojuz Akad. S-H Nauk. *Proc. Lenin Acad. Agric. Sci.*, **9** (10), 28–9. Cited in Weinmann. [180]

[27] Champeroux, A. (1962). Effects de la gibberelline et de la nutrition azotée sur la croissance et le metabolisme azoté du Dactyle. *Ann. Physiol. Veg.*, **4** (1), 99–114.

[28] Chatterjee, B. N. (1961). Analysis of ecotypic differences in tall fescue (*Festuca arundinacea* Schreb). *Ann. Appl. Biol.*, **49**, 560–2.

[29] Chinoy, J. J., and Nanda, K. K. (1951). Effect of vernalization and photoperiodic treatments on growth and development of crop plants. II. Varietal differences in stem elongation and tillering of wheat and their correlation with flowering under varying photoinductive and post-photoinductive treatments. *Physiol. Plantar.*, **4**, 427–36.

[30] Cooper, J. P. (1948). Resistance to inanition in grass seedlings. *Nature*, **161**, 894–5.

[31] Cooper, J. P. (1951). Studies on growth and development in *Lolium*. II. Pattern of bud development of the shoot apex and its ecological significance. *J. Ecol.*, **39**, 228–70.

[32] Cooper, J. P. (1963). Species and population differences in climatic response. In *Environmental Control of Plant Growth*, pp. 381–400, ed. L. T. Evans. Academic Press, New York.

[33] Cooper, J. P., and Edwards, K. J. R. (1959). Selection for leaf area in ryegrass. *Ann. Rept. Welsh Plant Breed. Sta.*, 71–5.

[34] Cooper, J. P., and Edwards, K. J. R. (1961). The genetic control of leaf development in *Lolium*. I. Assessment of genetic variation. *Heredity*, **16**, 63–82.

[35] Cooper, J. P., and Edwards, K. J. R. (1962). Selection for leaf and tiller development. *Rept. Welsh Plant Breed. Sta.*, 1961. 18.

[36] Crider, F. J. (1955). Root growth stoppage resulting from defoliation of grass. *Tech. Bull.* 1102. *U.S.D.A.*, 1–23.

[37] Darrow, R. A. (1939). Effects of soil temperature, pH and nitrogen nutrition on the development of *Poa pratensis*. *Bot. Gaz.*, **101**, 109–27.

[38] Dexter, S. T. (1936). Response of quack grass to defoliation and fertilization. *Plant Physiol.*, **11**, 843–51.

[39] Dibbern, J. C. (1947). Vegetative responses of *Bromus inermis* to certain variations in environment. *Bot. Gaz.*, **109**, 44–58.

[40] Dillewijn, C. van (1939). Wachstumserscheinungen bei Gramineae. *Rec. Trav. Bot. Neerl*, **36** (2), 799–809.

[41] Dillewijn, C. van (1952). Botany of sugar cane. p. 371. *Chronica Botanica*. Waltham, Mass. U.S.A.

[42] Dobben, W. H. van, and Hoogland, R. F. (1953). The influence of temperature on the length of leaves of winter cereals. *Verslag C.I.L.O.*, 97–101.

I

43 Dobrynin, G. M. (1960). (The laws of shoot formation in some grasses.) *Dokl. Akad. Nauk. SSSR. Transl. Bot. Sci. Sect.*, **130** (1–6), 61–4.

44 Donald, C. M. (1958). The interaction of competition for light and for nutrients. *Aust. J. Agr. Res.*, **9** (4) 421–35.

45 Engledow, F. L., and Wadham, S. M. (1924). Investigations on yield in cereals. *J. Agr. Sci.*, **14**, 80–5.

46 Esau, K. (1943). Ontogeny of the vascular bundle in *Zea mays*. *Hilgardia*, **15** (3), 327–68.

47 Etter, A. G. (1951). How Kentucky bluegrass grows. *Ann. Miss. Bot. Gard.*, **38**, 293–375.

48 Evans, M. W. (1927). The life history of timothy. *U.S.D.A. Bull.*, **1450**, 1–56.

49 Evans, M. W. (1946). The grasses: their growth and development. *Ohio Agric. Expt. Station. Agronomy mimeograph*, 105.

50 Evans, M. W. (1949). Kentucky bluegrass. *Ohio Agr. Expt. Sta. Res. Bull.*, **681**, 1–39.

51 Evans, M. W., and Ely, J. E. (1935). The rhizomes of certain species of grasses. *J. Amer. Soc. Agron.*, **27**, 791–7.

52 Evans, M. W., and Ely, J. E. (1941). Growth habits of reed canary grass. *J. Amer. Soc. Agron.*, **33**, 1017–27.

53 Evans, M. W., and Watkins, J. M. (1939). The growth of Kentucky bluegrass and Canada bluegrass in late spring and in autumn as affected by the length of day. *J. Amer. Soc. Agron.*, **31**, 767–74.

54 Fejer, S. O. (1960). Effects of gibberellic acid, indole-acetic acid, coumarin and perloline on perennial ryegrass (*Lolium perenne* L.). *N.Z. J. Agric. Res.*, **3** (4), 734–43.

55 Fisher, J. (1961). The growth of rhizomes in Kentucky bluegrass. *Forage Notes*, **7** (1), 11–12.

56 Friend, D. J. C., Helson, V. A., and Fisher, J. E. (1962). Leaf growth in Marquis wheat, as regulated by temperature, light intensity, and daylength. *Canad. J. Bot.*, **40** (10), 1299–1311.

57 Gall, H. J. F. (1947). Flowering of smooth brome grass under certain environmental conditions. *Bot. Gaz.*, **109** (1), 59–71.

58 Gardner, J. L. (1942). Studies in tillering. *Ecology*, **23**, 162–74.

59 Garwood, E. A. (1959). Seasonal root development of herbage species. Exp. Progr. 12, *Rep. Grassl. Res. Inst. Hurley*, 1958, 1959, 1960. 54–5.

60 Gericke, W. F. (1922). Certain relations between root development and tillering in wheat; significance in the production of high protein wheat. *Amer. J. Bot.*, **9**, 366–9.

61 Gericke, W. F. (1923). Further notes on effect of extent of root systems on tillering of wheat. *Bot. Gaz.*, **75**, 320–2.

62 Giddens, J., Perkins, H. F., and Walker, L. C. (1962). Movement of nutrients in coastal Bermuda grass. *Agron. J.*, **54** (5), 379.

63 Glenday, A. C. (1959). Mathematical analysis of growth curves replicated in time. *N.Z. J. Agric. Res.*, **2** (2), 297–305.

64 Hamilton, H. H. (1948). A developmental study of the apical meristem in four varieties of *Avena sativa* grown at two temperatures. *Amer. J. Bot.*, **35**, 656–65.

65 Harrison, C. M. (1934). Responses of Kentucky bluegrass to variations in temperature, light, cutting and fertilizing. *Plant Physiol.*, **9**, 83–106.

66 Hiesey, W. M. (1953). Growth and development of species and hybrids of *Poa* under controlled temperatures. *Amer. J. Bot.*, **40** (4), 205–21.

67 Ingle, M., and Rogers, B. J. (1961). The growth of a mid-western strain of *Sorghum halepense* under controlled conditions. *Amer. J. Bot.*, **48**, 392–6.

68 Jacques, W. A. (1956). Root development in some common New Zealand pasture plants. 9. The root replacement pattern in perennial ryegrass (*Lolium perenne*). *N.Z. J. Sci. Tech.*, **38A**, 160–5.

69 Jacques, W. A., and Schwass, R. H. (1956). Root development in some common New Zealand pasture plants. 7. Seasonal root replacement in perennial ryegrass (*Lolium perenne*), Italian ryegrass (*L. multiflorum*) and tall fescue (*Festuca arundinacea*). *N.Z. J. Sci. Tech.*, **37A** (6), 569–83.

70 Jewiss, O. R., and Robson, M. J. (1960–61). Studies on the growth of ecotypes of tall fescue. Exp. in Prog. 14. *Ann. Rept. Grassl. Res. Inst.*, Hurley, 23–5.

[71] Juhren, M., Hiesey, W. M., and Went, F. W. (1953). Germination and early growth of grasses in controlled conditions. *Ecol.*, **34** (2), 288–300.

[72] Julander, O. (1945). Drought resistance in range and pasture grasses. *Pl. Physiol.*, **20**, 573–99.

[73] Juska, F. V. (1959). The effect of gibberellic acid on Kentucky bluegrass root production. *Agron. J.*, **51** (3), 184–5.

[74] Kauter, A. (1933). Beitrage zur Kenntnis der Weigzelachstums der Graser. *Ber. Schweiz Bot. Ges.*, **42**, 37–109.

[75] Ketellapper, H. J. (1960). The effect of soil temperature on the growth of *Phalaris tuberosa* L. *Physiol. Plantar.*, **13**, 641–7.

[76] Khalil, M. S. H. (1956). The interrelation between growth and development of wheat as influenced by temperature, light, and nitrogen. *Meded. Landb. Wageningen*, **56** (7), 1–73.

[77] Knight, R. (1961). The relation between tillering and dry matter production in cocksfoot (*Dactylis glomerata* L.) grown under spaced and sward conditions. *Aust. J. Agr. Res.*, **12** (4), 566–77.

[78] Knight, W. E. (1955). The influence of photoperiod and temperature on growth, flowering, and seed production of Dallis grass, *Paspalum dilatatum* Poir. *Agron. J.*, **47**, 555–9.

[79] Knight, W. E., and Bennett, H. W. (1953). Preliminary report of the effect of photoperiod and temperature on the flowering and growth of several southern grasses. *Agron. J.*, **45**, 268–9.

[80] Knoblauch, H. C., Ahlgren, G. H., and Gausman, H. W. (1955). Persistence of timothy as determined by physiological response to different management systems. *Agron. J.*, **47**, 434–9.

[81] Konekamp, A., and Zimmer, E. (1955). Ergebnisse der Wurzeluntersuchungen Völkenrode, 1949–53. *Z. Pfl. Ernahr. Dung.*, **68**, 158–69.

[82] Koryakina, V. F. (1957). (The influence of daylength on growth and development of meadow timothy.) *Dokl. Akad. Nauk. SSSR.*, **115** (2), 396–9.

[83] Krassovsky, I. V. (1926). Physiological activity of the seminal and nodal root of crop plants. *Soil Sci.*, **21**, 307–25.

[84] Labanauskas, C. K., and Dungan, G. H. (1956). Interrelationships of tillers and main stems in oats. *Agron. J.*, **48** (6), 265–8.

[85] Langer, R. H. M. (1954). A study of leaf growth in timothy (*Phleum pratense*). *J. Brit. Grassl. Soc.*, **9** (4), 275–84.

[86] Langer, R. H. M. (1956). Growth and nutrition of timothy (*Phleum pratense*), I. The life history of individual tillers. *Ann. Appl. Biol.*, **44** (1), 166–87.

[87] Langer, R. H. M. (1958). A study of growth in swards of timothy and meadow fescue. 1. Uninterrupted growth. *J. Agric. Sci.*, **51** (3), 347–52.

[88] Langer, R. H. M. (1959). A study of growth in swards of timothy and meadow fescue. 2. The effects of cutting treatments. *J. Agric. Sci.*, **52** (3), 273–81.

[89] Larsen, E. C. (1947). Photoperiodic responses of geographical strains of *Andropogon scoparius*. *Bot. Gaz.*, **109**, 132–49.

[90] Laude, H. M. (1953). The nature of summer dormancy in perennial grasses. *Bot. Gaz.*, **114**, 284–92.

[91] Laude, H. M., and Chaugule, B. A. (1953). Effect of stage of seedling development upon heat tolerance in bromegrasses. *J. Range Mgmt.*, **6** (5), 320–4.

[92] Leopold, A. C. (1949). The control of tillering in grasses by auxin. *Amer. J. Bot.*, **36** (6), 437–40.

[93] Lovvorn, R. L. (1945). The effect of defoliation, soil fertility, temperature and length of day on the growth of some perennial grasses. *J. Amer. Soc. Agron.*, **37**, 570–82.

[94] Lucanus, R., Mitchell, K. J., Pritchard, G. G., and Calder, D. M. (1960). Factors influencing survival of strains of ryegrass during the summer. *N.Z. J. Agric. Res.*, **3** (1), 185–93.

[95] McAlister, D. F. (1944). Determination of soil drought resistance in grass seedlings. *J. Amer. Soc. Agron.*, **36**, 324–36.

[96] McCarty, E. C. (1938). The relation of growth to the varying carbohydrate content of mountain brome. *U.S. Dept. Agric. Tech. Bull.*, **598**, 1–24.

[97] McCarty, E. C., and Price, R. (1942). Growth and carbohydrate content of important mountain forage plants in Central Utah as affected by clipping and grazing. *U.S. Dept. Agric. Tech. Bull.*, **818**, 1–51.

[98] May, L. H. (1960). The utilization of carbohydrate reserves in pasture plants after defoliation. *Herb. Abs.*, **30** (4), 239–45.

[99] Mes, M. G. (1952). The influence of some climatic factors on the growth and seed production of grasses. *Veld Gold*, 39–51. Published by Nat. Veld Trust, Johannesburg.

[100] Miller, V. J. (1960). Temperature effect on the rate of apparent photosynthesis of seaside bent and Bermuda grass. *Proc. Amer. Soc. Hort. Sci.*, **75**, 700–3.

[101] Mitchell, K. J. (1953). Influence of light and temperature on the growth of ryegrass (*Lolium* spp.). 1. Pattern of vegetative development. *Physiol. Plantar.*, **6**, 21–46.

[102] Mitchell, K. J. (1953). Influence of light and temperature on the growth of ryegrass (*Lolium* spp.). 2. The control of lateral bud development. *Physiol. Plantar.*, **6** (3), 425–43.

[103] Mitchell, K. J. (1954). Influence of light and temperature on growth of ryegrass (*Lolium* spp.). 3. Pattern and rate of tissue formation. *Physiol. Plantar.*, **7** (1), 51–65.

[104] Mitchell, K. J. (1954). Growth of pasture species. I. Perennial and short rotation ryegrass. *N.Z. J. Sci. Tech.*, **36A**, 193–206.

[105] Mitchell, K. J. (1955). Growth of pasture species. II. Perennial ryegrass, cocksfoot, and paspalum. *N.Z. J. Sci. Tech.*, **37A**, 8–26.

[106] Mitchell, K. J. (1956). Growth of pasture species under controlled environment. I. Growth at various levels of constant temperature. *N.Z. J. Sci. Tech.*, **38A**, 203–15.

[107] Mitchell, K. J., and Calder, D. M. (1958). The light regime within pastures. *N.Z. J. Agric. Res.*, **1** (1), 61–8.

[108] Mitchell, K. J., and Coles, S. T. J. (1955). Effects of defoliation and shading on short-rotation ryegrass. *N.Z. J. Sci. Tech.*, **36A**, 586–604.

[109] Mitchell, K. J., and Lucanus, R. (1960). Growth of pasture species in controlled environment. II. Growth at low temperatures. *N.Z. J. Agric. Res.*, **3** (4), 647–55.

[110] Monsi, M., and Saeki, T. (1953). Über den Lichtfaktor in den Pflanzengesellschaften und seine Bedeutung für die Stoffproduktion. *Japan. J. Bot.* **14**, 22–52.

[111] Nakamura, K. (1956). On the translocation of P^{32} between panicle bearing shoots and barren shoots in rice plants. *Proc. Crop. Sci. Soc. Japan*, **25** (2), 71–2.

[112] Nanda, K. K. (1958). Effects of photoperiod on stem elongation and lateral bud development in *Panicum miliaceum* and its correlation with flowering. *Phyton*, **10**, 7–16.

[113] Naylor, A. W. (1939). Effects of temperature, calcium, and arsenous acid on seedlings of *Poa pratensis*. *Bot. Gaz.*, **101**, 366–79.

[114] Newell, L. C. (1951). Controlled life cycles of bromegrass, *Bromus inermis* Leyss. used in improvement. *Agron. J.*, **43**, 417–24.

[115] Nichiporovitch, A. A. (1961). Properties of plant crops as an optical system. *Fiziol. Rasten.*, **8**, 536–46.

[116] Nitsch, J. P. (1963). The mediation of climatic effects through endogenous regulating substances. In *Environmental Control of Plant Growth*, pp. 175–92, ed. L. T. Evans. Academic Press, New York.

[117] Noda, K., Kumamoto, T., and Ibaragi, K. (1957). Effect of shading treatment upon the plant compositions and respiratory intensity of wheat and barley. *Proc. Crop. Sci. Soc. Japan*, **25** (3), 128–9.

[118] Oda, Y., and Honda, T. (1963). Environmental control of tillering in rice plants. *Sci. Rep. Res. Inst. Tohoku Univ.*, **14** D (1), 15–36.

[119] Olmsted, C. E. (1941). Growth and development in range grasses. I. Early development of *Bouteloua curtipendula* in relation to water supply. *Bot. Gaz.*, **102**, 499–518.

[120] Olmsted, C. E. (1942). Growth and development in range grasses. II. Early development of *Bouteloua curtipendula* as affected by drought periods. *Bot. Gaz.*, **103** (3), 531–42.

[121] Olmsted, C. E. (1944). Growth and development in range grasses. IV. Photoperiodic responses in twelve geographic strains of side oats grama. *Bot. Gaz.*, **106**, 46–74.

[122] Olmsted, C. E. (1945). Growth and development in range grasses. V. Photo-periodic responses of clonal divisions of three latitudinal strains of side oats grama. *Bot. Gaz.*, **106**, 382–401.

[123] Palfi, G., and Dezsi, L. (1960). The translocation of nutrients between fertile and sterile shoots of wheat. *Acta Bot. Acad. Sci. Hungaricae*, **6** (1–2), 65–74.

[124] Palmer, J. H. (1956). The nature of the growth response to sunlight shown by certain stoloniferous and prostrate tropical plants. *New Phytol.*, **55** (3), 346–55.

[125] Pan, C. L. (1936). Length of exposure to light in relation to plant growth in rice. *J. Amer. Soc. Agron.*, **28** (1), 58–63.

[126] Parks, W. L., and Fisher, W. B. (1958). Influence of soil temperature and nitrogen on ryegrass growth and chemical composition. *Proc. Soil Sci. Soc. Amer.*, **22** (3), 257–9.

[127] Patel, A. S., and Cooper, J. P. (1961). The influence of seasonal changes in light energy on leaf and tiller development in ryegrass, timothy, and meadow fescue. *J. Brit. Grassl. Soc.*, **16** (4), 299–308.

[128] Peterson, M. L., and Loomis, W. E. (1949). Effects of photoperiod and temperature on growth and flowering of Kentucky bluegrass. *Pl. Physiol.*, **24**, 31–43.

[129] Phillips, M. E. (1953). Studies on the quantitative morphology and ecology of *Eriophorum angustifolium* Roth. *J. Ecol.*, **41** (2), 295–318.

[130] Pohjakallio, O. (1951). On the effect of the intensity of light and length of day on the energy economy of certain cultivated plants. *Acta Agric. Scand.*, **1**, 153–75.

[131] Pohjakallio, O. (1954). On the effect of light conditions on the dry matter yield, dry matter content, and root-top ratio of certain cultivated plants. *Acta Agric. Scand.*, **4** (2), 289–301.

[132] Prat, H. (1960). Vers une classification naturelle des Graminées. *Bull. de la Soc. Bot. Fr.*, **107**, 32–79.

[133] Pritchett, W. L., and Nelson, L. B. (1951). The effect of light intensity on the growth characteristics of alfalfa and bromegrass. *Agron. J.*, **43**, 172–7.

[134] Purvis, O. N. (1934). An analysis of the influence of temperature during germination on the subsequent development of certain winter cereals and its relation to the effect of length of day. *Ann. Bot.*, **48**, 919–56.

[135] Quinlan, J. D., and Sagar, G. R. (1962). An autoradiographic study of the movement of ¹⁴C-labelled assimilates in the developing wheat plant. *Weed Res.*, **2**, 264–73.

[136] Roberts, R. A., and Hunt, I. V. (1936). The effect of shoot cutting on the growth of root and shoot of perennial ryegrass and timothy. *Welsh J. Agric.*, **12**, 158–74.

[137] Rogler, G. A. (1943). Response of geographical strains of grasses to low temperature. *J. Amer. Soc. Agron.*, **35**, 547–59.

[138] Rosenquist, D. W., and Gates, D. H. (1961). Responses of four grasses at different stages of growth to various temperature regimes. *J. Range Management*, **14** (4), 198–202.

[139] Sampson. A. W., and McCarty, F. C. (1930). The carbohydrate metabolism of *Stipa pulchra*. *Hilgardia*, **5**, 61–100.

[140] Satilov, I. S., and others. (1957). (Photosynthesis of perennial herbage and winter wheat under negative temperatures.) *Isv. Timirjazevsk. Seljsk. Akad.*, **3**, 207–12. (Herb. Abs., **23**, 713.)

[141] Schwass, R. H., and Jacques, W. A. (1956). Root development in some common New Zealand pasture plants. 8. The relationship of top growth to root growth in perennial ryegrass (*Lolium perenne*), Italian ryegrass (*L. multiflorum*) and tall fescue (*Festuca arundinacea*). *N.Z. J. Sci. Tech.*, **38A**, 109–19.

[142] Schultz, H. K., and Hayes, H. K. (1938). Artificial drought tests of some hay and pasture grasses and legumes in sod and seedling stages of growth. *J. Amer. Soc. Agron.*, **30**, 676–82.

[143] Scurfield, G. (1958). The effect of gibberellic acid on the early growth of species of *Phalaris*. *Aust. J. Sci.*, **21** (2), 48–9.

[144] Scurfield, G. (1963). The effects of temperature on the early vegetative growth of *Phalaris canariensis* L. and *P. tuberosa* L. *Aust. J. Agric. Res.*, **14** (2), 165–79.

[145] Sharman, B. C. (1942). Developmental anatomy of the shoot of *Zea mays* L. *Ann. Bot. N.S.*, **6** (22), 245–82.

[146] Sharman, B. C. (1945). Leaf and bud initiation in the Gramineae. *Bot. Gaz.*, **106** (3), 269–89.

[147] Shen, G. M. (1960). (Translocation and distribution of assimilates from the leaves of rice plant during its various developing periods – experiments with radio-active carbon (C^{14})). *Acta Agric. Sinica*, **11**, 30–40.

[148] Smith, H. F. (1933). The physiological relations between tillers of a wheat plant. *J. Counc. Sci. Ind. Res. Aust.*, **6**, 32–42.

[149] Soper, K. (1956). The anatomy of the vegetative shoot of *Paspalum dilatatum* Poir. *N.Z. J. Sci. Tech.*, **37A** (6), 600–5.

[150] Soper, K. (1958). Effects of flowering on the root system and summer survival of ryegrass. *N.Z. J. Agr. Res.*, **1** (3), 329–40.

[151] Soper, K., and Mitchell, K. J. (1956). The developmental anatomy of perennial ryegrass (*Lolium perenne* L.). *N.Z. J. Sci. Tech.*, **37A** (6), 484–504.

[152] Sprague, H. B. (1933). Root development of perennial grasses and its relation to soil conditions. *Soil Sci.*, **36**, 189–209.

[153] Sprague, V. G. (1943). The effects of temperature and daylength on seedling emergence and early growth of several pasture species. *Proc. Soil Sci. Soc. Amer.*, **8**, 287–94.

[154] Stapledon, R. G., and Milton, W. E. J. (1930). The effect of different cutting and manurial treatments on tiller and root development of cocksfoot. *Welsh, J. Agric.*, **6**, 166–74.

[155] Stern, W. R. (1962). Light measurements in pastures. *Herb. Abs.*, **32** (2), 91–6.

[156] Stuckey, I. H. (1941). Seasonal growth of grass roots. *Amer. J. Bot.*, **28**, 486–91

[157] Stuckey, I. H. (1942). Some effects of photoperiod on leaf growth. *Amer. J. Bot.*, **29**, 92–7.

[158] Stuckey, I. H. (1942). Influence of soil temperature on the development of colonial bent grass. *Plant Physiol.*, **17** (1), 116–22.

[159] Sullivan, E. F. (1961). Effect of temperature and phosphorus fertilization on yield and composition of Piper Sudangrass. *Agron. J.*, **53** (5), 357–8.

[160] Sullivan, J. T., and Sprague, V. G. (1949). The effect of temperature on the growth and composition of the stubble and roots of perennial ryegrass. *Pl. Physiol.*, **24**, 706–19.

[161] Takahashi, N., Okajima, H., Takagi, S., and Honda, T. (1956). The mechanism of tiller development in the rice plant. *Proc. Crop. Sci. Soc. Japan.*, **25** (2), 73–4.

[162] Takeda, T. (1961). Studies on the photosynthesis and production of dry matter in the community of rice plants. *Japanese J. Bot.*, **17** (3), 403–37.

[163] Tanaka, A. (1958). Studies on peculiarities in the physiological processes of rice leaves in each leaf position. The assimilative capacity of leaves at each leaf position and the transfer of assimilation products. *Japanese J. Soil and Manure*, **29** (8), 1–7.

[164] Teel, M. R. (1956). The physiological age of bromegrass (*Bromus inermis* Leyss) as it affects growth rate following defoliation. *Diss. Abstr.*, **16** (5), 844.

[165] Templeton, W. C., Mott, G. O., and Bula, R. J. (1961). Some effects of temperature and light on growth and flowering of tall fescue, *Festuca arundinacea* Schreb. *Crop Sci.*, **1**, 216–9.

[166] Tincker, M. A., and Jones, M. G. (1931). Yield studies on Oats. III. The inter-relationship of the parts of the oat plant during development. *Ann. Appl. Biol.*, **18**, 37–53.

[167] Trowbridge, P. F., Haigh, L. D., and Moulton, C. R. (1915). Studies on the timothy plant. Part II. *Res. Bull.*, 20. *Missouri Agric. Expt. Sta.*, p. 67.

[168] Troughton, A. (1951). Studies on the roots and storage organs of herbage plants. *J. Brit. Grassl. Soc.*, **6**, 197–206.

[169] Troughton, A. (1955). The application of the allometric formula to the study of the relationship between the roots and shoots of young grass plants. *Agric. Prog.*, **30**, 59–65.

[170] Troughton, A. (1955). Cessation of tillering in young grass plants. *Nature*, **176**, 514.

[171] Troughton, A. (1956). Studies on the growth of young grass plants with special reference to the relationship between root and shoot systems. *J. Brit. Grassl. Soc.*, **11**, 56–65.

[172] Troughton, A. (1960). Growth correlations between the root and shoot of grass plants. *Proc. 8th Int. Grassl. Congr. Paper*, 12 A/3, 280–3.

[173] Virgin, H. I. (1962). Light-induced unfolding of the grass leaf. *Physiol. Plantar.*, **15**, 380–9.

[174] Vose, P. B. (1962). Nutritional response and shoot/root ratio as factors in the composition and yield of genotypes of perennial ryegrass, *Lolium perenne* L. *Ann. Bot. N.S.*, **26**, 425–37.

[175] Ward, C. Y., and Blaser, R. E. (1961). Carbohydrate food reserves and leaf area in regrowth or Orchardgrass. *Crop. Sci.*, **1** (5), 366–70.

[176] Warren-Wilson, J. (1959). Analysis of the distribution of foliage area in grassland. In *The Measurement of Grassland Productivity*, pp. 51–61, ed. J. D. Ivins. Butterworth, London.

[177] Waters, H. J. (1915). Studies on the timothy plant. Part I. *Bull.* 19 *Miss. Agric. Exp. Sta.*, 1–68.

[178] Watkins, J. M. (1940). The growth habits and chemical composition of bromegrass, *Bromus inermis* Leyss, as affected by different environmental conditions. *J. Amer. Soc. Agron.*, **32**, 527–38.

[179] Watson, D. J. (1936). The effect of supplying nitrogenous fertilizer to wheat at different stages of growth. *J. Agric. Sci.*, **26**, 391–414.

[180] Weinmann, H. (1948). Underground development and reserves of grasses. A review. *J. Brit. Grassl. Soc.*, **3**, 115–40.

[181] Wiggans, S. C. (1959). Responses of oat plants to various percentages of continuous shade. *Bot. Gaz.*, **121** (1), 55–60.

[182] Willard, C. J., and McClure, S. M. (1932). The quantitative development of tops and roots of bluegrass with an improved method of obtaining root yields. *J. Amer. Soc. Agron.*, **24**, 509–13.

[183] Wilson, D. B. (1962). Effects of light intensity and clipping on herbage yields. *Canad. J. Pl. Sci.*, **42**, 270–5.

[184] Youngner, V. B. (1959). Growth of U.3 Bermuda grass under various day and night temperatures and light intensities. *Agron. J.*, **51**, 557–9.

[185] Youngner, V. B. (1961). Growth and flowering of *Zoysia* species in response to temperatures, photoperiods, and light intensities. *Crop. Sci.*, **1**, 91–3.

8

Reproduction

By L. T. Evans

GRASSES are among the most successful plants occupying adverse environments. Their success is due to a variety of morphological and physiological
characters, among which are the effective protection of their florets and the
reduction to a minimum of the time when the florets are open. The developing
inflorescences are enclosed by the leaf sheaths until fully differentiated, while
each floret is in turn protected by a lemma and palea, except for the one brief
period when they are forced apart by the lodicules to allow pollen dispersal
and to expose the stigmas to cross pollination.

To keep this period to a minimum for outbreeding populations requires close
control of the season of flowering and of the daily time of flower opening, and
in both respects the grasses are pre-eminent. In more equable climates this
pressure for a close control of flowering time may be relaxed. Nevertheless,
marked uniformity in flowering time is evident, not only in the cereals and
hay grasses where it has been selected for, but in many native grass populations.

This uniformity may, however, conceal a great variety in the paths by which
the individuals in a population reach anthesis. This is exposed when populations are transferred to other environments and provides a reservoir of genetic
variation when the species invades new areas.

Control of flowering time can fit the life cycle of a plant to the climate in
which it finds itself, and such control is best mediated by climatic factors. To
the extent that the climate in any area is broadly the same from year to year,
the seasonal change in daylength – identical from one year to the next – is the
most suitable controlling factor. Control by daylength alone would be too
rigid however, particularly at the later stages of reproductive development,
and among the grasses daylength usually sets the theme by controlling the
time of inflorescence initiation, while variations are played on it by the effects
of temperature, light intensity, and nutritional status, on the rate of development of the initiated inflorescence.

A similar flexibility exists in the breeding system of the grasses, which may
vary greatly with environmental conditions. Whether the florets are normal or
proliferous, cleistogamous or chasmogamous, self-fertilized or crossed, sexual
or apomictic, in many species depends on, and is adapted to, the climatic conditions prevailing during inflorescence development.

Induction

Control of the reproductive cycle in grasses by environmental conditions is
most rigorous at its onset, at the changeover from vegetative growth. Beyond
certain minimum requirements this change is relatively independent of the
rate and amount of prior vegetative growth. Moreover, it is not immediately

apparent in any morphological change in the shoot apex, and only becomes evident in subsequent development. It is therefore referred to as induction. In some grasses induction may follow exposure to only one day of appropriate length,[54] in others it may require several months at low temperatures followed by a period in long days. The unit induced is the individual tiller. It should be noted that Cooper's use of the term induced[40-51] is different, denoting those tillers which are ready to respond to the appropriate daylength, rather than those which have responded.

Inflorescence initiation is often considered as a fundamental and permanent change in a shoot apex, but in grasses the change need not be permanent, nor does it seem so fundamental. Although induction usually results in the development of an inflorescence, this is by no means always the case, and initiated inflorescences may revert to the vegetative condition. Moreover, with few exceptions the basic morphogenic pattern of vegetative growth is retained during inflorescence development, as pointed out in Chapter 4. One exception is rice, where the phyllotaxy changes from 1/2 to 2/5.[87]

The appearance of fascicle or spikelet primordia at the shoot apex (the double ridges stage) is the first clear sign of inflorescence initiation. The essential morphological change at this stage is thus a precocity in lateral branching. That induction is more than precocious branching, however, is indicated in those grasses where gibberellic acid applications lead to the initiation of spikelet primordia, without further differentiation.[93] The double ridges stage may be preceded by a sudden increase in the length of the shoot apex, associated with a more rapid initiation of leaf primordia. At initiation also, the basal internodes of the tiller may elongate rapidly. This would be an extremely useful index of inflorescence initiation were it not that elongation sometimes occurs in its absence.[94, 102, 125, 141]

Induction can occur so soon after germination in some grasses that they appear to have no obligate vegetative phase. For example *Lolium remotum* has been found to flower at the third node, and *L. gaudini* and *L. temulentum* at the fourth node, when sown in Arctic summer conditions.[50] Since 3 leaf primordia are present in their embryos, the plants must have been induced shortly after the appearance of the coleoptile. In *Zea* inflorescence primordia have been found even in the embryo.[71] In those grasses requiring vernalization in the seedling stage, rather than as seeds, there is obviously an obligate vegetative stage. In some the first formed leaves are relatively unresponsive to inductive daylengths[55] or even wholly so in some perennial grasses.[26] In these plants the obligate vegetative phase may be of considerable duration.

Vernalization by Low Temperatures

Many grasses, especially perennials from the temperate zones, will not initiate inflorescences under favourable daylengths without prior exposure to low temperatures. Low temperature treatment brings these plants to a state equivalent to that reached in spring, and is therefore known as vernalization. Initially the term was used for low temperature treatment of seeds, but as there is no evidence that the processes requiring low temperatures are any different in established plants, the term may be extended to all stages of plant growth.

Some grasses, such as *Lolium perenne*, can be vernalized by cold treatment of imbibed seeds.[21, 43, 69] The seeds may then be dried without loss of effect and sown, a practice which may be of some value in range management. Developing caryopses may even be vernalized on the mother plant by low autumn temperatures.[76] On the other hand cold treatment of the seed is ineffective in many vernalizable grasses.[10, 21, 67] Even in *Lolium perenne*, where the imbibed seeds are vernalizable, the rate of vernalization is greater with seedlings.[58] In *Phalaris tuberosa* cold treatment becomes effective only after several leaves have expanded[88] and the need for some vegetative growth as a pre-requisite for vernalization may be widespread among temperate perennial grasses. This could be due to a need to accumulate photosynthates, or to a need for short day perception along with the experience of low temperatures.

The vernalization of embryos is made possible by two important features of the process. The first is that the vernalization process is apparently localized in the shoot apex; the second, that the change induced in the shoot apex can be conserved there until the plant is exposed to daylengths resulting in inflorescence initiation. Thus fully vernalized plants of *Lolium perenne* held in short days throughout summer,[41] or even in darkness for 4 weeks,[165] remained vernalized and able to initiate inflorescences in subsequent long days (cf. 153). Where vernalization is only partial, intervening periods at high temperatures may lead to devernalization. However, moderate but non-vernalizing day temperatures do not negate the vernalizing effects of cool nights.[58, 114] Thus, low temperature treatment need not be continuous to be effective, and provided devernalizing temperatures do not occur, the accumulated time at temperatures within the vernalizing range may be taken as the period of effective vernalization.

Perennial grasses requiring vernalization need to be revernalized each year. As there is no evidence of dilution of the vernalized state of an apex through growth, or of devernalization of fully vernalized apices, the need for annual revernalization implies that vernalized apices cannot induce later-formed neighbouring apices, i.e. that the change induced in them is not transmissible to other apices.

The range of vernalizing temperatures is from about −6°C to about 14°C. Below 0°C the rate of vernalization is greatly reduced,[77] as it is above 10°C.[134] Between these extremes, temperatures are about equally effective, although in *Lolium perenne* the rate of vernalization increases with increase in temperature from 4°C to 10°C.[58]

In some genera vernalization response increases with the perenniality of the species, although there may be marked differences between races of any one species. In Figure 8.1 some vernalization response curves are given for several *Lolium* species. Here it can be seen that no flowering occurred in *L. perenne* with less than 2 weeks of cold treatment, while longer periods led to progressively more rapid flowering. In the winter annual, *L. multiflorum*, there was a slight response and in the annual, *L. temulentum*, no response to cold treatment. However, some races of *L. temulentum* show a marked vernalization response, while *L. perenne* plants of Mediterranean origin may show none.[47] Among *Phalaris tuberosa* strains the length of cold treatment required for induction increases with the coldness of the winter of the place of origin.[88] Variation in response of populations of *Lolium perenne* and other grasses in relation to their origin have been discussed at length by Cooper,[40, 42, 43, 44, 46] and appear to be under polygenic control. It is interesting to note in this connection that populations in their natural environments may be fully vernalized long before the end of winter.[41, 107] This suggests that the role of vernalization may be more to prevent inflorescence initiation in the autumn than to permit it in spring.

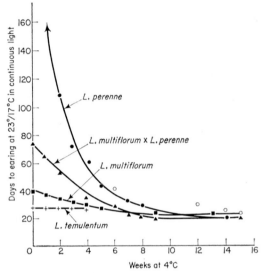

FIG. 8.1. Responses by several ryegrass species to vernalization in short days at 4°C (Data from Evans, 1960, *J. Agric. Sci.*, **54**, 410.)

With the point now made that strains within a species may differ widely in their vernalization responses, we can refer to the responses listed in Table 8.1, in which Prat's arrangement of genera and tribes[133] has been used. With this arrangement it may be seen that vernalization responses have been recorded only among the tribes of the subfamily Festucoideae. It is also evident that nearly all the grasses responding to vernalization also require long days for inflorescence initiation. However, the nature of the relation between vernalization and long day response is not clear. As vernalization proceeds fewer long days are required for induction (Fig. 8.1), and the critical daylength may fall.[107, 127] This suggests that vernalization in some way increases the responsiveness of the shoot apex to substances translocated from leaves in long-day conditions.

Short-day Vernalization

Exposure to winter conditions is an essential prelude to flowering in many temperate grasses, but in a number of them it is not known whether it is the low temperatures or the short days which are effective. Short days at temperatures above the vernalizing range may substitute for low temperatures in some species, and such induction has been called short-day vernalization. It is unlikely that the same processes are involved in the two conditions, however, since the leaf is the perceptive organ in one case, the shoot apex in the other. Short-day vernalization is known in *Arrhenatherum elatius*,[20,48] *Bromus inermis*,[49,118] *Dactylis glomerata*,[78,155] *Hordeum bulbosum*,[92] *Lolium perenne*,[46,47,58] *L. temulentum*,[47,127] *Phalaris tuberosa*,[88] *Poa pratensis*,[129] *P. palustris*, *Trisetum flavescens*, and *Agrostis tenuis*[49] all long-day Festucoid species vernalizable by low temperatures. It also occurs in *Agrostis canina, A. alba* and *A. stolonifera*, Festucoid species which do not respond to cold.[48,49]

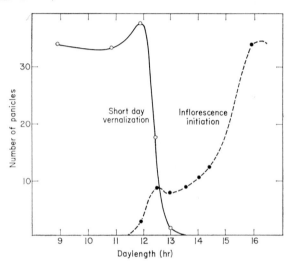

FIG. 8.2. Effect of daylength on short day vernalization and on inflorescence initiation in *Dactylis glomerata*. (Data from Allard and Evans, 1941, *J. Agric. Res.*, **62**, 193, and Gardner and Loomis, 1953, *Plant Physiol.*, **28**, 201).

The range of daylengths within which short day vernalization occurs has been examined only in *Dactylis glomerata*. In some strains it is limited to daylengths of less than 12·5 hours [74] (see Fig. 8.2), while in others it can take place in much longer days.[26]

Short day vernalization is usually effective only at higher temperatures, but in *Dactylis glomerata* short days at low temperatures are effective,[74] while in *Poa pratensis* the short days are effective only at low temperatures.[129] This is in sharp contrast to induction in short-day plants, where low temperatures prevent induction. Other grasses behaving like *Dactylis glomerata* and *Poa pratensis* should be sought, for their implication is twofold. First, since neither low temperatures nor short days alone are effective, these two conditions are unlikely to be activating alternate pathways to induction, but rather one or sequential steps on a common pathway. Secondly, if they operate on only one step, such short-day induction is likely to involve quite different processes from those in short-day plants, where moderately high temperatures are needed for induction.

Daylength Control of Inflorescence Initiation

Of all the climatic components affecting the timing of the reproductive cycle in grasses, daylength is the most decisive in its effects: and of all the stages in the cycle, inflorescence initiation is the most susceptible to its control. There are few grasses, such as *Coix lacryma-jobi* (Fig. 8.3(d)) and *Poa annua*, in which inflorescence initiation appears to be relatively indifferent to it. Some are obligate long-day plants, flowering only when the photoperiod exceeds a critical length, while others are quantitative long day plants, able to flower in short days, but more rapidly in longer photoperiods. The strains of *Phleum pratense* whose response to daylength is shown in Figure 8.3(a) are all

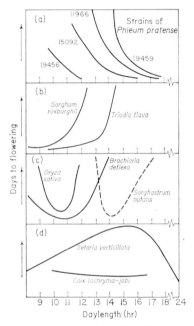

(a) in several strains of a long-day grass (data from Evans and Allard, 1934, *J. Agric. Res.*, **48**, 571.)

(b) in two short day species (data from Allard and Garner, 1940, *U.S.D.A. Tech. Bull.*, 727, 1, and Sen Gupta and Saha, 1950, *Nature*, **166**, 75.)

(c) in three intermediate day species (data from Allard and Evans, 1941, *J. Agric. Res.*, **62**, 193; Chandraratna, 1954, *New Phytol.*, **53**, 397; Porteres, 1947, *Agron. Trop.*, **2**, 47.

(d) in a daylength—indifferent and in an ambiphotoperiodic grass (data from Allard and Garner, 1940, *U.S.D.A. Tech. Bull.*, **727**, 1; and Mathon and Stroun, 1960, *Proc. 3rd. Int. Congr. Photobiol* 381.)

Fig. 8.3. Control of flowering by daylength.

long-day plants, differing in their critical daylength. Short-day plants, on the other hand, flower only when the photoperiod is less than a critical length, or flower more rapidly in short days. Two examples of these, differing in their critical daylengths and in the sharpness of their responses, are illustrated in Figure 8.3(b). Intermediate daylength plants which flower only, or most rapidly, at near equinoctial daylengths are much less common. In some of these, e.g. *Sorghastrum nutans* and some rice strains, daylength dependence is remarkably sharp (Fig. 8.3(c)).

It has often been said that daylength is unlikely to be an important controlling influence in plants of the tropics, where the range of daylength is slight. But response curves like those in Figure 8.3(c) suggest that the small seasonal changes in tropical daylengths may have marked effects on inflorescence initiation. Several varieties of rice are sensitive to differences in daylength of 10 minutes or less.[52, 120]

TABLE 8.1

Requirement for Low Temperatures and Daylength for Flowering
in the Gramineae

Vernalization: O = no response, (+) = response, + = obligate requirement.
Daylength: L = long days obligate, (L) = accelerated by long days, S = short days
obligate, (S) = accelerated by short days, M = intermediate daylengths required,
A = intermediate daylengths inhibitory, I = indifferent.

	Vernalization	Daylength	References
FESTUCOIDEAE			
Festuceae			
Briza gracilis	O		43
Br. minor	O	(L)	44
Bromus arduennensis		L	110
B. carinatus		(L)	5
B. cartharticus		(L), L	114, 135
B. commutatus	+	(L)	44
B. inermis	(+)	(L), L	2, 65, 72, 114, 118, 155
B. mollis	O, (+), +	(L), L	44, 110, 112
B. racemosus	+	(L)	44
B. rigidus		(L)	5
B. rubens		(L)	5
Cynosurus cristatus	+	L	57, 165
Dactylis glomerata	+	L	2, 74, 155, 160, 165
Desmarezia sicula	O	(L)	40
Festuca arundinacea	(+)	(L)	159
F. elatior		L	155
F. ovina	+	L	167
F. pratensis	(+), +	L	67, 143, 157
F. rubra	+		157
F. vivipara	+	L	167
Melica imperfecta		(L)	5
Poa alpina	+	L	167
P. annua	O	I	32, 43, 160
P. bulbosa	(+)	L	2, 111, 139, 169
P. compressa		(L), L	2, 64, 155
P. palustris	(+)		49
P. pratensis	+	(L), L	2, 32, 129
Hordeae			
Aegilops crassa	(+)	L	110
Ae. cylindrica	O	L	105, 110
Ae. ovata	O, (+), +	(L), L	44, 108, 110
Ae. speltoides	O, (+)	L	108, 110
Ae. triuncialis	(+), +	(L), L	108, 110
Ae. ventricosa	(+), +	L	108, 110
Agropyron cristatum	+		157
A. intermedium	+		69
A. junceum	O	(L), L	108, 110
A. repens		L	139
A. sibiricum	+		157
A. smithii	O	L	12
A. tenerum	O		157
Elymus canadensis		L	106
E. cinereus	(+)		69
E. sibiricus	O		157
Hordeum bulbosum	+	L	92

TABLE 8.1 (*Continued*)

	Vernalization	Daylength	References
Hordeae			
H. distichum		(L), L	143
H. jubatum	O	(L)	44
H. marinum	(+)		49
H. murinum	+	L	108
H. vulgare		I, (L), L	143
Hystrix patula		L	2
Lolium gaudini	O	L	40, 43
L. loliaceum	O	(L)	44
— L. multiflorum	O, (+)	L	21, 40, 47, 58 — NoTS
— L. perenne	(+), +	L	40, 42, 47, 57, 58, 155, 160 — NoTS
L. remotum	O	(L)	40
L. rigidum	O, (+)	L	40, 42, 43, 44
L. temulentum	O, (+)	(L), L	40, 43, 47, 54, 55, 57, 127
Secale anatolicum	+		153
S. cereale	O, (+), +	(L), L	75, 143
S. montanum	+		69
Triticum aegilopoides	(+)		42, 43
T. compactum		(L)	143
T. dicoccum		(L)	143
T. durum		(L), L	143
T. monococcum	O	(L)	42, 43, 143
T. vulgare	O, (+)	I (L), L,	42, 43, 143
Agrostideae			
— Agrostis alba	O, +		157 — Unavailable
— A. nebulosa		L	3 improper experimental technique
— A. palustris		L	2
Alopecurus myosuroides	+	(L)	44
A. pratensis	(+), +	(L)	19, 157, 160
Calamagrostis cinnoides		I	3
Mibora verna		I	32
Phleum nodosum	O	L	2, 45
Phleum pratense	O	(L), L	2, 44, 45, 62, 95, 155, 160
Aveneae			
Aira flexuosa	(+)	L	32
Arrhenatherum elatius	(+)	(L), L	20, 32, 48, 108, 110
Avena abyssinica		L	143
A. elatior	O		10
A. nudibrevis		L	143
A. sativa	O, (+)	(L), L	143, 160
Corynephorus canescens	O	L	32
Deschampsia caespitosa	+	L	167
Holcus lanatus	(+), +		18
Koeleria cristata		(L)	106
Trisetum flavescens	(+)		21, 49
T. spicatum	O	I	37
Phalarideae			
Anthoxanthum odoratum		(L)	160
Phalaris arundinacea		L	2, 139
P. canariensis	O, (+)	(L)	44
P. tuberosa	(+), +	L	88

TABLE 8.1 (*Continued*)

	Vernalization	Daylength	References
Stipeae			
Stipa comata		I	106
S. lepida		(L)	5
S. spartea		I	106
PANICOIDEAE			
Paniceae			
Acroceras macrum		I	114
Axonopus affinis		(L)?	90
Brachiaria deflexa		M	132
Digitaria eriantha		I	115
Echinochloa pyramidalis		I	115
Panicum crus-galli		(S), S	33, 143
P. lineare		(S)	143
P. miliaceum		S	117, 139
P. sanguinale	O	(S), I	33, 111
P. virgatum	O	S, I, (L)?	11, 106
Paspalum dilatatum		L?	89, 90
P. notatum		L?	90
Pennisetum alopecuroides		(S)	3
P. ruppellii		I	3
P. villosum		I	3
Setaria italica		(S)	33, 143
S. glauca		(S)	143
S. moharica		(S)	143
S. tenuiseta	O	L?	116
S. verticillata		(S), A	33, 109, 113, 143
S. viridis		(S), I	32, 143
Andropogoneae			
Andropogon furcatus	O	S	11
A. gerardii-hallii		L?	106
A. scoparius		M, L?	102, 106
A. virginicus		S	3
Dichanthium aristatum		S	91
Hyparrhenia hirta		(S)	114
Rottboellia exaltata		S	60, 80
R. formosa		S	60
Saccharum officinarum		M, S	1, 25
Sorghastrum nutans		M?	2
Sorghum halepense		(S)	73, 84, 90
S. roxburghii		S	150
S. sudanense		(S), I	143
Themeda australis		(S), M (L)	Evans – unpublished
Maydeae			
Coix lacryma-jobi		(S), I	3, 33
Euchlaena mexicana		S	53, 101
Tricholaena rosea		I	3
Tripsacum dactyloides		(S)	2, 3
Zea mays		S, (S), I	71, 101, 143
CHLORIDOIDEAE			
Chlorideae			
Bouteloua curtipendula	O	S, M. I. L?	106, 124, 125
B. eriopoda		M?	124

Table 8.1 (*Continued*)

	Vernalization	Daylength	References
Chlorideae			
B. filiformis	O	S	124
B. gracilis	O	(S), I, L?	11, 106, 124
B. hirsuta	O	(S)	124
B. rothrockii	O	(S)	124
Cynodon dactylon		L	116
Eleusine coracana		S, M	132, 143
Zoysieae			
Zoysia japonica		S	68, 172
Z. matrella		S	68, 172
Z. tenuifolia		S	68
Eragrosteae, etc.			
Eragrostis curvula	O	I	74, 104
E. lehmanniana		I	114
Muhlenbergia mexicana		I	2
M. schreberi		S	2
Triodia flava		S	3
ORYZOIDEAE			
Oryzeae			
Oryza sativa		S, (S), M, I	15, 29, 143

A most unusual response to daylength is that shown in Figure 8.3(d) for *Setaria verticillata*, in which flowering is most rapid at the daylength extremes, regardless of light quality.[109] Such ambiphotoperiodism is known only in one other species, and requires further investigation.

In assessing natural daylengths the twilight periods (which may be prolonged at high latitudes) should be included, since quite low intensities are photoperiodically effective. Light of 4-foot candles intensity is sufficient for photoperiod extension in *Phleum pratense*,[45] and 10 f.c. for *Dactylis glomerata* and species of *Lolium*[43,155] while light of 20 f.c. intensity prevents flowering in *Panicum miliaceum*.[117] Flashes of light near the middle of the dark period may prevent flowering in intermediate and short-day plants and are used for this purpose in sugar cane crops. In several long-day grasses on the other hand similar flashes of light permit flowering.[31,155]

As with vernalization responses, races within a species may differ in their photoperiod responses. Differences in critical photoperiod among strains of *Phleum pratense* are evident in Figure 8.3(a), and similar differences occur in other grasses.[46,160] In species such as *Bouteloua curtipendula* the differences may be more marked, responses ranging from great sensitivity to virtual indifference to daylength.[125] Such intra-species variation should be borne in mind when considering the responses to daylength listed in Table 8.1, since most of the entries are based on work with only one strain or clone. Moreover, many of the entries are based on data for flowering time rather than time of inflorescence initiation, and often only over a restricted range of photoperiods.

K

Nevertheless, the entries show a striking degree of homogeneity in daylength response within tribes and subfamilies.

All members of the subfamily Festucoideae are either long-day plants or indifferent to daylength. Nearly all species in the other subfamilies are either short or intermediate day plants, or are indifferent to daylength. Possible exceptions are *Axonopus affinis*, *Panicum virgatum*, *Paspalum dilatatum*, *P. notatum*, and *Setaria tenuiseta* among the Paniceae; *Andropogon gerardii-hallii* and *Themeda australis* among the Andropogoneae; and *Bouteloua curtipendula* and *Cynodon dactylon* among the Chlorideae.

Olmsted's work with *Bouteloua curtipendula*[124, 125, 126] is often cited as indicating that both short and long-day strains may exist within a species. Strains from Texas flowered most rapidly and completely in short days; those from the middle latitudes of the U.S.A. flowered relatively sparsely and indifferently over the range of daylengths used; while the strains from North Dakota flowered only in daylengths of more than 13 hours. All populations, particularly those from the middle latitudes, were heterogeneous in their responses. No dissections of the shoot apices were made so it is by no means certain that inflorescence initiation was either delayed or prevented in the North Dakota strain by daylengths of less than 13 hours. This doubt gains force from the fact that the northern strains were extremely dormant in short days, so that even if initiation had occurred further development of the inflorescences is likely to have been suppressed. Further, the fact that flowering occurred sooner in a daylength of 14 hours than in 15 hours casts doubt on the long-day status of the strain, and suggests it may be an intermediate day plant with a fairly long optimum photoperiod.

Similar doubts may be held for all the exceptions listed above, since the data on them refer only to flowering time, not to time of initiation, while marked dormancy in short days occurs in most of the species. In the *Paspalum* species, as in *Bouteloua*, flowering was earlier and more abundant in 14 hours than in 16 hours. Thus there are as yet no established exceptions to long-day or indifferent responses among the Festucoid grasses, and short-day, intermediate or indifferent responses among the Panicoid, Chloridoid and Oryzoid grasses. Exceptions may well be established in the future, but this degree of conservatism is truly remarkable in a character of such adaptive significance.

Effect of Temperature on Daylength Response

The effect of daylength on inflorescence initiation can be considerably modified by temperature. In many long-day grasses night temperatures above 12–18°C inhibit flowering in long-days, though 'blind shoots' may be formed.[45, 58, 65, 139, 140, 164] For example, *Poa compressa* and *P. ampla* may flower at a day temperature of 30°C when night temperatures are low, whereas night temperatures above 17°C are inhibitory regardless of day temperatures.[82] This suggests that the inhibitory effect of high temperatures is largely confined to the dark periods. However, in *Phleum pratense* high day temperatures may also be inhibitory.[45]

Short-day grasses, on the other hand, may not flower in short days unless

night temperatures exceed 12–16°C.[11, 22, 84, 90] Thus, increase in night temperatures has opposite effects on long- and short-day grasses. On the basis of their
temperature responses, *Axonopus affinis* and the *Paspalum* species[90] behave
like short-day plants, while *Cynodon dactylon*[116] could be a long-day plant.

The opposite responses of long- and short-day grasses to temperature may
explain the preponderance of short-day plants in the tropics where daylengths
during the growing season would permit both long- and short-day plants to
flower. However, the high night temperatures at these intermediate daylengths would favour flowering of short-day grasses and inhibit that of the
long-day ones.

The dependence of daylength response on temperature may also explain
why inflorescence initiation in intermediate day plants such as sugar cane is
often limited to autumn, although identical daylength conditions occur in the
spring. This has been ascribed to a need for progressively decreasing daylength, but more probably is due to the higher temperatures of autumn.[25]

Effects of Other Factors

The grasses have evolved under grazing, and defoliation usually has little
effect on their flowering.[43, 45, 129] In *Pennisetum clandestinum*, where inflorescences are borne only on the lateral shoots, inflorescence initiation will not
occur without defoliation and decapitation of the main shoots.[28, 170] It is not
clear, however, whether induction is due to loss of apical dominance or to
removal of an inhibitory effect of the leaves. The latter is possible since, in
Rottboellia exaltata, the older leaves are inhibitory to induction even under
favourable daylengths.[60]

Nitrogenous fertilizers increase the number of inflorescences in several
perennial long-day grasses.[27, 65, 98, 118, 129, 155, 164] In *Phleum pratense* nitrogen
not only increases the number of flowering tillers, but may increase still more
the number of tillers of higher orders of origin.[98]

Little attention has been paid to the effect of light intensity on flowering of
grasses. Reduction of natural light intensities reduces the proportion of plants
flowering in *Bouteloua gracilis*,[12] and delays flowering, and reduces the
number of inflorescences and the number of florets on them, in *Phleum
pratense*.[141]

Defoliation, nutrition, and light intensity do not seem to play a specific role
in the control of inflorescence initiation in grasses. Rather, they may reduce
the flowering response as determined by daylength and temperature conditions. This is evident in perennial grasses where the position of a tiller on a
plant, affecting its nutritional status and light environment, plays a major role
in determining whether or not it bears an inflorescence, as in the more sterile
strains of *Bromus inermis*[94] and *Phleum pratense*.[96, 98, 100]

Nature of the Daylength Response

By what mechanism does daylength control the initiation of flowering, and
temperature modify this control? In long-day plants, long days may stimulate

inflorescence initiation, or short days may inhibit it. The latter is the usual interpretation, and in *Lolium temulentum* long dark periods at high temperatures have been shown to lead to the export from leaves in short days of substances inhibitory to initiation.[56] On the other hand, leaves in long days export a stimulus to inflorescence initiation, which is much more than the mere absence of inhibition.[59] It would seem to be the balance between these two opposed processes, controlled by daylength, which determines behaviour at the shoot apex.

In short-day plants, it is usually considered that long nights and warm temperatures lead to the production in the leaves of a transmissible stimulus to initiation, and this has been shown to occur in *Rottboellia exaltata*.[60] Here too the non-inductive daylength is not merely neutral but inhibitory. Such dual daylength control of initiation confers high sensitivity on the photoperiod response. Those grasses less sensitive to daylength may well have environmental control restricted to only one of the opposed processes, while in the indifferent plants both processes must be shifted beyond environmental influence.

In those grasses in which short days provide an alternative to vernalization, a sequence of short followed by long days is needed for induction. Here both short- and long-day processes may be limited by environmental conditions. Intermediate day plants may be similar in this respect, only equinoctial daylengths favouring both processes sufficiently for induction to occur.[142] However, the taxonomic association between intermediate and short-day plants suggests that the intermediate response is a special type of short-day response, possibly one more than usually limited by photosynthetic activity.

Thus, the diversity of response to daylength illustrated in Figure 8.3 may be due to differences in the extent to which various steps in the path to induction are under environmental control, rather than to diversity in the path itself.

Inflorescence Development

The course of inflorescence development following initiation has been described in Chapter 4. This stage in the cycle is susceptible to many environmental influences, and where these are unfavourable the shoot apices may undergo imperfect differentiation or even revert to the vegetative condition.[93] The rate of development is particularly subject to daylength and temperature, but in most grasses the time from inflorescence initiation to earing in the field falls in the range of 25–70 days.[19,41,136,155,164] In *Bouteloua curtipendula* it may be as short as 15 days. Strains within a species may differ markedly in their rate of inflorescence development, and the late flowering habit of S23 ryegrass is due largely to slow growth of the inflorescence.[57]

The rate of inflorescence development increases with temperature, even at temperatures well above the optimum for vegetative growth, and flowering time may therefore depend markedly on spring temperatures.[41,61]

Vernalization has no effect on the rate of inflorescence development,[43,57] but daylength does, though usually less critically than on initiation. An exception in this respect is *Hordeum bulbosum* which is indifferent to daylength at initiation, but demands long days for the development of the inflorescences.[92] In most long-day grasses inflorescence development takes place in longer days than initiation, and is often adapted to them.[20, 57, 72] Some sugar canes on the other hand require intermediate daylengths for initiation, followed by short days for inflorescence development.[1, 25]

The intensity of induction also has a pronounced effect on the rate of inflorescence development in both long- and short-day grasses.[57, 60] The more inductive cycles given, and the more favourable their daylength, the greater is the subsequent rate of inflorescence development. When temperature and other conditions are standardized, this rate provides the most sensitive index we have of the intensity of induction. [54, 57]

The greater the intensity of induction the more rapidly are spikelet primordia initiated[55] and the sooner is the terminal spikelet differentiated and further spikelet formation precluded. The number of spikelets in each ear is thus the outcome of two opposed processes, and may be very sensitive to environmental conditions. Little work has been done with grasses on the effect of environmental conditions on the numbers of spikelets, and numbers and weight of seed, and on the relations between these.

Seasonal Flowering Time in Retrospect

Having now looked at the many steps in the path to flowering it will be clear that flowering time represents the cumulative effect of environmental conditions on all steps, and similar flowering times among individuals and strains may conceal large differences in their paths to flowering.[106]

Flowering time may be affected by differences in:

(1) the time of germination or breaking of dormancy, as in *Bouteloua curtipendula* and *Andropogon scoparius*,

(2) the minimum requirements for vegetative growth, as in several range grasses,[136]

(3) the requirements for vernalization, as in strains of *Lolium perenne* and *Phalaris tuberosa*, and for photoperiodic induction, as in *Phleum pratense*,

(4) the time required from inflorescence initiation to earing, as in strains of *Lolium perenne*, or from earing to anthesis, as in the mid-west prairie grasses.[136]

By and large, differences in the earlier stages tend to diminish during later ones. For example, in the many temperate perennial grasses examined by Bommer[19] inflorescence initiation occurred over a 7 months' interval, whereas earing occurred over an interval of less than 2 months.

Anthesis

The beauty of flowering in the grasses lies not only in the appearance of the floral organs at anthesis (see Frontispiece), but also in the coordination of their extremely rapid movements.

In *Festuca pratensis*, for example, the first sign of flowering is the spreading apart of the panicle branches. Proceeding from the tip of the panicle downwards, and from the lowest floret upwards in each spikelet, the pales of each floret are forced apart to an angle of up to 60° within about 7 minutes, and the filaments of the anthers stretch out and topple over while the stigmas spread upwards. The anthers then dehisce and liberate their pollen within about 10 minutes. The florets open between 5 a.m. and 6 a.m. and close at about 8 a.m.[8] In self-fertile annuals, such as *Lolium temulentum* and *Bromus tectorum*, the pales open only slightly, the stigmas are not exserted, and the anthers shed their pollen within the pales. In a few grasses lacking lodicules, flowering may be proterogynous, the stigmas maturing first and forcing the pales apart.[4,16] In *Alopecurus myosuroides*, the stigmas may be exserted even before the panicle emerges from the sheath, while the anthers are not exserted until 3–5 days later.[8]

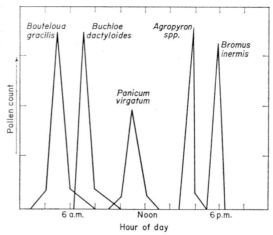

FIG. 8.4. Pollination cycles in several grasses (data from Jones and Newell, 1946, *Univ. Nebr. Coll. Agric. Exp. Sta. Res. Bull.*, 148.)

The movements of the various floral organs is probably accomplished by a redistribution of water among them. Movement of the panicle branches is due to swelling of pulvini at their bases; the opening of the pales is likewise due to a sudden swelling of the lodicules; while the sudden extension of the filaments coincides with the withdrawal of water from the anthers, leading to their dehiscence. The most active tissue in the elongation of the filaments is the epidermis,[144] and mobilization of the sugars in this tissue – possibly by endogenous gibberellins – may be responsible for the sudden extension of the epidermal cells.[145]

The daily timing of these events varies with the species, and does not seem to be determined by atmospheric and soil moisture status.[13] Rather, photoperiod may set the rhythm while the actual timing of opening depends on temperature conditions.[14] In *Paspalum dilatatum*, for example, flowers open later at lower temperatures; they open at 6–7 a.m. on plants grown at 20°C or above, but not until 2–3 p.m. on plants grown at 10°C.

Pollination in many grasses is restricted to a very brief period each day, as is evident from pollen counts, some of which are given in Figure 8.4. Moreover, the pollen of grasses, although it may travel great distances, does not remain viable for long in sunlight.[86] Closely related species growing together and flowering at the same time of the year, like *Festuca sulcata* and *F. pseudovina*, may therefore be prevented from interbreeding by small differences in the daily flowering cycle.[130]

There appears to be no consistent relation between diurnal flowering time and the taxonomic position of grasses, or the conditions in which they grow. Many warm season grasses, e.g. *Bothriochloa intermedia*,[123] flower during the night, but others, like *Panicum virgatum*, may flower at midday. Most cool season grasses flower in the early morning, but others may flower in the afternoon, e.g. *Festuca elatior*, or evening, e.g. *Festuca ovina*, or during the night, e.g. *Poa pratensis*. A few, such as *Holcus lanatus* and *Bromus arvensis*, may flower twice each day.[8]

Breeding System

The grasses have exploited a wide range of breeding systems, as is evident from Figure 8.5, which is based on data from Fryxell.[70]

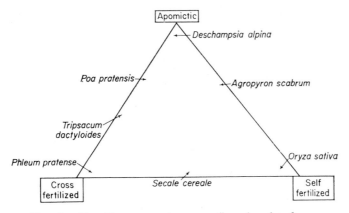

FIG. 8.5. Breeding systems in grasses (based on data from Fryxell, 1957, *Bot. Rev.*, **23**, 135.)

Many of the annual grasses, are self-fertilized, while the majority of perennials are cross-fertilized and show inbreeding depression and self-incompatibility. Stebbins[156] has drawn attention to trends from self-incompatible perennials to self-pollinated annuals in a number of genera, including *Bromus, Hordeum, Elymus, Agropyron, Festuca*, and *Poa*. He regards the annual habit and self-fertilization as derived, specialized characteristics, of value where conditions are unfavourable towards the end of the growing season, or where species undergo long distance dispersal. Hence the existence of crossed, self-incompatible species of *Bromus, Hordeum*, and *Secale* at their centres of distribution, while self-compatible species occur at the margins. There are, however, many exceptions to these trends (see [8, 70, 154]) and no clear examples of them among tropical grasses. Of 35 annual grasses examined by Beddows[8], 4 were of low self-fertility, while 9 of 26 perennials were highly self-fertile. Even more striking is the fact that only 4 out of 21 perennial New Zealand grasses are self-sterile.[38]

The breeding system of grasses can be profoundly modified by environmental conditions. Sometimes this is due to a change in floral behaviour, as in wheat and rice. In these normally self-fertilized cereals the degree to which cross-fertilization occurs is greatly affected by weather conditions [83, 138] The incompatibility system in grasses (see Chapter 9) is probably beyond environmental influence, but the occurrence of apomixis, male sterility, cleistogamy, monoecism, and dioecism are all subject to climatic influence.

The anthers of grasses appear to be among the most susceptible of floral organs to adverse environmental conditions during their differentiation. The male florets of monoecious species may be delayed, inhibited, or even replaced by female florets under unfavourable photoperiods and low temperatures. Frost may emasculate wheat and barley,[158] while long days and low temperatures lead to low fertility in normally male-fertile *Pennisetum clandestinum*.[171]

Apomixis is common among the grasses (see Chapter 9) and in most it is facultative rather than obligate. In fact, doubt exists as to whether there are any wholly obligate apomicts[36] and it is becoming apparent that environmental conditions may influence the degree of apomixis in grasses. In *Calamagrostis purpurea* early panicles may be sexual, late ones apomictic,[122] and in *Dichanthium* daylength during inflorescence development influences the degree of apomixis.[91] Such facultative apomicts have exploited an extremely effective solution to the contrasting demands of sufficient reproducibility to perpetuate successful gene combinations, and sufficient variability to adapt to changing environments.

Cleistogamy

Cleistogamy, or pollination and fertilization within closed florets, was recognized in the grasses by Linnaeus in the name *Panicum clandestinum*. Its occurrence, limited of course to self-fertile species and particularly those with reduced lodicules, permits reproduction by seed in conditions unfavourable for open flowering and cross pollination.

In many grasses cleistogamy is facultative, occurring only when conditions are adverse during the late stages of inflorescence development. In grasses such as *Bromus carinatus* and *Stipa leucotricha* individual inflorescences, and even spikelets, may bear both chasmogamous and cleistogamous florets under changing conditions.[24, 79] The cleistogamous panicles are usually smaller and less branched, stigmas, lodicules and stamens are reduced in size, and meiosis and fertilization take place precociously.

The adverse conditions precipitating facultative cleistogamy seem to be quite diverse and unspecific, and races within a species may differ in their response to them. Cleistogamy occurs in several species of *Stipa* under drought or low temperature conditions;[24, 131] in *Bromus carinatus* under low light intensity, poor nutrition and short daylengths; in *Bromus cartharticus* in daylengths of less than 10½ hours, or more than 12½ hours;[135] in *Bothriochloa decipiens* in short days;[81] and in *Rottboellia exaltata* following exposure to short days while the plants are still young.[80]

In other grasses cleistogamy may be obligate, occurring regardless of environmental conditions. *Triodia decumbens* is doubly cleistogamous, since fertilization takes place in the closed floret while the panicle is still within the sheath.[8] Besides bearing normal aerial panicles, several grasses, including species of *Danthonia* and *Triplasis*,[30, 162] regularly bear cleistogamous, one-flowered spikelets in the axils of basal leaves. These highly reduced spikelets are enclosed by the leaf sheaths and, as Chase[30] remarks, 'if their source were unknown they would not be placed in the same tribe'.

The most specialized cleistogamy occurs in three grasses which bear fertile spikelets on underground stems.[163] The cleistogamous inflorescences are often reduced to a single spikelet, while the florets have a large ovary with small stigmas, small lodicules, and small anthers closely applied to the stigmas.

Monoecism and Dioecism

The antithesis of obligate cleistogamy is dioecism, where the male and female inflorescences are borne on separate plants. Bews[16] lists 12 genera, belonging to several tribes, as dioecious. *Arundo richardii* is gynodioecious, individuals being either hermaphrodite or female.[39]

In *Buchloe dactyloides*, the male and female plants are so unalike they were originally allotted to different genera. It now appears[9] (cf. 146), however, that male and female inflorescences can be borne on one plant, on distinct branches, which produce their own kind when propagated vegetatively. Further, plants may even bear hermaphrodite florets, particularly in southern areas. An examination of the effect of age and climate on sex expression in this grass should be rewarding.

Monoecism is characteristic of the Phareae and Maydeae[16] and also occurs in other grasses. Here again environmental conditions play a major role in determining the numbers and relative earliness of the male and female inflorescences. In *Euchlaena*, short days lead to silking before anthesis, long days to the opposite.[53] Similarly, in *Zea mays*, short days increase the tendency to femaleness, even to the extent of suppressing development of the male flowers in the terminal inflorescence.[35, 71, 137, 147]

Nearer to the usual hermaphrodite condition are grasses such as *Zizania* and *Coix lacryma-jobi* in which the spikelets of the two sexes occur in the one inflorescence, the male spikelets being below in *Zizania*, above in *Coix*. Finally, there are the many grasses in which the spikelets include both hermaphrodite and unisexual florets, as in *Poa annua*, *Holcus lanatus*, and *Arrhenatherum avenaceum*.

Inflorescence Proliferation

This condition, common in some grasses at certain seasons of the year, is due to a failure of determination in developing spikelets with the result that their apical meristems continue growth, producing leafy shoots. These may be detached from the mother plant and carried some distance before establishment as independent plants. In less extreme cases only the glumes assume a leafy form, while in more extreme cases there may be additional orders of branching in the inflorescence, additional spikelets and a changed arrangement of them.[57,151] As Arber[4] has pointed out, the abnormalities in one genus frequently resemble the normal features of another.

Proliferation of the inflorescence is usually ephemeral and due to unfavourable environmental conditions, although it may also follow spraying with growth substances.[66,85] The component of the environment most specifically involved is daylength. In many long-day grasses exposure to short days during inflorescence development induces proliferation,[34,64,99,121,160,167] and proliferous inflorescences in these grasses occur most commonly in autumn. Proliferation is less common among short-day grasses, but has been noted in *Zea mays*,[71] *Sorghum*,[103] and *Panicum virgatum*.[119] In short-day maize the tassels developing in long days may be proliferous.

Ephemeral proliferation may be associated with a limited stimulus to induction. The fewer the long days to which *Cynosurus cristatus* is exposed, the slower is the rate of inflorescence development and the greater the degree of proliferation:[57,167] the earlier wheat is returned to short days, the more extensive are the teratological features:[17] the lower the temperature during long-day treatment the more proliferous are the spikelets of *Poa bulbosa*,[169] an effect which could be due to the limited efficiency of long-day induction at low temperatures.[56]

In certain Arctic–Alpine grasses proliferation of the inflorescences is not ephemeral and seasonal, but constant in occurrence, as in *Festuca vivipara*, *Poa alpina vivipara*, and *Deschampsia alpina*.[166] What is essentially an error of development in other grasses has become genetically assimilated in these species, to the extent that it is referred to as a form of apomixis. The advantage of this character in Arctic–Alpine environments, where the growing season is short, cool, and often humid, is the great acceleration in reproduction which it allows. The disadvantage, as in agamospermous apomixis, is the reduced chance of genetic recombination and adaptation to a changing environment. But as with apomixis it seems unlikely that the trend to proliferation has been shifted entirely beyond environmental influence in any species. *Poa alpina*[148] and the proliferous fescues[167] occasionally produce flower-bearing panicles, while the great variability of the proliferous species[166] suggests that sexuality is not entirely suppressed in them.

Flowering and the Annual Habit in Grasses

Perenniality is regarded as the primitive condition in grasses, but the annual habit has arisen in all groups. According to Bews[16] 'the mere shortening of the life history is a fairly simple matter'. It may be, but we are still by no means clear how it is accomplished. Certainly more is involved than rapid flowering and seed production, to which annuality is usually ascribed.

The tillers of grasses are monocarpic organs in which flowering leads to death, and the term perennial applies only to the population of tillers comprising a plant. Even vegetative tillers may die, as in *Phleum pratense* where no generation of tillers survives for more than one year.[96] Perenniality of grasses therefore depends on the rate at which new tillers are initiated, grow and become self-sufficient in relation to the rate at which they die following flowering or senescence.

Tiller primordia are initiated at most potential sites for them in both annuals and perennials. In annuals particularly, the presence of a developing inflorescence tends to inhibit growth of the tiller initials. According to Skripcinskii[152] these wither at seed setting in the annual cereals, but grow in profusion if the florets are removed from the developing inflorescences. With perennial cereals, on the other hand, rendering the ears sterile does not affect the growth of the initials, and new tillers may be formed in profusion on the flowering tillers. This striking difference between annuals and perennials needs to be confirmed in other grasses. In at least three perennials, *Phleum pratense*,[96] *Bromus inermis*,[94] and *Lolium perenne*,[51] heading is accompanied by a decrease in tiller production, though tillering may increase again in the later stages of head production. Even in the annual cereals, in which tiller bud inhibition by the inflorescence appears to be a form of apical dominance mediated by auxin,[7] nutritional and moisture status also affect tiller development,[6] and the difference between annuals and perennials is less absolute than Skripcinskii suggests. Perhaps more important in the perennial habit is diageotropism of the new tillers, which can root and become independent more readily than the upright tillers of many annuals.

The other determinant of perenniality is the rate at which tillers die. To a large extent this depends on the rate at which they flower. This is fastest in those grasses which have no vernalization or daylength requirement for inflorescence induction and development, and in which all tillers are induced after a minimum of growth, as in *Poa annua*.[32] When inflorescence development is prevented by close cutting,[168] or rendered sparse by infection,[149] *Poa annua* may become perennial. The existence of a strict daylength requirement does not confer perenniality, but delays flowering and death until the appropriate season. Such annuals may be grown as perennials under non-inductive conditions. Similarly, a vernalization requirement may confer only bienniality. However, there is often a broad relation between vernalization requirement and perenniality, as in species of *Lolium*. In some grasses, such as *Agropyron repens* and certain bamboos,[151] the primary shoot never develops an inflorescence. It would be interesting to know whether this is due to a mechanism like that operating in *Geum*, where plants remain perennial by virtue of a rosette axis which never flowers in nature. When vernalized for 50 weeks, however, both this axis and axillary buds not vernalizable under normal conditions can be made to flower.[34] In *Geum* then, perenniality is conferred by a cold requirement which has been pushed beyond normal field experience, and it is possible that a similar mechanism is responsible for perenniality in some of the sparse flowering temperate grasses.

Flowering and Growth

After considering the inhibition of fertility in certain grasses cultivated for their vegetative organs, such as sugar cane, Kikuyu grass and the oil-grasses, Arber[4] remarks that the grasses 'offer a suitable field in which to study the relation, or rather the antagonism, which prevails between the vegetative and the reproductive phases'. This concept of antagonism between growth and flowering is widespread and is at the root of much of our thinking about pasture production (cf. 128). It is in a sense true of annuals, where abundant flowering leads to death of the plant, but in perennial grasses flowering may often be associated with vigorous growth. In both meadow fescue and timothy swards the relative growth rate was highest by far in the period immediately after earing, although this occurred at different times and under different conditions in the two species.[97] These high rates of growth may be associated with the changed spatial relations of the leaves due to shooting, permitting greater light penetration and utilization. It is noted above that tillering in at least three perennial grasses may decrease during heading, only to rise to a maximum rate in the early stages of seed maturation.[96] In *Agrostis tenuis*, however, suppression of panicle production by cutting or by choke disease does result in greater tiller production and in more tillers per unit area of sward.[23]

Rhizome growth in many grasses only occurs, or is most active, in long-day conditions. In short-day grasses, such as *Zoysia*,[172] flowering and rhizome growth are therefore mutually exclusive. However, when *Sorghum halepense* is grown at a range of temperatures in 12 hour photoperiods, in which both flowering and rhizome growth can occur, the latter increases with increase in the vigour of flowering.[84] Similarly, rhizome growth and flowering are correlated in long-day grasses such as *Agropyron repens*,[139] and *Bromus inermis*.[72, 161] Flowering is frequently associated with reduced root growth, but in *Bouteloua* strains roots were most abundant under the photoperiods in which the strains flowered best.[124]

Enough has been said to indicate that there is no simple antagonism between growth and flowering in the grasses.

Conclusion

Looking back, the two most striking features of flowering in the grasses are the broad conservatism of response to temperature and daylength at the first step in the reproductive cycle, and the great flexibility in the later stages when the breeding system is finally determined.

The conservatism within taxonomic groups in climatic requirements for inflorescence initiation was not expected to be so marked, for two reasons. Firstly, because the extremes of daylength response may be found within single genera in other families, and could therefore be expected within tribes of grasses. Secondly, because these responses are of such adaptive importance that one would expect them to be under considerable selection pressure to change. They do change, but mainly to the extent of becoming more or less indifferent to daylength. A possible explanation is that further change is not required as distribution is limited by other physiological characteristics, such as heat or cold tolerance, and that it is these which are conservative (see Chapter 7).

In sharp contrast is the great variety in breeding system within most grass tribes, and the extent of the influence of environment upon it. Whether flowering is cleistogamous or chasmogamous, whether fertilization follows self or cross pollination; whether reproduction is apomictic or sexual, or even whether reproduction by seed is abandoned in favour of more rapid but more localized reproduction by vegetative propagules from proliferous inflorescences, depends, in many grasses, on environmental conditions in the later stages of inflorescence development. The extent of this adaptability in the grasses must surely be a major component in their success.

REFERENCES

[1] Allard, H. A. (1938). Complete or partial inhibition of flowering in certain plants when days are too short or too long. *J. Agr. Res.*, **57**, 775.

[2] Allard, H. A., and Evans, M. W. (1941). Growth and flowering of some tame and wild grasses in response to different photoperiods. *J. Agr. Res.*, **62**, 193.

[3] Allard, H. A., and Garner, W. W. (1940). Further observations on the response of various species of plants to length of day. *U.S.D.A. Tech. Bull.*, **727**, 1.

[4] Arber, A. (1934). *The Gramineae.* Univ. Press, Cambridge.

[5] Ashby, W. C., and Hellmers, H. (1959). Flowering and growth responses to photoperiod and temperature for six southern California grasses. *Bot. Gaz.*, **120**, 151.

[6] Aspinall, D. (1961). The control of tillering in the barley plant I. The pattern of tillering and its relation to nutrient supply. *Aust. J. Biol. Sci.*, **14**, 493.

[7] Bakhuyzen, van der S. (1947). Bloei en bloeihormonen in het bijzonder bij tarwe I. *Minist. Landb. Verslag. Onderz.* **53**, 145.

[8] Beddows, A. R. (1931). Seed setting and flowering in various grasses. *Welsh Plant Breed. Sta. Ser.*, H 12.

[9] Beetle, A. A. (1960). Distribution as a key to the age and origin of grasses. *Univ. Wyoming Publicn.*, **24**, 1.

[10] Bellini, P. (1959). Vernalizzazione di graminaceae foraggene polienne 2. *Ann. Sper. Agr.*, **13**, 143.

[11] Benedict, H. M. (1940). Effect of daylength and temperature on the flowering and growth of four species of grasses. *J. Agr. Res.*, **61**, 661.

[12] Benedict, H. M. (1940). Growth of some range grasses in reduced light intensities at Cheyenne, Wyoming. *Bot. Gaz.*, **102**, 582.

[13] Bennett, H. W. (1959). The effect of moisture and light on flowering in *Paspalum* species. *Agron. J.*, **51**, 169.

[14] Bennett, H. W. (1959). The effect of temperature upon flowering in *Paspalum*. *Agron. J.*, **51**, 191.

[15] Best, R. (1959). Photoperiodism in rice. *Field Crop Abs.*, **12**, 85.

[16] Bews, J. W. (1929). *The World's Grasses. Their differentiation, distribution, economics, and ecology.* Longmans, Green & Co., London.

[17] Blum, F., and Kriz, J. (1956). Effects of daylength on the development and morphogenesis of wheat spikes. *Fiziol. Rasten.*, **3**, 414.

[18] Bocher, T. W., and Larsen, K. (1958). Geographical distribution of initiation of flowering, growth habit and other characters in *Holcus lanatus* L. *Bot. Notis.*, **111**, 289.

[19] Bommer, D. (1959). Über Zeitpunkt und Verlauf der Blüten-differenzierung bei perennierenden Grassern. *Zeit f. Acker u. pflanzenbau.*, **109**, 95.

[20] Bommer, D. (1960). Trennung von Schossvorgang und Blutenanlage bei Glatthafer *Arrhenatherum elatius* (L.). *J. et. Pr. Naturwiss.*, **47**, 71.

[21] Bommer, D. (1961). Samen-vernalisation perennierender Graserarten. *Zeit. f. pflanzenzucht.*, **46**, 105.

[22] Bommer, D. (1961). Vernalisations-bedürfnis und photoperiodisches Verhalten der Futtergraser und ihre Bedeutung für Anbau und Züchting. Neue Ergebn. Futterbaulich Forschung. 120. D.L.G. Verlag. Main.

[23] Bradshaw, A. D. (1959). Population differentiation in *Agrostis tenuis* Sbth. II. The incidence and significance of infection by *Epichloe typhina*. *New Phytol.*, **58**, 310.

[24] Brown, W. V. (1952). The relation of soil moisture to cleistogamy in *Stipa leucotricha*. *Bot. Gaz.*, **113**, 438.

[25] Burr, G. O. *et al.* (1957). The sugarcane plant. *Ann. Rev. Plant Physiol.*, **8**, 275.

[26] Calder, D. M. (1963). Erocronnental control of flowering in *Dactylis glomerata* L. *Nature*, **197**, 882.

[27] Calder, D. M., and Cooper, J. P. (1961). Effect of spacing and nitrogen level on floral initiation in cocksfoot (*Dactylis glomerata* L.). *Nature*, **191**, 195.

[28] Carr, D. J., and Ng. E. K. (1956). Experimental induction of flower formation in Kikuyu grass (*Pennisetum clandestinum* Hochst. ex Chiov.). *Aust. J. Ag. Res.*, **7**, 1.

[29] Chandraratna, M. F. (1954). Photoperiod response in rice (*Oryza sativa* L.) I. Effects on inflorescence initiation and emergence. *New Phytol.*, **53**, 397.

[30] Chase, A. (1918). Axillary cleistogenes in some American grasses. *Amer. J. Bot.*, **5**, 254.

[31] Chouard, P. (1947). Sur le photopériodisme chez les plantes vivaces. *Bull. Soc. Bot. France*, **94**, 399.

[32] Chouard, P. (1949). Expériences de longue durée sur le photopériodisme; leçons qui decoulent. *Mem. Soc. Bot. France*, 106.

[33] Chouard, P. (1950). Le nyctopériodisme chez des plantes de la flore tempérée de France. *Bull. Soc. Bot. de France*, **97**, 234.

[34] Chouard, P. (1960). Vernalization and its relations to dormancy. *Ann. Rev. Plant Physiol.*, **11**, 191.

[35] Choudri, R. S., and Krishnan, R. (1946). Sex differentiation in *Zea mays*. *Sci. and Cult*, **11**, 472.

[36] Clausen, J. (1954). Partial apomixis as an equilibrium system in evolution. *Caryologia suppl.*, 469.

[37] Clebsch, E. E. C. (1961). Comparative morphological and physiological variation in Arctic and Alpine populations of *Trisetum spicatum*. *Diss. Abs.*, **21**, 2865.

[38] Connor, H. E. (1960). Breeding systems in New Zealand grasses. III. Festuceae, Aveneae, Agrostideae. *N.Z. J. Agric. Res.*, **3**, 728.

[39] Connor, H. E., and Penny, E. D. (1960). Breeding systems in New Zealand grasses. II. Gynodioecy in *Arundo richardii* Endl. *N.Z. J. Agric. Res.*, **3**, 725.

[40] Cooper, J. P. (1951). Studies on growth and development in *Lolium*. II. Pattern of bud development of the shoot apex and its ecological significance. *J. Ecol.*, **39**, 228.

[41] Cooper, J. P. (1952). Ibid. III. Influence of season and latitude on ear emergence. *J. Ecol.*, **40**, 352.

[42] Cooper, J. P. (1954). Ibid. IV. Genetic control of heading responses in local populations. *J. Ecol.*, **42**, 521.

[43] Cooper, J. P. (1956). Developmental analysis of populations in the cereals and herbage grasses. I. Methods and techniques. *J. Agric. Sci.*, **47**, 262.

[44] Cooper, J. P. (1957). Ibid. II. Response to low temperature vernalization. *J. Agric. Sci.*, **49**, 361.

[45] Cooper, J. P. (1958). The effect of temperature and photoperiod on inflorescence development in strains of timothy (*Phleum* species). *J. Brit. Grassl. Soc.*, **13**, 81.

[46] Cooper, J. P. (1959). Selection and population structure in *Lolium*. I. The initial populations. *Heredity*, **13**, 317.

[47] Cooper, J. P. (1960). Short day and low temperature induction in *Lolium*. *Ann. Bot. N.S.*, **24**, 232.

[48] Cooper, J. P. (1963). Species and population differences in climatic response. In *Environmental Control of Plant Growth*, pp. 381–400. Ed. L. T. Evans. Academic Press. New York.

[49] Cooper, J. P., and Calder, D. M. (1962). Flowering responses in herbage grasses. *Welsh Plant Breed. Sta. Rept.* (1961), 20–22.

[50] Cooper, J. P., and Money-Kyrle, A. F. (1952). Inflorescence development in *Lolium* during the Arctic summer. *Nature*, **169**, 158.

[51] Cooper, J. P., and Saeed, S. W. (1949). Studies on growth and development in *Lolium*. I. Relation of the annual habit to head production under various systems of cutting. *J. Ecol.*, **37**, 233.

[52] Dore, J. (1959). Response of rice to small differences in length of day. *Nature*, **183**, 413.

[53] Emerson, R. A. (1924). Control of flowering in teosinte. *J. Hered.*, **15**, 41.

[54] Evans, L. T. (1958). *Lolium temulentum* L., a long day plant requiring only one inductive photocycle. *Nature*, **182**, 197.

[55] Evans, L. T. (1960). Inflorescence initiation in *Lolium temulentum*. I. Effect of plant age and leaf area on sensitivity to photoperiodic induction. *Aust. J. Biol. Sci.*, **13**, 123.

[56] Evans, L. T. (1960). Ibid. II. Evidence for inhibitory and promotive photoperiodic processes involving transmissible products. *Aust. J. Biol. Sci.*, **13**, 429.

[57] Evans, L. T. (1960). The influence of environmental conditions on inflorescence development in some long day grasses. *New Phytol.*, **59**, 163.

[58] Evans, L. T. (1960). The influence of temperature on flowering in species of *Lolium* and in *Poa pratensis*. *J. Agric. Sci.*, **54**, 410.

[59] Evans, L. T. (1962). Inflorescence initiation in *Lolium temulentum* L. III.The effect of anaerobic conditions during photoperiodic induction. *Aust. J. Biol. Sci.*, **15**, 281.

[60] Evans, L. T. (1962). Daylength control of inflorescence initiation in the grass *Rottboellia exaltata* L.f. *Aust. J. Biol. Sci.*, **15**, 291.

[61] Evans, M. W. (1939). Relation of latitude to certain phases of the growth of timothy. *Amer. J. Bot.*, **26**, 212.

[62] Evans, M. W., and Allard, H. A. (1934). Relation of length of day to growth of timothy. *J. Agric. Res.*, **48**, 571.

[63] Evans, M. W., Allard, H. A., and McConkey, O. (1934). Time of heading and flowering of early, medium, and late timothy plants at different latitudes. *Sci. Agric.*, **15**, 573.

[64] Evans, M. W., and Watkins, J. M. (1939). The growth of Kentucky bluegrass and of Canada bluegrass in late spring and in autumn as affected by the length of day. *J. Amer. Soc. Agron.*, **31**, 767.

[65] Evans, M. W., and Wilsie, C. P. (1946). Flowering of Bromegrass, *Bromus inermis*, in the greenhouse, as influenced by length of day, temperature, and level of fertility. *J. Amer. Soc. Agron.*, **38**, 923.

[66] Faivre-Dupaigne, R., Leroux, R., and Longchamp, R. (1961). Modifications morphologiques provoquées chez le Ray-grass d'Italie (*Lolium italicum* A. Braun) varieté 'Mayenne' par les acides 2.4 dichlorophenoxyacetique (2.4 D), 2 methyl, 4 chlorophenoxyacetique (MCPA) et 2 methyl-4 chlorophenoxybutyrique (MCPB). *C.R. Acad. Sci.*, **252**, 3107.

[67] Fedorov, A. K. (1954). Some data concerning the development of perennial forage grasses. *Dokl. Akad. Nauk. S.S.S.R.*, **98**, 673.

[68] Forbes, I. (1952). Chromosome numbers and hybrids in *Zoysia*. *Agron. J.*, **44**, 194.

[69] Frischknecht, N.C. (1959). Effects of presowing vernalization on survival and development of several grasses. *J. Range Management*, **12**, 280.

[70] Fryxell, P. A. (1957). Mode of reproduction in higher plants. *Bot. Rev.*, **23**, 135.

[71] Galinat, W. C., and Naylor, A. W. (1951). Relation of photoperiod to inflorescence proliferation in *Zea mays* L. *Amer. J. Bot.*, **38**, 38.

[72] Gall, H. J. F. (1947). Flowering of smooth Bromegrass under certain environmental conditions. *Bot. Gaz.*, **109**, 59.

[73] Garner, W. W., and Allard, H. A. (1923). Further studies in photoperiodism, the response of the plant to relative length of day and night. *J. Agr. Res.*, **23**, 871.

[74] Gardner, F. P., and Loomis, W. E. (1953). Floral induction and development in orchard grass. *Plant Physiol.*, **28**, 201.

[75] Gott, M. B., Gregory, F. G., and Purvis, O. N. (1955). Studies in vernalization of cereals. XIII. Photoperiodic control of stages in flowering between initiation and ear formation in vernalized and unvernalized Petkus winter rye. *Ann. Bot. N.S.*, **21**, 87.

[76] Gregory, F. G., and Purvis, O. N. (1938). Ibid. II. The vernalization of excised mature embryos, and of developing ears. *Ann. Bot. N.S.*, **2**, 237.

[77] Hansel, H. (1953). Vernalization of winter rye by negative temperatures and the influence of vernalization upon the lamina length of the first and second leaf in winter rye, spring barley, and winter barley. *Ann. Bot. N.S.*, **17**, 417.

[78] Hanson, A. A., and Sprague, V. G. (1953). Heading of perennial grasses under greenhouse conditions. *Agron. J.*, **45**, 248.

[79] Harlan, J. R. (1945). Cleistogamy and chasmogamy in *Bromus carinatus* Hook et. Arn. *Amer. J. Bot.*, **32**, 66.

[80] Heslop-Harrison, J. (1959). Photoperiod and fertility in *Rottboellia exaltata* L.f., *Ann. Bot N.S.*, **23**, 345.

[81] Heslop-Harrison, J. (1961). The function of the glume pit and the control of cleisto-gamy in *Bothriochloa decipiens* (Hack). C. E. Hubbard, *Phytomorphol.*, **11**, 378.

[82] Hiesey, W. M. (1953). Growth and development of species and hybrids of *Poa* under controlled temperatures. *Amer. J. Bot.*, **40**, 205.

[83] Howard, A., and G. L. C. (1909). The varietal characters of Indian wheats. *Mem. Dept. Agric. India. Bot. Ser.*, **2**, 66.

[84] Irgle, M., and Rogers, B. J. (1961). The growth of a midwestern strain of *Sorghum halepense* under controlled conditions. *Amer. J. Bot.*, **48**, 392.

[85] Jeater, R. S. L. (1958). The effect of growth regulating weedkillers on the morpho-logy of grasses. *J. Brit. Grassl. Soc.*, **13**, 7.

[86] Jones, M. D., and Newell, L. C. (1946). Pollination cycles and pollen dispersal in relation to grass improvement. *Univ. Nebr. Coll. Agric. Exp. Sta. Res. Bull.*, 148.

[87] Kawahara, H., Ota, T., and Chonan, N. (1959). Observations on the differentiating process of panicle in rice plant by dissecting binocular microscope. *Proc. Crop. Sci. Soc. Japan*, **23**, 197.

[88] Ketellapper, H. J. (1960). Growth and development in *Phalaris*. I. Vernalization response in geographic strains of *P. tuberosa Ecol.*, **41**, 298.

[89] Knight, W. E. (1955). The influence of photoperiod and temperature on growth, flowering, and seed production of Dallas grass, *Paspalum dilatatum. Poir., Agron. J.*, **47**, 555.

[90] Knight, W. E., and Bennett, H. W. (1953). Preliminary report of the effect of photoperiod and temperature on the flowering and growth of several southern grasses. *Agron. J.*, **45**, 268.

[91] Knox, R. B., and Heslop-Harrison, J. (1963). Experimental control of aposorous apomixis in a grass of the Andropogoneae. *Bot. Notis*, **116**, 40.

[92] Koller, D., and Highkin, H. R. (1960). Environmental control of reproductive de-velopment in *Hordeum bulbosum*, a perennial pasture grass. *Amer. J. Bot.*, **47**, 843.

[93] Koller, D., Highkin, H. R., and Caso, O. H. (1960). Effects of gibberellic acid on stem apices of vernalizable grasses. *Amer. J. Bot.*, **47**, 518.

[94] Lamp, H. F. (1952). Reproductive activity in *Bromus inermis* in relation to phases of tiller development. *Bot. Gaz.*, **113**, 413.

[95] Langer, R. H. M. (1955). Ear formation in timothy grass (*Phleum pratense*) following vernalization and short day treatments. *Nature*, **176**, 263.

[96] Langer, R. H. M. (1956). Growth and nutrition of timothy (*Phleum pratense* L.). I. The life history of individual tillers. *Ann. Appl. Biol.*, **44**, 166.

[97] Langer, R. H. M. (1958). A study of growth in swards of timothy and meadow fescue. I. Uninterrupted growth. *J. Agr. Sci.*, **51**, 347.

[98] Langer, R. H. M. (1959). Growth and nutrition of timothy (*Phleum pratense* L.). V. Growth and flowering at different levels of nitrogen. *Ann. Appl. Biol.*, **47**, 740.

[99] Langer, R. H. M., and Ryle, G. J. A. (1958). Vegetative proliferations in herbage grasses. *J. Brit. Grassl. Soc.*, **13**, 29.

[100] Langer. R. H. M., and Ryle, G. J. A. (1959). The effect of time of sowing on flowering and fertile tiller production in S48 timothy. *J. Agric. Sci.*, **53**, 145.

[101] Langham, D. G. (1940). The inheritance of intergeneric differences in *Zea-Euch-laena* hybrids. *Genetics*, **25**, 88.

[102] Larsen, E. C. (1947). Photoperiodic responses of geographical strains of *Andro-pogon scoparius*. *Bot. Gaz.*, **109**, 132.

[103] Laude, H. H., and Gates, F. C. (1929). A head of Sorghum with greatly proli-ferated spikelets. *Bot. Gaz.*, **88**, 447.

[104] Leigh, J. H. (1960). Temperature, moisture, and daylength effects on lovegrass (*Eragrostis curvula* (Schrad.)) Nees. *Sth. Afric. J. Sci.*, **56**, 268.

[105] McMillan, C. (1956). Nature of the plant community. II. Variation in flowering behaviour within populations of *Andropogon scoparius*. *Amer. J. Bot.*, **43**, 429.

[106] McMillan, C. (1959). The role of ecotypic variation in the distribution of the cen-tral grasslands of North America. *Ecol. Monogr.*, **29**, 285.

[107] Margadant, W. D. (1951). Jarowisatie van weidergrassen, speciaal *Lolium perenne. Versl. Centraal. Inst. Landb. Onderz.*, 39.

[108] Mathon, C. C. (1960). Récherches experimentales sur le photopériodism de quel-ques especes de la flore de France. *Bull. mens. Soc. Linn. Lyon*, **29**, 188.

[109] Mathon, C. C. (1961). Efféts de la temperature, de l'energie et de la qualité de l'éclairement sur la mise a fleur de l'espece ambiphotoperiodique: *Setaria verti-cillata* Beauv. *C.R. Acad. Sci.*, **253**, 2102.

[110] Mathon, C. C. (1961). Contribution a l'étude des exigences thermiques préalables et du photopériodisme chez differentes espèces de phanerogames. *Bull. Mus. Natl. Hist. Nat. Ser.*, 2, **33**, 228.

[111] Mathon, C. C. (1961). *Ibid.*, **33**, 348.

[112] Mathon, C. C., and Nehou, J. (1960). Contribution a l'étude de la bisannualité. A propos de la précocite de trois formes de *Bromus mollis* L. *C.R. Soc. Biol.*, **154**, 1056.

[113] Mathon, C. C., and Stroun, M. (1960). A propos d'un cas d'ambiphotopériodism: *Setaria verticillata* Beauv. Proc. 3rd Int. Congr. Photobiol, 381.

[114] Mes, M. G. (1952). The influence of some climatic factors on the growth and seed production of grasses. *Veld Gold*, Publ. by Nat. Veld Trust, Johannesburg 39.

[115] Mes, M. G. (1956). The effect of some climatic factors on the growth, flowering, and seed production of three species of grasses. *Plant. Physiol. Res. Inst. Pretoria Ann. Report*, 1955/56, 10.

[116] Mes, M. G. (1958). Influence of climate on the growth and flowering of grasses. *Ibid.*, 1958, 30.

[117] Nanda, K. K. (1958). Effect of photoperiod on stem elongation and lateral bud development in *Panicum miliaceum* and its correlation with flowering. *Phyton*, **10**, 7.

[118] Newell, L. C. (1951). Controlled life cycles of bromegrass, *Bromus inermis* Leyss., used in improvement. *Agron. J.*, **43**, 417.

[119] Nielsen, E. L. (1941). Grass studies. V. Observations on proliferation. *Bot. Gaz.*, **103**, 177.

[120] Njoku, E. (1959). Response of rice to small differences in length of day. *Nature*, **183**, 1598.

[121] Nygren, A. (1949). Studies on vivipary in the genus *Deschampsia. Hereditas*, **35**, 27.

[122] Nygren, A. (1951). Form and biotype formation in *Calamagrostis purpurea. Hereditas*, **37**, 519.

[123] Oke, J. G. (1951). Flowering habits of *Dichanthium annulatum* Stapf, *Dichanthium caricosum* A. Camus, and *Bothriochloa intermedia* (Br.) A. Camus. *Indian Acad. Sci. Proc.* Ser., B., **34**, 165.

[124] Olmsted, C. E. (1943). Growth and development in range grasses. III. Photoperiodic responses in the genus *Bouteloua Bot. Gaz.*, **105**, 165.

[125] Olmsted, C. E. (1944). *Ibid.* IV. Photoperiodic responses in twelve geographic strains of side-oats grama. *Bot. Gaz.*, **106**, 46.

[126] Olmsted, C. E. (1945). *Ibid.* V. Photoperiodic responses of clonal divisions of three latitudinal strains of side-oats grama. *Bot. Gaz.*, **106**, 382.

[127] Peterson, M. L., Cooper, J. P., and Bendixen, L. F. (1961). Thermal and photoperiodic induction of flowering in darnel (*Lolium temulentum*). *Crop Sci.*, **1**, 17.

[128] Peterson, M. L., Cooper, J. P., and Vose, P. B. (1958). Non-flowering strains of herbage grasses. *Nature*, **181**, 591.

[129] Peterson, M. L., and Loomis, W. E. (1949). Effects of photoperiod and temperature on growth and flowering of Kentucky bluegrass. *Plant Physiol.*, **24**, 31.

[130] Ponomarev, A. N. (1959). (Biological isolation of *Festuca sulcata* Hack. and *Festuca pseudovina* Hack.) Transl. *Dokl. Akad. Nauk. S.S.S.R. Bot. Sci.*, **127**, 203.

[131] Ponomarev, A. N. (1961). (Cleistogamy in the feather grasses (Stipa spp.).) *Bot. Zhur.*, **46**, 1236.

[132] Porteres, R. (1947). Thermophase et photophase chez *Eleusine coracana* (Gaertner) et *Brachiaria deflexa* (C. E. Hubbard). *Agron. Trop.*, 2, 47.

[133] Prat, H. (1960). Revue d'Agrostologie. Vers une classification naturelle des Graminees. *Bull. Soc. Bot. France*, **107**, 32.

[134] Purvis, O. N. (1948). Studies in vernalization of cereals. XI. The effect of date of sowing and of excising the embryo on the responses of Petkus winter rye to different periods of vernalisation treatment. *Ann. Bot. N.S.*, **12**, 183.

[135] Ragonese, A. E., and Marco, P. R. (1943). Influencia del fotoperiodo sobre la formacion de flores cleistogamas y chasmogamas en cebadilla criolla. *Rev. Argentina Agron.*, **10**, 178.

[136] Rice, E. L. (1950). Growth and floral development of five species of range grasses in central Oklahoma. *Bot. Gaz.*, **111**, 361.

[137] Richey, F. D., and Sprague, G. F. (1932). Some factors affecting the reversal of sex expression in the tassels of maize. *Amer. Nat.*, **66**, 433.

L

[138] Roberts, E. H., Craufurd, R. Q., and Cochec, F. L. (1961). Estimation of percentage natural cross pollination: Experiments on rice. *Nature*, **190**, 1084.

[139] Roberts, R. H., and Struckmeyer, B. E. (1938). The effects of temperature and other environmental factors upon the photoperiodic responses of some of the higher plants. *J. Agric. Res.*, **56**, 633.

[140] Roberts, R. H., and Struckmeyer, B. E. (1939). Further studies on the effect of temperature and other environmental factors upon the photoperiodic responses of plants. *J. Agric. Res.*, **59**, 699.

[141] Ryle, G. J. A. (1961). Effects of light intensity on reproduction in S48 timothy (*Phleum pratense* L). *Nature*, **191**, 196.

[142] Sachs, R. M. (1956). Floral initiation in *Cestrum nocturnum*. I. A long-short day plant. *Plant Physiol*, **31**, 185.

[143] Samygin, G. A. (1946). (Photoperiodism in plants.) *Akad. Nauk. S.S.S.R.*, Inst. Fiziol Rast. im K.A. Timiriazeva Trudy, **3**, 129.

[144] Schaeverbeke, J. (1959). Observations preliminaires sur l'allongement des filets staminaux du *Poa annua* L. *C.R. Acad. Sci.*, **249**, 444.

[145] Schaeverbeke, J. (1960). Action de la gibberelline sur l'allongement des filets staminaux chez les graminées. *C.R. Acad. Sci.*, **251**, 1176.

[146] Schaffner, J. H. (1920). The dioecious nature of buffalo grass. *Bull. Torrey Bot. Club*. **47**, 119.

[147] Schaffner, J. H. (1927). Control of sex reversal in the tassel of Indian corn. *Bot. Gaz.*, **84**, 440.

[148] Schwarzenbach, F. H. (1956). Die Beeinflussung der Viviparie bei einer gronländischen Rasse von *Poa alpina* L. durch den Jahreszeitlichen Licht und temperaturwechsel. *Ber. Schweiz. Bot. Ges.*, **66**, 204.

[149] Segretain, G., and Schmidt, P. (1960). Perennité et symbiose de *Poa annua* L. en montague. *C.R. Acad. Sci.*, **251**, 1091.

[150] Sen Gupta, J. C., and Saha, J. (1950). Effect of sowing time and photoperiods in *Sorghum roxburghii* var. Lions, Stapf. (Jowar). *Nature*, **166**, 75.

[151] Sharman, B. C. (1947). The biology and developmental morphology of the shoot apex in the Gramineae. *New Phytol.*, **46**, 20.

[152] Skripcinskii, V. V. (1958). (The relation between the work of organs of vegetative propagation in perennial and annual cereals and the process of seed formation.) *Dokl. Akad. Nauk. S.S.S.R.*, **118**, 1046.

[153] Skripcinskii, V. V. (1958). Removal of vernalization changes in the process of vegetative reproduction of plants. *Fiziol. Rasten* (Transl.), **5**, 158.

[154] Smith, D. C. (1944). Pollination and seed formation in grasses. *J. Agric. Res.*, **68**, 79.

[155] Sprague, V. G. (1948). The relation of supplementary light and soil fertility to heading in the greenhouse of several perennial forage grasses. *J. Amer. Soc. Agron.*, **40**, 144.

[156] Stebbins, G. L. (1957). Self-fertilization and population variability in the higher plants. *Amer. Nat.*, **91**, 337.

[157] Stepanov, N. V. (1958). (Peculiarities of development in perennial herbage grasses.) *Isv. Timirjazevsk. S.-H. Akad.*, **2**, 7.

[158] Suneson, C. A. (1953). Frost induced natural crossing in barley, and a corollary on stem rust persistence. *Agron. J.*, **45**, 388.

[159] Templeton, W. C., Mott, G. O., and Bula, R. J. (1961). Some effects of temperature and light on growth and flowering of tall fescue, *Festuca arundinacea* Schreb II. Floral development. *Crop Sci.*, **1**, 283.

[160] Tincker, M. A. H. (1925). The effect of length of day upon the growth and reproduction of some economic plants. *Ann. Bot.*, **39**, 721.

[161] Watkins, J. M. (1940). The growth habits and chemical composition of bromegrass, *Bromus inermis* Leyss., as affected by different environmental conditions. *J. Amer. Soc. Agron.*, **32**, 527.

[162] Weatherwax, P. (1928). Cleistogamy in two species of *Danthonia*. *Bot. Gaz.*, **85**, 104.

[163] Weatherwax, P. (1934). Flowering and seed production in *Amphicarpon floridanum*. *Bull. Torrey. Bot. Club*, **61**, 211.

[164] Wilson, J. R. (1959). The influence of time of tiller origin and nitrogen level on the floral initiation and ear emergence of four pasture grasses. *N.Z. J. Agric. Res.*, **2**, 915.

[165] Wycherley, P. R. (1952). Temperature and photoperiod in relation to flowering in three perennial grass species. *Meded. Landbouwh. Wageningen*, **52**, 75.

[166] Wycherley, P. R. (1953). Proliferation of spikelets in British grasses. I. The taxonomy of the viviparous races. *Watsonia*, **3**, 41.

[167] Wycherley, P. R. (1954). Vegetative proliferation of floral spikelets in British grasses. *Ann. Bot. N.S.*, **18**, 199. 119

[168] Youngner, V. B. (1959). Ecological studies on *Poa annua* in turfgrasses. *J. Brit. Grassl. Soc.*, **14**, 233.

[169] Youngner, V. B. (1960). Environmental control of initiation of the inflorescence, reproductive structures, and proliferations in *Poa bulbosa*. *Amer. J. Bot.*, **47**, 753.

[170] Youngner, V. B. (1961). Observations on the ecology and morphology of *Pennisetum clandestinum*. *Phyton*, **16**, 77.

[171] Youngner, V. B. (1961). Low temperature induced male sterility in male fertile *Pennisetum clandestinum*. *Science*, **133**, 577.

[172] Youngner, V. B. (1961). Growth and flowering of *Zoysia* species in response to temperatures, photoperiods and light intensities. *Crop Sci.*, **1**, 91.

9

Cytogenetics

By J. R. McWilliam

DURING the preliminary stages of a grass breeding programme, a knowledge of the cytological behaviour and characteristics of the material is valuable. The chromosome number of species with respect to other members of the genus, the level of ploidy, meiotic behaviour, and the mode of reproduction (sexual or apomictic), are all factors which have a direct influence on breeding procedures. In more advanced breeding programmes, involving interspecific hybridization and the induction of polyploidy, close cytological control is necessary throughout.

The chromosome numbers and their behaviour at meiosis have been studied in most of the important cultivated grass species, and details can be found in a number of reviews.[6, 7, 15, 33, 49, 66] The cytological situation in the Gramineae is complicated because most species are, in fact, polyploids, or contain chromosome races forming polyploid series. In addition, many of the apomictic genera such as *Poa* form extensive aneuploid series.

The basic chromosome number in the Gramineae varies and is related to the taxonomic grouping. Carnahan and Hill[15] have listed the chromosome numbers of more than 1550 species, and an analysis of these shows that over 90 per cent fall into one of two major groups. The tropical and subtropical species with small chromosomes representative of the tribes Andropogoneae, Maydeae, Paniceae, Chlorideae, Eragrosteae, and Danthonieae have a basic number $n = 10$ or simple derivatives such as 9 or 12. Those species with a mainly temperate distribution, including the Agrostideae, Aveneae, Phalarideae, Festuceae, and Hordeae, have larger chromosomes, and the basic number is usually 7.

Cytogenetic evidence has provided valuable information on phylogenetic relationships in the Gramineae and has been useful in the identification of species in certain genera in which morphological characters alone are insufficient for this purpose.[45, 56] A knowledge of the chromosome numbers and the recognition of chromosome races within a species complex may influence the choice of particular races or species for crossing, or the direction in which the crosses are made.[44] Investigations of chromosome homology in interspecific hybrids can lead to a better understanding of species relationships and evolutionary history, suggesting possible avenues for further hybridization.[64, 71] Also cytogenetic studies can contribute fundamental information on the nature of polyploidy and apomixis and the existence of aneuploidy and other chromosomal irregularities.

Because of the importance of interspecific hybridization, polyploidy, and apomixis as evolutionary mechanisms in the Gramineae, the following discussion will be confined to a cytogenetical evaluation of these phenomena and their possible application in grass breeding programmes.

Interspecific Hybridization

The frequency of natural hybrids between grasses and the obvious importance of hybridization in the evolution of many important commercial species, has led geneticists to believe that hybridization is a potentially useful tool for the improvement of grasses by breeding.

The relative abundance of naturally occurring interspecific hybrids in the Gramineae appears to be related to the occurrence of different species growing together in dense stands, the production of large amounts of wind-borne pollen, and the existence of self-incompatibility systems which promote cross-pollination. The survival and successful establishment of many of these new hybrids is associated with their perenniality and effective means of vegetative reproduction. Also, the high frequency of polyploidy in the family has provided a means of fixing and spreading hybrid combinations.

Extensive interspecific hybridization has been achieved in a number of genera including *Agropyron, Bromus, Hordeum, Festuca, Lolium, Poa,* and *Sorghum.* A detailed record of these hybrids, and information on their cytological behaviour has been given in earlier reviews.[6, 39, 40, 49, 61] In the most recent review, Carnahan and Hill[15] list 256 interspecific and 95 intergeneric hybrids, composed mostly of controlled hybrids but including also a number of sterile natural hybrids.

The existence of many intergeneric hybrids such as *Agropyron* × *Elymus, Elymus* × *Hordeum* and *Festuca* × *Lolium* [for detailed list see Carnahan and Hill[15]] suggests that hybrids between species, unrelated taxonomically, can be more readily achieved in the Gramineae than in other groups of flowering plants. The cytogenetical evidence, however, indicates a closer relationship between such genera than is apparent on morphological grounds alone. In general, the most successful controlled hybrids in the family have been produced between species which are closely related.

Interspecific hybridization offers particular opportunities in the breeding of pasture grasses where yield rather than quality is often the more important consideration. Moreover, hybrids between species adapted to different climatic conditions are likely to have an increased range of adaptation in any particular region, provided it is not too far removed from the requirements of the parents. The increased genetic variability characteristic of populations of hybrid ancestry, may also be an advantage in a pasture plant which occupies a relatively heterogeneous environment, and in which only a small proportion of the initial population survives to constitute the final pasture.

One of the limitations to the use of interspecific hybridization in plant breeding is the sterility often associated with F_1 hybrids or later segregates. The evidence bearing on theories of hybrid inviability, sterility, and breakdown in plants, has been adequately reviewed by Stebbins.[68] When the F_1 sterility is complete, various techniques have been used for circumventing this problem in grasses. Valuable F_1 individuals may be propagated by vegetative offsets, as with *Cynodon dactylon,*[12] or by utilizing apomixis as has been demonstrated with *Poa* hybrids by Clausen.[18] The commercial production of F_1 hybrid seed may also be possible in some cases by incorporating self-incompatibility or male sterility factors in one or both parents. Where such techniques are not possible, the production of artificial allopolyploids from sterile interspecific hybrids is often the most rapid means of producing fertile and stable types.

When the sterility in the F_1 hybrid is not complete, a marked increase in fertility can be obtained by rigorous selection for fertility in the F_2 and later generations. This techique has been used successfully to restore fertility in *Triticum* × *Agropyron* hybrids [5], in the breeding of short rotation rye grass,[20] and also by Stebbins in self-fertilized groups such as *Bromus* and *Elymus*.[66] The partially sterile F_1 hybrids can also be back-crossed to the best adapted parent, a process resembling introgressive hybridization, which has played a dominant role in the evolution of many grasses.[1,2]

The production of successful hybrids frequently depends on the extent of hybridization, and failure to produce certain crosses does not constitute proof of complete incompatibility between the species concerned. Often hybrid seeds are set but they degenerate after an initial period of development. In such cases embryo culture can increase the chances of establishing hybrid populations as demonstrated with interspecific hybridization in *Hordeum*.[46] The use of parents selected for good agronomic characters and the incorporation of a broad range of genotypes of both species are prerequisites for any comprehensive hybridization programme.

In crossing species that differ in chromosome number, doubling the chromosome complement of the lower chromosome parent often facilitates the cross and results in improved chromosome pairing and fertility in the F_1 hybrid.[31,35,59] It has also been suggested[21] that the possibility of achieving such a cross is greater if the species with the higher chromosome number is used as the male parent. Special techniques such as the use of ionizing radiations to treat pollen or entire inflorescences before crossing have also been employed to increase the yield of hybrids, or to obtain successful hybrids in otherwise incompatible crosses.[51,57,73]

Probably the greatest use of interspecific hybridization in forage crop breeding in recent years has been in the transfer of individual characters from one species to another through a careful combination of hybridization, back-crossing, and selection.[65] The best example of such an approach in the grasses is the transfer of the desirable characteristics of the various species of cereal grains to related species of forage grasses. Among these examples are attempts to transfer genetic material from wheat and rye into species of *Agropyron*;[5,60] efforts to produce a variety of *Hordeum bulbosum* with a non-shattering rachis and reduce awns by introgression with *Hordeum vulgare*;[4,66] and the introduction of perenniality and rhizomatous habit from *Sorghum halepense* into the annual grain sorghums.[31] Another successful example of this approach has been the release of a relatively stable, fertile, *Phalaris tuberosa* × *Phalaris arundinacea* hybrid (S 230), developed at the Welsh Plant Breeding Station.[3]

Interspecific hybridization has also been used in the production of entirely new genotypes possessing new character combinations and ranges of adaptation. This form of transgressive segregation in the hybrid progeny is the product of new genetic recombinations resulting in the breakdown of existing linkages and the establishment of novel allelic combinations which have acquired a positive adaptive value. The isolation of such genotypes may be achieved by selecting in the segregating hybrid progeny at the diploid level, or, in the case of sterile hybrids, by chromosome doubling and isolating fertile stable allopolyploids.

The commercial exploitation of heterosis in pasture grasses has been infrequent, possibly due to the high cost of producing F_1 hybrid seed. In cases where the parent species are cross-compatible, the commercial production of heterotic F_1 seed is possible by using a self-incompatible clone of each species, selected on the basis of their high specific combining ability, and interplanted in isolation. This technique has been used successfully to obtain large quantities of F_1 seed of the hybrid *Phalaris tuberosa* × *Phalaris arundinacea* 6 × 44 and also for producing intraspecific hybrid seed in diploid *Paspalum notatum*.[12] Where this technique is not applicable, the use of genetic male sterility or chemical gametocides can be of value, as in the use of cytoplasmic male sterility in the production of hybrid sorghum.[72] One of the advantages of heterosis breeding, apart from the improvement in yield characteristics, is that it provides maximum performance in optimal growing conditions, and at the same time confers phenotypic stability in times of environmental stress.[27] This stability and consistency of performance over a range of environments is the basis of the success of many double-cross hybrids in maize.[42] It also permits the inclusion, in individuals, of genetic diversity from very different parents, without destroying the complex interrelationships which confer agronomic value.

One further use of hybridization has been to create a bridge for obtaining still wider crosses. *Triticum dicoccoides*, a wild wheat of the Mediterranean region, has been used in this way to transfer leaf rust resistance from *Aegilops umbellulata* to wheat.[59]

The production of new interspecific hybrids, followed by selection, with or without doubling the chromosome number, is likely to be most rewarding in countries such as Australia which possesses few if any productive native forage species suitable for cultivation in improved pastures. In Australia, many of the introduced species, although more successful than the native species in this role, require genetic adjustment. The progenies of interspecific hybridization with their wealth of variability will provide valuable raw material for this purpose, and are more likely to contain genotypes adapted to new and marginal environments.

Polyploidy

Occurrence and Characteristics

Polyploidy has also undoubtedly played an important role in the evolution of the Gramineae, for about 70 per cent of the known wild species of grasses are of polyploid origin.[63] The major role of polyploidy in evolution has been in the fixing and spreading of hybrid combinations either at the varietal, subspecies or species level. It has also provided one of the most rapid known methods of producing radically different, but nevertheless vigorous and well adapted genotypes. This has been achieved through the production of new combinations of characters rather than the origin of new characters themselves, and has thus tended to be a conservative rather than a progressive force in evolution.

The classification of natural polyploids is usually based on four main criteria: morphological resemblance to diploid species, chromosome number and behaviour, the presence or absence of tetrasomic ratios, and the fertility or sterility of the diploid from which the polyploid was derived. On this basis Stebbins[63] has described four categories of polyploids: autopolyploids, segmental allopolyploids, true or genomic allopolyploids, and autoallopolyploids, all of which involve the duplication of entire chromosome sets. These types, however, represent only general classes which may be interconnected by intermediate forms. Positive identification is difficult in most cases because of the lack of information on their mode of origin.

An understanding of the characteristics of natural polyploids is perhaps the best guide to the successful use of induced polyploidy as a tool in plant breeding. Some of the more important of these which may explain the success of polyploids in nature are as follows:

Polyploids in general display wider ranges of tolerance of extreme climatic and edaphic conditions and, as a consequence, have wider geographic distributions than their diploid ancestors.[34, 43, 67, 69, 71] One of the main external factors favouring the spread of polyploidy is undoubtedly the availability of new ecological niches. Radically new genotypes created by polyploidy will thus have their greatest adaptive value in rapidly changing environments. They will be less important in species that are widespread and still rich in ecotypic differentiation.[67]

Practically all successful polyploids show evidence of hybridization, either between diploids prior to chromosome doubling, or between similar polyploids derived from related diploids. As a result, they contain genes or entire genomes derived from a number of different diploid ancestors. The increasing dominance of polyploidy in the evolution of many genera is thus related to an increasing diversification of existing polyploids rather than the formation of an increasing number of new forms. Another feature of polyploids is the genetic barrier between them and their diploid progenitors. This sudden acquisition of reproductive isolation, although not always complete,[79] provides added stimulus for independent evolution of polyploids.

Certain features of the inter-relationships between species of a group favour the establishment and spread of polyploidy. Extensive polyploid complexes are most likely to develop in groups where the species are sufficiently closely related to each other to form vigorous F_1 hybrids, but differentiated strongly enough for the chromosomes to be nearly or entirely incapable of pairing with each other. A good example of such a situation which has favoured the spread of polyploidy is in the genus *Bromus*.[64] Polyploidy also tends to be more common in cross-pollinated and long-lived perennial species with efficient means of vegetative reproduction. These features enable 'raw' polyploids to survive the initial period of partial sterility before becoming stabilized and fully fertile.[65]

True autopolyploids represent a relatively small proportion of the successful natural polyploids, and chromosome doubling *per se* has probably played very little part in the differentiation of species.[63] Grasses reported to be natural autopolyploids include *Agrostis canina*,[41] *Agropyron desertorum*,[22] and *Hordeum bulbosum*.[56] These tetraploids may have been formed from the spontaneous doubling of relatively homozygous diploids, but most of the so called autopolyploids have probably been derived from hybridization between varieties or sub-species of a diploid species, as in the case of *Dactylis glomerata*,[50, 71] and would be more accurately classified as segmental allopolyploids.

Allopolyploidy on the other hand has undoubtedly been the most important form of polyploidy in the ancestry of cultivated plants, which serves to amplify the earlier statement that successful polyploidy has been invariably associated with hybridization. In general, the most fertile and genetically stable allopolyploids are those in which the original genomes are highly divergent as indicated by the extent of chromosome homology in the F_1 hybrids. The nature and basis of infertility and instability in polyploids has been reviewed by Stebbins.[63, 65] This initial disadvantage, presumably a feature of most 'raw' polyploids, has been overcome through natural selection and recombination leading to an increase in preferential pairing and more efficient co-adaption in the respective gene systems.

One other important property of many allopolyploids, particularly during the early stages of their development, is the ability of the chromosomes to undergo occasional heterogenetic associations, and to segregate with respect to some of the characters that separated their parent species. This mechanism has undoubtedly provided many wild allopolyploids with a valuable source of new variation and may, in fact, have contributed more in this respect than gene mutations.

At levels of polyploidy higher than tetraploidy, true autopolyploidy is rare or absent. It is likely that a large proportion, if not the majority of hexaploids, octaploids, and higher polyploids represent some variant of the autoallapolyploid condition, resulting from autopolyploids and allopolyploids combined in different ways.

Role in Plant Breeding

The induction of polyploidy by the use of colchicine has provided the plant breeder with a valuable tool for the synthesis of new polyploid species. This technique has been used in grass breeding in a number of different ways. Autopolyploids have been produced in a wide range of species by doubling individual diploids, but with few exceptions this approach has not proved very profitable.[37, 64] Some success has been achieved in the case of tetraploid rye (*Secale cereale*)[47] and tetraploid *Lolium multiflorum*.[77] Both these autotetraploids were produced, however, only after a programme of hybridization and selection at the tetraploid level. The most common defect of 'raw' autopolyploids lies in their slower growth rate, genetic instability, and reduced fertility. They are also characterized by multivalent chromosome associations at meiosis, tetrasomic ratios, and are rarely successful at levels above tetraploidy.

Chromosome doubling has been, and will continue to be, of more value in the production of fertile allopolyploids from the sterile products of interspecific and intergeneric hybridization. It has also been used successfully to facilitate the transfer of desirable genes from one species to another.[59] Allopolyploids have been produced from species hybrids in a number of grass genera including *Bromus*, *Agropyron*, *Elymus*, *Sitanion*, *Lolium*, *Festuca*, and *Phalaris*.[14, 44, 62, 64, 70] Some of these have been vigorous and particularly fertile, but to date, none of them represent a marked improvement over their respective parents, and none have yet found a place in agriculture.

The finding that induced allopolyploids have been less successful than established species is not unexpected. The need for genetic adjustment exists as it does in the autopolyploids. The main source of weakness in newly synthesized allopolyploids is the sterility and instability which results both from irregular chromosome behaviour, and disharmonies of a physiological nature due to the genetic imbalance between the parent species. Stebbins,[64] in a survey of a wide range of allopolyploids, has shown that the vigour and fertility of allopolyploids cannot be predicted from either the systematic position of their parents, or from the chromosome behaviour of the undoubled F_1 hybrids. In general, allopolyploids combine in a blending fashion the characteristics of the species from which they are derived.

Induced polyploidy has been used successfully in maize breeding in the production of homozygous diploids from monoploids.[16] This has reduced the time required in the breeding and testing of inbreds of corn. Although monoploids are not commonly found in the grasses, homozygous lines derived from haploids or polyhaploids have provided useful evidence on the nature of polyploidy and may be useful in inheritance studies.[22, 36]

Another way in which induced polyploidy may be of value is in the partial stabilization of an intermediate hybrid condition of particular value, such as hybrid vigour. This is relevant in the case of allopolyploids, and is dependent largely on the amount of preferential pairing between chromosomes belonging to the same parental species.

The most stable and fertile allopolyploids will be those between varieties or species in which the doubled hybrid shows a minimum of multivalent chromosome associations. Any technique, therefore, for increasing preferential pairing will speed up this process. The induction of structural alterations of the chromosomes has been suggested by Stebbins[67] to reduce heterogenetic associations. He obtained a reduction in the frequency of multivalents at meiosis in *Dactylis* allopolyploids derived from F_1 hybrids made with irradiated pollen. Also, hybridization at the polyploid level and selection pressure in favour of increasing fertility favours mutations which make the chromosomes more different from each other, with the result that the 'raw' allopolyploid is likely to become progressively diploidized.[26, 48] The genetic control of such a mechanism in wheat, a natural allopolyploid, has been reported.[58]

Polyploidy is now widely recognized as one of the principal methods for the formation of new species among the higher plants. It is a broad scale evolutionary process and may be a potentially valuable plant breeding tool, particularly in the Gramineae. Induced polyploidy will probably find its most useful application when the objective is the production of entirely new types, embracing new properties or increased adaptation. For this reason it cannot be expected to provide striking improvements in established highly selected crop plants where uniformity and quality are of primary consideration.

Raw allopolyploids are thus unlikely to play a major role in plant breeding as an end in themselves, but since they represent radically new plants with the potential in the initial stages for considerable variation, they should provide a valuable source of new variants on which to base a breeding programme. The production of useful forage plants from them, however, may require a considerable period of time. In this role, induced polyploidy will probably be of greatest value in the production of stable allopolyploids from the sterile products of interspecific and intergeneric hybridization. This approach, provided it has a broad genetic basis and is combined with hybridization and selection at the polyploid level, is likely to prove more rewarding than breeding at the autopolyploid level.

Hybridization combined with chromosome doubling has not achieved the success predicted at an earlier date by its more optimistic proponents, and so far has contributed relatively little to the development of new crop plants. However, applied with understanding and ingenuity, it can undoubtedly lend versatility and increased scope to grass breeding programmes. The ultimate value of the polyploid derivatives will depend on how successfully they can be adjusted to meet the requirements of the plant breeder.

Apomixis

Apomixis is a term covering all types of reproduction which replace or substitute for the usual sexual process. Two main types are recognized;[29] vegetative apomixis where reproduction is by means of vegetative proliferation (vivipary), and agamospermy where reproduction is by means of seed. Both types may also be facultative or obligate.

Apomixis is common in the Gramineae; agamospermous apomixis is known to occur in 74 species, and 12 other species reproduce, at least occasionally, by vivipary.[10, 15, 24, 29, 49, 55] The greatest number of species with an agamospermous type of apomixis occur in genera from tropical and sub-tropical regions. In the subfamily Panicoideae, for example, agamospermy has been recorded in 22 genera and is particularly common in *Bothrichloa, Paspalum, Pennisetum, Urochloa,* and *Dichanthium.* In the Festucoideae, grasses of the temperate regions, only three genera, *Poa, Eragrostis,* and *Calamagrostis* are known to contain agamospermous species. Vivipary, on the other hand, tends to be more common in this latter group.

The importance of vegetative apomixis is often overlooked, though, under certain conditions, it can substitute entirely for normal seed production and be genetically comparable to obligate agamospermy. Of the various forms of vegetative apomixis, vivipary or inflorescence proliferation is probably of greatest significance in the Gramineae. It is common in certain alpine and arctic grasses such as *Festuca vivipara*, *Poa alpina* var. *vivipara* and *Deschampsia alpina*.[78] In these environments with a short growing season and humid conditions, it provides an efficient alternative mode of reproduction. The influence of environmental conditions on the expression of vivipary is discussed in Chapter 8.

In agamospermy, seeds are produced without the instrumentality of meiosis and fertilization and the resulting embryo is usually identical with its maternal parent in chromosome number and genotype. In the simplest type, adventitious embryony, the diploid embryo arises directly from the sporophyte tissue of the ovule, but this type has not been recorded among the grasses. The types most commonly found in grasses are collectively termed gametophytic apomixis;[65] in these, the new sporophyte develops from a diploid gametophyte and involves a morphological alternation of generations. The two principal ways in which meiosis is bypassed and an unreduced gametophyte obtained are: apospory, in which a diploid embryo sac is formed from a somatic cell by mitotic divisions, and diplospory, in which the embryo sac arises from the megaspore mother cell without reduction division, due to the omission of meiosis or to the failure of the chromosomes to synapse.

Apospory is the most common form of apomixis in the grasses and occurs in many genera of the Andropogoneae and Paniceae[10] and also in the genus *Poa*.[54] Diplospory has been reported in comparatively few genera, e.g. *Calamagrostis*,[55] *Agropyron*,[32] *Poa*,[54] and *Tripsacum*,[10] and there is some evidence that it occurs in certain South African species of *Eragrostis*.[10]

Diploid gametophytes formed by apospory or diplospory may give rise to embryos through the multiplication of either the egg cell (parthenogenesis) or some other cell (apogamety). Both processes may be autonomous, or may require pollination and partial fertilization for the development of the embryo (pseudogamy). Autonomous parthenocarpy has been reported in a few grasses including *Calamagrostis purpurea*[53] and in certain *Poa* species.[28, 54] More commonly apomictic grasses are pseudogamous as found for *Heteropogon contortus*,[23] *Bothriochloa ischaemum*,[9] *Paspalum dilatatum*,[8] and *Panicum maximum*,[76] and this situation may be characteristic of all apomicts in the Andropogoneae and Paniceae.[10]

In a broad survey of the subfamily Panicoideae, Brown and Emery[10] found apomixis in 28 per cent of the species examined. All but one of these formed 4-nucleate unreduced embryo sacs, whereas in all the sexual species examined the embryo sacs had the usual 8 nuclei. On the basis of this survey they considered that the 4-nucleate embryo sac was a reliable indication of apomixis in panicoid genera. Further, because of the uniformity of this character, they concluded that apomixis in the subfamily is based on a common gene pool which is of ancient origin. Although this conclusion has been questioned,[25] it is clear that apomixis is widespread in the Panicoideae and has undoubtedly played a significant role in its evolution. The difference between reduced and unreduced embryo sacs does not exist in the Festucoideae, as in this subfamily, apomictic species always have 8-nucleate unreduced embryo sacs.[32, 52, 74]

Both vivipary and agamospermy in the grasses are almost invariably associated with polyploidy. Also the sexual ancestors of agamospermic complexes are nearly all cross-fertilized perennials, possessing accessory methods of vegetative reproduction such as rhizomes or stolons.[30] Possible exceptions to these generalizations include the annual species *Urochloa trichopus* and the diploid *Pennisetum ramosum*, both of which are apomictic.[10] There is no evidence that polyploidy promotes apomixis, but in association with hybridization it tends to reinforce the action of genes conditioning apomixis which are not manifest in a diploid genetic background.[52, 65] There is also a strong selective advantage for a mechanism such as apomixis during the evolution of new polyploids because of their meiotic irregularities and other disharmonies which often cause a reduction in fertility.

Facultative apomixis is much commoner than obligate apomixis in the grasses, and, indeed, the existence of wholly obligate apomictic species has been questioned.[17] In *Poa* where it has been studied in most detail facultative apomixis is an advantage in permitting the formation of new types, and at the same time preserving certain superior types once they have developed. The establishment of an equilibrium between apomixis and sexual processes in a population depends on the relative frequency, fertility, and vigour of the apomictic and sexual fractions. Also environmental conditions may influence the expression of apomixis (see Chapter 8). In most facultative apomicts, the apomictic and sexual processes occur concurrently; the apomictic fraction however is usually more fertile and vigorous, and enjoys a strong selective advantage. In new populations arising from hybridization between facultative apomicts this balance is destroyed. The F_1 generation usually contains both apomictic and sexual forms and for a few generations sexual recombination is possible. Finally, however, apomixis is restored in the most successful recombinations through natural selection and a new equilibrium is established. By this means the characteristics of distinct species may be recombined through hybridization and incorporated into new stable apomictic forms. This process has been studied in a wide range of interspecific crosses between partially apomictic species of *Poa*.[19] One of these, *P. pratensis*, has demonstrated its ability to absorb genomes from many different sources and occasionally give rise to valuable new apomictic segregates. This may explain the polymorphism characteristic of this apomictic complex, and account for its adaptability, and wide distribution throughout the Northern Hemisphere.[18]

Many facultative apomicts are also characterized by variation in chromosome number. This is particularly true of species of *Poa*; e.g. *P. pratensis* can exist in the wild with any number of chromosomes between $2n = 38$ and $2n = 147$.[18] Aneuploidy of this type arises following hybridization, and is perpetuated by the failure of apomixis to eliminate the chromosomally unbalanced genotypes. In obligate apomicts, however, chromosomal variation, although maintained by the same process, is thought to arise as a result of autosegregation.[29]

The occurrence of apomixis in a number of important pasture grasses such as *Cenchrus ciliaris, Paspalum dilatatum, P. notatum, Chloris gayana, Panicum maximum, Pennisetum clandestinum* and *Poa pratensis*[15] has led geneticists to define procedures for the breeding of such species. The presence of apomixis must first be determined by detailed studies of megasporogenesis and embryogeny, or by properly conducted progeny tests involving emasculaton (where possible) and hybridization, preferably with genotypes bearing a dominant gene marker.[11] Once the existence of apomixis has been definitely established, efforts should be made to determine if the plants behave as obligate or facultative apomicts, as this will influence the subsequent breeding procedures.[75] In facultative apomicts inter- and intra-specific hybridization should be used to develop new sexual recombinants from which stable apomictic forms may be derived. Clausen[18] has used this technique successfully in *Poa*. Hybridization between two facultative apomicts, *P. ampla* and *P. pratensis*, produced a highly fertile and sexual F_1. A stable apomictic segregate selected from the F_3 generation combined the desirable features of both parents and, in addition, an increased range of adaptation. In species containing mostly obligate apomicts, efforts should be made to explore a wide range of ecotypes to locate more desirable forms. This should include a search for the occasional sexual species which may provide a means of overcoming barriers to hybridization. Hybrids, if obtained, often reproduce apomictically and produce adequate seed if grown in the presence of a suitable pollen source. This technique has been used by Burton[12,13] to fix heterosis in an apomictic hybrid derived from a cross between a sexual and apomictic form of *Paspalum notatum*. Also the induction of mutations in obligate apomicts by irradiation may provide useful variants which could be perpetuated by apomixis.[38]

When useful variation latent in many apomictic species can be released by these or any other means, the apomictic mode of reproduction can greatly facilitate the subsequent selection and testing of new varieties for commercial use.

REFERENCES

[1] Anderson, E. (1949). *Introgressive hybridization*. Wiley and Sons, New York.
[2] Anderson, E., and Stebbins, G. L. (1954). Hybridization as an evolutionary stimulus. *Evolution*, **8**, 378–88.
[3] Anon. (1959). *Rep. Welsh Pl. Breed. Sta.*, 1956–58, p. 69.
[4] Anon. (1960). *Annual Report Div. Plant Industry, C.S.I.R.O., Australia*, 1960–61, p. 17.
[5] Armstrong, J. M., and White, W. J. (1952). *Triticum–Agropyron* hybridization. *6th Int. Grassl. Cong. Proc.*, Vol. **1**, 222–7. Pennsylvania.
[6] Atwood, S. S. (1947). Cytogenetics and breeding of forage crops. *Adv. in Genetics*, **1**, 1–67.
[7] Avdulov, N. P. (1931). Karyo – systematische Untersuchung der Familie Gramineen. *Bull. Appl. Bot., Suppl.*, **44**, 428 pp.
[8] Bashaw, E. C., and Holt, E. C. (1958). Magasporogenesis, embryo-sac development and embryogenesis in Dallisgrass, *Paspalum dilatatum* Poir. *Agron. J.*, **50**, 753–6.
[9] Brown, W. V., and Emery, W. H. P. (1957). Apomixis in the Gramineae, tribe Andropogoneae: *Themeda triandra* and *Bothriochloa ischaemum*. *Bot. Gaz.*, **118**, 246–53.
[10] Brown, W. V., and Emery, W. H. P. (1958). Apomixis in the Gramineae: Panicoideae. *Amer. J. Bot.*, **45**, 253–63.
[11] Burton, G. W. (1948). The method of reproduction in common Bahia grass, *Paspalum notatum*. *Amer. Soc. Agron. J.*, **40**. 443–52.
[12] Burton, G. W. (1956). Utilization of heterosis in pasture plant breeding. *7th Int. Grassl. Cong. Proc.*, pp. 439–49. Palmerston North, N.Z.

[13] Burton, G. W., and Forbes, I. (1960). The genetics and manipulation of obligate apomixis in common Bahia grass (*Paspalum notatum* Flugge). *8th Int. Grassl. Cong. Proc.*, pp. 66–71. Reading University, U.K.

[14] Carnahan, H. L., and Hill, H. D. (1955). *Lolium perenne* L. × tetraploid *Festuca elatior* L. triploid hybrids and colchicine treatments for inducing autoallohexaploids. *Agron. J.*, **47**, 258–62.

[15] Carnahan, H. L., and Hill, H. D. (1961). Cytology and genetics of forage grasses. *Bot. Rev.*, **27**, 1–162.

[16] Chase, S. S. (1952). Production of homozygous diploids of maize from monoploids. *Agron. J.*, **44**, 263–7.

[17] Clausen, J. (1954). Partial apomixis as an equilibrium system in evolution. *Caryo logia*, **6**, 469–79.

[18] Clausen, J. (1961). Introgression facilitated by apomixis in polyploid *Poas*. *Euphytica*, **10**, 87–94.

[19] Clausen, J., Hiesey, W. M., and Nobs, M. (1959). Evolutionary processes in apomictic species of *Poa*. *Carnegie Inst. Wash. Year Book*, No. 58, 358–60.

[20] Corkhill, L. (1945). Short rotation ryegrass, its breeding and characteristics. *N.Z. J. Agric.*, **71**, 465–70.

[21] Crowder, L. V. (1953). A survey of meiotic behaviour in tall fescue grass. *Amer. J. Bot.*, **40**, 348–54.

[22] Dewey, D. R. (1961). Hybrids between *Agropyron repens* and *Agropyron desertorum*. *J. Hered.*, **52**, 13–21.

[23] Emery, W. H. P., and Brown, W. V. (1958). Apomixis in the Gramineae tribe Andropogoneae: *Heteropogon contortus*. *Madroño*, **14**, 238–46.

[24] Fryxell, P. A. (1957). Mode of reproduction in higher plants. *Bot. Rev.*, **23**, 135–233.

[25] Gildenhuys, P. J., and Brix, K. (1958). Cytological abnormalities in *Pennisetum dubium*. *Heredity*, **12**, 441–52.

[26] Gilles, A., and Randolph, L. F. (1951). Reduction of quadrivalent frequency in autotetraploid maize during a period of 10 years. *Amer. J. Bot.*, **38**, 12–7.

[27] Griffing, B., and Langridge, J. (1963). Phenotypic stability for growth in the self-fertilized species, *Arabidopsis thaliana*. *In Statistical Genetics and Plant Breeding*. (Ed. W. D. Hanson and H. F. Robinson). Nat. Acad. Sci. Nat. Res. Council Publ. **982**, 368–94.

[28] Grun, P. (1955). Cytogenetic studies in *Poa*. III. Variation within *Poa nervosa*, an obligate apomict. *Amer. J. Bot.*, **42**, 778–84.

[29] Gustafsson, Å. (1946–47). Apomixis in higher plants. *Lunds Univ. Arsskrift.*, **42**, 1–66; **43**, 71–178; **43**, 183–370.

[30] Gustafsson, Å. (1948). Polyploidy, life-form, and vegetative reproduction. *Hereditas*, **34**, 1–22.

[31] Hadley, H. H. (1958). Chromosome numbers, fertility and rhizome expression of hybrids between grain sorghum and Johnson grass (*Sorghum halepense*). *Agron. J.*, **50**, 278–82.

[32] Hair, J. B. (1956). Subsexual reproduction in *Agropyron*. *Heredity*, **10**, 129–60.

[33] Hanson, A. A., and Carnahan, H. L. (1956). Breeding perennial forage grasses. *U.S.D.A. Tech. Bull.* 1145.

[34] Hayman, D. L. (1960). The distribution and cytology of the chromosome races of *Themeda australis* in southern Australia. *Aust. J. Bot.*, **8**, 58–68.

[35] Hertzsch, W. (1961). Gattungskreuzungen Zwischen den Gattungen *Festuca* und *Lolium* C. Die F_1 – Bastarde, ihr Verhalten und ihr Aussehen. *Z. Pflanzen*, **45**, 345–60.

[36] Hovin, A. (1958). Meiotic chromosome pairing in amphihaploid *Poa annua* L. *Amer. J. Bot.*, **45**, 131–38.

[37] Hutton, E. M. (1957). Some effects of induced autopolyploidy in white clover, barrel medic and Wimmera ryegrass. *Aust. Inst. Agric. Sci. J.*, **23**, 227–31.

[38] Hutton, E. M. (1961). Inter-variation in Rhodes grass (*Chloris gayana* Kunth). *British Grassl. Soc. J.*, **16**, 23–9.

[39] Jenkin, T. J. (1954). Interspecific and intergeneric hybrids in herbage grasses. IV–VIII. *J. Genet.*, **52**, 239–331.

[40] Jenkin, T. J. (1955). Interspecific and intergeneric hybrids in herbage grasses. IX–XVIII. *J. Genet.*, **53**, 81–130; 380–486.

[41] Jones, K. (1952). Autotetraploidy in *Agrostis canina*. *Nature*, **169**, 159–60.

[42] Jones, D. F. (1958). Heterosis and homeostasis in evolution and applied genetics. *Amer. Nat.*, **42**, 321–8.

[43] Kihara, H. (1954). Considerations of the evolution and distribution of *Aegilops* species based on the analyser-method. *Cytologia*, **19**, 336–57.

[44] McWilliam, J. R. (1962). Interspecific hybridization in *Phalaris*. Hybrids between *Phalaris tuberosa* and the hexaploid race of *Phalaris arundinacea. Aust. J. Agric. Res.*, **13**, 1–9.

[45] Morrison, J. W. (1959). Cytogenetic studies in the genus *Hordeum*. I. Chromosome morphology. *Canad. J. Bot.*, **37**, 527–38.

[46] Morrison, J. W., Hannah, A. E., Loiselle, R., and Symko, S. (1959). Cytogenetic studies in the genus *Hordeum*. II. Interspecific and intergeneric crosses. *Canad. J. Plant Sci.*, **39**, 375–83.

[47] Müntzing, A. (1954). An analysis of hybrid vigour in tetraploid rye. *Hereditas*, **40**, 265–277.

[48] Müntzing, A., and Prakken, R. (1940). The mode of chromosome pairing in *Phleum* twins with 63 chromosomes and its cytogenetic consequences. *Hereditas*, **26**, 463–501.

[49] Myers, W. M. (1947). Cytology and genetics of forage grasses. *Bot. Rev.*, **13**, 319–421.

[50] Myers, W. M. (1948). Studies on the origin of *Dactylis glomerata* L. (Abstract). *Genetics*, **33**, 117.

[51] Nishiyama, I., and Iizuka, M. (1952). Successful hybridization by means of X-rayed pollens in otherwise incompatible crosses. *Bull. Res. Inst. Food Sci. Kyoto Univ.*, **3**, 1–7.

[52] Nygren, A. (1946). The genesis of some Scandinavian species of *Calamagrostis*. *Hereditas*, **32**, 131–262.

[53] Nygren, A. (1949). Apomictic and sexual reproduction in *Calamagrostis purpurea*. *Hereditas*, **35**, 285–300.

[54] Nygren, A. (1953). Studies in the inheritance of apomixis in the genus *Poa*. *9th Int. Cong. Genet. Proc.*, pp. 842–3. Como, Italy.

[55] Nygren, A. (1954). Apomixis in the Angiosperms. *Bot. Rev.*, **20**, 577–649.

[56] Rajhathy, T., and Morrison, J. W. (1961). Cytogenetic studies in the genus *Hordeum*. V. *H. jubatum* and the New World species. *Canad. J. Genet. and Cytol.* **3**, 378–90.

[57] Reusch, J. D. H. (1960). The effects of gamma-radiation on crosses between *Lolium perenne* and *Festuca pratensis*. *Heredity*, **14**, 51–60.

[58] Riley, R., and Chapman, V. (1958). Genetic control of the cytologically diploid behaviour of hexaploid wheat. *Nature*, **182**, 713–5.

[59] Sears, E. R. (1956). The transfer of leaf-rust resistance from *Aegilops umbellulata* to wheat. Brookhaven. *Symp. Biol.*, **9**, 1–21.

[60] Smith, D. C. (1942). Intergeneric hybridization of cereals and other grasses. *J. Agric. Res.*, **64**, 33–47.

[61] Smith, D. C. (1956). Progress in grass breeding. *Adv. in Agron.*, **8**, 127–62.

[62] Starling, J. L. (1961). Cytogenetic study of interspecific hybrids between *Phalaris arundinacea* and *P. tuberosa*. *Crop. Sci.*, **1**, 107–11.

[63] Stebbins, G. L. (1947). Types of polyploids: their classification and significance. *Adv. Genet.*, **1**, 403–29.

[64] Stebbins, G. L. (1949). The evolutionary significance of natural and artificial polyploids in the family Gramineae. *8th Int. Cong. Genet. Proc.* (1948), Stockholm, 461–85.

[65] Stebbins, G. L. (1950). *Variation and evolution in plants*. Columbia Univ. Press, New York.

[66] Stebbins, G. L. (1952). Species hybrids in grasses. *6th Int. Grassl. Cong. Proc.*, Pennsylvania, **1**, 247–53.

[67] Stebbins, G. L. (1956). Artificial polyploidy as a tool in plant breeding. *Brookhaven Symp. Biol.*, **9**, 37–50.

[68] Stebbins, G. L. (1958). The inviability, weakness, and sterility of interspecific hybrids. *Adv. in Genet.*, **9**, 147–215.

[69] Stebbins, G. L., and Love, R. M. (1941). A cytological study of California forage grasses. *Amer. J. Bot.*, **28**, 371–82.

[70] Stebbins, G. L., and Vaarama, A. (1954). Artificial and natural hybrids in the Gramineae, tribe Hordeae. VII. Hybrids and allopolyploids between *Elymus glaucus* and *Sitanion* spp. *Genetics*, **39**, 378–95.

[71] Stebbins, G. L., and Zohary, D. (1959). Cytogenetic and evolutionary studies in the genus *Dactylis*. I. Morphology, distribution and interrelationships of the diploid subspecies. *Univ. Calif. Publ. Bot.*, **31** (1), 1–40.

[72] Stephens, J. C., and Holland, R. F. (1954). Cytoplasmic male-sterility for hybrid sorghum seed production. *Agron. J.*, **46**, 20–3.

[73] Swaminanthan, M. S., Iyer, R. D., and Sulbha, K. (1961). Morphology, cytology, and breeding behaviour of hybrids between *Corchorus olitorius* and *C. capularis*. *Curr. Sci.*, **30**, 67–8.

[74] Tinney, F. W. (1940). Cytology of parthenogenesis in *Poa pratensis*. *J. Agric. Res.*, **60**, 351–60.

[75] Tinney, F. W., and Aamodt, G. S. (1940). The progeny test as a measure of the type of seed development in *Poa pratensis* L. *J. Hered.*, **31**, 457–64.

[76] Warmke, H. E. (1954). Apomixis in *Panicum maxumum*. *Amer. J. Bot.*, **41**, 5–11.

[77] Wit, F. (1958). Tetraploid Italian ryegrass (*Lolium multiflorum*. Lam.). *Euphytica*, **7**, 47–58.

[78] Wycherley, P. R. (1953). Proliferation of spikelets in British grasses. I. The taxonomy of the viviparous races. *Watsonia*, **3**, 41–56.

[79] Zohary, D., and Nur, U. (1959). Natural triploids in the orchard grass, *Dactylis glomerata* L., polyploid complex and their significance for gene flow from diploid to tetraploid levels. *Evolution*, **13**, 311–7.

M

10

Selection Methods in the Breeding of Cross-fertilized Pasture Species

By B. D. H. Latter

In recent years there have appeared two comprehensive reviews of the problems of pasture plant breeding and of the techniques which have been developed to deal with them. Hanson and Carnahan[5] have given an excellent survey of the literature concerned with breeding objectives, breeding procedures, and experimental and plot techniques; while Cooper[2] has discussed the physiological basis of local adaptation, the general philosophy of plant introduction, and the basic methods of testing and selection in the grasses. It will therefore be assumed in this chapter that the reader has a general understanding of the problems and practice of pasture plant breeding as outlined in these reviews: the present discussion can then be devoted to a brief survey of the fundamental concepts of quantitative inheritance theory as it pertains to populations of a cross-fertilized species, and to a consideration of their implications in the choice of efficient methods of testing and selection in a pasture breeding programme.

Metric Characters

The characters of economic importance in a pasture species are predominantly quantitative, with continuous expression throughout the available parental material: forage yield, seedling vigour, growth rhythm, winter hardiness, high temperature tolerance, drought resistance, and maturity time are typical examples. Within this range of characters, however, there is an obvious classification into two groups: in one category fall those characters such as forage yield, seedling vigour, growth rhythm and maturity time, which are intrinsically continuous in expression under any normal set of environmental conditions; in the other category are those traits typified by winter hardiness, drought resistance and high temperature tolerance, which are continuous in expression if defined in terms of parameters describing the curves of response to the appropriate environmental factor, but which will usually be scored in terms of *survival* at a chosen extreme level of temperature or moisture. There are, in addition, those characters whose expression is of necessity discontinuous, but whose behaviour is most simply interpreted in terms of a threshold model involving an underlying continuous variable. An excellent example of economic interest is the presence or absence of rhizomatous root growth in *Agropyron intermedium*,[6] and of creeping root in lucerne.[3, 14]

The theory of quantitative inheritance is in general applicable to characters of each of these three types, since in all cases the observed variation may be due to the segregation of alleles at many loci, and to environmental effects which differ from one individual to the next. In the following discussion, the value of each of the available techniques of testing and selection will be considered in relation to the type of character, or combination of characters, which dominates the objectives of the breeding programme.

Heritability and Combining Ability

For a particular quantitative character in a population of a cross-fertilized species, the *general combining ability* of a genotype is defined to be the average performance of the half-sib progeny which are produced by crossing the specified genotype with a large random sample of genotypes from the population. In this context, performance is taken to be measured as a deviation from the overall population mean. The variation among the means of such half-sib groups is known as the variance in general combining ability. The *specific combining ability* of a pair of genotypes is defined to be the average performance of the full-sib group of offspring produced by crossing the two genotypes, measured as a deviation from the sum of the parental values for general combining ability. It is therefore a measure of departure from the additive scheme, due to dominance and non-allelic interaction.

The character concerned may be one which can be measured on the parents themselves (i.e. a single-plant character): time of flowering, seed size, and seedling vigour are typical examples of agronomic importance. The *heritability* of single-plant characters showing continuous expression can in general be defined as the regression of offspring mean on mid-parent value (the mean performance of the two parents from which the progeny group is derived). Experimental estimates of heritability derived in this way can be used to make accurate predictions of progress under selection, despite the existence of complications due to maternal effects, assortative mating, non-additive genetic effects or genotype $\times$ season interactions. However, in selection for a character which shows little evidence of these complications, such as seed size, heritability can also be measured as a function of the variance in general combining ability. The appropriate expression is $h^2 = 4\sigma^2_{g \cdot c \cdot a}/\sigma^2_p$, where h^2 denotes the heritability of the character, $\sigma^2_{g \cdot c \cdot a}$ the variance in general combining ability, and σ^2_p the total phenotypic variance among the individuals in the population.

Many characters of agronomic value in a pasture species cannot be observed satisfactorily in a spaced-plant nursery; e.g. forage yield, aggressiveness in competition with an associated legume or weeds, and resistance to repeated defoliation. In this context the concept of heritability is of limited value, and the parameters of importance become (1) the variance in general combining ability; (2) the variance in specific combining ability; (3) the repeatability of general combining ability value from season to season and from location to location (i.e. the measures of genotype $\times$ environment interactions); and (4) the experimental errors to which plot values are subject. Estimates of these genetical and environmental parameters can be used to predict potential improvement per generation for any proposed selection scheme and to give an indication of the optimal structure of the testing programme as regards the numbers of families, replications, locations, and seasons per test.

Individual Selection

The term *individual selection* is to be used in the following discussion to mean the selection of individuals from a spaced-plant trial which has been set out without clonal replication: individual plants, selected on the basis of their own performance for one or more characters, are removed to the glasshouse, their time of flowering synchronized by appropriate environmental treatment, and intercrossed at random to produce seed for the establishment of a further generation. For characters whose performance in spaced plants is highly correlated with that under sward conditions, the method of individual selection is of great importance and is often the most efficient procedure, when consideration is given to the expected genetic improvement per annum relative to the operational difficulties inherent in the use of more elaborate procedures.

Individual selection is always to be preferred to other methods when the heritability is high: heritability being defined as the regression of offspring performance on mid-parent performance, parents and offspring normally being measured in consecutive seasons so that genotype × season interactions are taken into account. For characters with a heritability of the order of 50 per cent or more, as for example seed weight and time of flowering, aids to selection such as clonal replication, progeny testing, and attention to the performance of full-sibs, can give at best only minor increases in the rate of progress: and they may often result in a decreased rate of response, due either to a reduction in the selection intensity which can be applied, or to a lengthening of the generation interval.

When a programme involves selection for a number of single-plant characters which are genetically independent, individual selection is especially efficient in that plants with inferior performance for characters scored early in the season may be ignored when later performance is being assessed. In the *Phalaris tuberosa* improvement programme at present in progress at Canberra, the objectives include high seedling vigour as an aid to successful establishment, greater autumn and winter growth rates, late maturity, increased seed retention and greater seed size. The breeding population has been produced by the intercrossing of a number of promising introductions of the species, each with excellent performance in one or other of the characters concerned, followed by a generation of random mating without selection to allow for genetic recombination. Since the heritability of the characters is likely to be quite high in such a heterogeneous population, individual selection with independent culling levels for the different traits has been adopted for the first generations of the programme.

The procedure has been to germinate a large population of 60,000 seeds in petri dishes and to reduce this number to 15,000 on the basis of 'germination vigour'; i.e. the ease and rate of germination, which is known to be highly correlated with seedling vigour. The selected seedlings are grown under relatively uniform conditions in flats for a period of two months during the autumn, and at the end of this period the most vigorous (as judged by size of tops and tiller number) are transplanted to the field. The plants are then passed through a further series of selection sieves for first-year winter growth, habit, flowering time, seed retention, and second-year autumn and winter growth. The plants passing through the final screening are removed from the field prior to flowering and recombined under controlled conditions.

Discontinuous characters present a somewhat different problem in that the efficiency of individual selection depends not only on the heritability of the character on the underlying scale, but also on the position of the population mean in relation to the threshold value. Individual selection may still be an efficient procedure, particularly when the incidence of the desirable phenotype is low. However, as the level of expression of the character in the population increases, aids to selection become progressively more useful to discriminate among potential parents; without some information as to the incidence of the desired phenotype among relatives, there is a rapid decline in the intensity of selection which can be achieved.

Clonal Evaluation

In programmes devoted to the breeding of perennial species, genotypes selected on the basis of performance in unreplicated spaced-plant nurseries are frequently dug up and broken into propagules for seed production and for further study. A number of the plantlets of each genotype are set out in isolated polycross blocks to produce seed for the progeny testing of the selected clones under sward conditions, and the remainder may be planted for further observation as space-planted clones, as tiller rows, or as tiller plots. It is important therefore to discuss both the theoretical and practical merits of this procedure as an aid in the screening of parental material.

In the study of *single-plant* characters of *high* heritability, clonal evaluation is rarely likely to be worthwhile unless the material is to be screened at more than one location. Consider first the use of clonal replication in the establishment of a spaced-plant trial in a single location. To show that clonal evaluation leads only to marginal increases in the rate of improvement of characters of high heritability, consider a nursery which is to be planted either with 5000 genotypes without replication, 2500 genotypes each with two replicates, or 1000 genotypes each replicated five times, etc.; and suppose that the best 50 genotypes for an additive genetic character of heritability 50 per cent are to be selected. With the optimal degree of replication (which turns out to be two replicates per genotype in this instance) the anticipated improvement per generation is roughly 5 per cent more than that expected without replication; and it is doubtful if this is sufficient to compensate for the expense of splitting the original seedlings and the increased complexity introduced by separate randomization of the genotypes in the blocks of the field design.

For single-plant characters of *low* heritability, which are not affected by the mechanical process of subdivision of the parent plant, clonal evaluation may be a valuable aid to selection: however, the efficiency of the procedure depends on the nature of the genetic variance displayed by the quantitative characters concerned, being most useful for those showing no non-additive genetic effects. In the context of the preceding example, for an additive genetic character of heritability 20 per cent the optimal number of replicates per genotype is five and, at this optimum, the rate of improvement per generation is almost 30 per cent more than that expected without clonal replication: however, for a character of heritability 20 per cent, with a further 20 per cent of its phenotypic variability due to non-additive genetic effects, the optimal number of clonal replicates per genotype can be shown to be three, and the rate of improvement per generation at this optimum is only 10 per cent greater than that expected without replication.

Clonal evaluation has undoubtedly its greatest potential in dealing with characters which cannot adequately be studied on a single individual. Some obvious examples are the determination of average performance over a set of locations or systems of management; the screening of material for characters with discontinuous expression, such as survival under extreme environmental regimes; the study of the response of a set of genotypes to simple cutting treatments; and the measurement of forage yield under an approximation to sward conditions.

If a set of genotypes is to be tested at each of a number of stations in spaced-plant trials, and selection is to be based on their average performance for each of a number of single-plant characters known to show important genotype × location interactions, clonal replication of the material may be an attractive alternative to the study of family groups. Once again the efficiency of this method of testing depends on the degree to which the expression of the characters concerned is influenced by the mechanical process of replication, and also on the extent to which differences in mean performance over the set of environments are a reflection of differences in general combining ability. Where specific combining ability effects are large, the study of family groups represented in each environment, and selection based on their average performance over the series of tests, is likely to make more efficient use of the available variance in general combining ability.

Clonal material is particularly valuable for the preliminary study of the response of genotypes to a variety of simulated management practices. Dewey[4] has reported the results of a study of clipping frequency on the relative yields and persistency of thirty orchardgrass clones, which illustrates the potential value of such a testing phase in the early stages of a breeding programme. The parental clones were the product of previous selection for their ability to yield under the conditions of 'controlled interplant competition' described by Keller[11] – a technique which involves the interplanting of spaced plants of different species in such an arrangement that each plant is subject to the same intensity of intra- and inter-specific competition. Three clipping frequencies simulating continuous grazing, rotational grazing, and hay management, were imposed on the material set out in tiller rows of five plants each. The genotypes were found to differ widely in their response to defoliation as measured by forage yields and persistency over a period of three years, and the genotype × management interaction effects were negligible by comparison, though they could be shown to be statistically significant. Performance in the year of establishment was poorly correlated with subsequent performance and, as might have been anticipated, clonal differences were greatest under hay management and least under simulated continuous grazing.

Such studies have obvious limitations: the competitive conditions in a row or plot containing only one genotype may be very different from those prevailing in a plot sown to seed representing, for example, a polycross progeny group; and the existence of non-additive genetic effects will of course reduce the efficiency of selection based on genotypic performance rather than breeding value. The importance of these effects can however be determined by the simultaneous progeny testing and clonal evaluation of selected genotypes at intervals throughout the course of a breeding programme. A comparison of performance in clonal plots and in polycross progeny tests will readily indicate the more profitable testing regime and will, in addition, provide basic information of value to those dealing with material having a comparable history of selection.

Progeny Testing

The role of the progeny test in a grass-breeding programme involving a species which is predominantly cross-fertilized, depends to a considerable extent on the particular phase through which the programme is passing and on the immediate breeding objectives. In the following discussion, therefore, the practical and theoretical merits of the progeny test as compared with other testing schemes will be considered in each of three main contexts. In the first instance, the breeder's immediate plan may involve the rapid improvement of a small set of characters of outstanding economic value, each of which can be scored satisfactorily on individual spaced plants: he may envisage a phase of three or four generations devoted to such characters (for example, high seed retention, seedling vigour or perhaps rhizomatous root development) to produce a useful interim strain. A subsequent phase may involve a number of generations of testing and selection for productivity under sward conditions, possibly necessitating the evaluation of the material at each of a few locations over a number of seasons. Alternatively, the programme may be concerned jointly with the testing of spaced plants for important individual characters and the measurement of sward performance under plot conditions: the selection of breeding material in each generation is then dependent on the relative economic importance of the two sets of objectives.

The essence of a progeny testing scheme is simply that the breeding potential of each of a set of genotypes is determined by measuring the mean performance of its offspring. For this purpose, one may use either inbred progeny produced by self-fertilization or progeny produced by open pollination in isolated, replicated, 'polycross' blocks. The genotypes judged to be superior on the basis of the progeny test are then isolated from the remainder of the population and allowed to intercross to produce the next generation: the resulting genotypes form the available parental material for a further cycle of progeny testing and selection.

Inbred Progeny

The advantages of basing such a scheme on the performance of inbred progenies (produced by one generation of self-fertilization of the parental genotypes) are twofold. On the practical side, the individual plants to be progeny tested can be selfed under bags in situ in the nursery, whereas the production of polycross seed requires their removal, clonal replication and open pollination in isolated blocks. However, if seed is required in appreciable quantities, it may be necessary clonally to replicate the genotypes to be selfed, so that the two procedures are then more comparable from an operational point of view. On the theoretical side, a progeny test based on inbred progeny may be more accurate than that utilizing polycross progeny groups, due to the very appreciable increase in variance among progeny group means. For an additive genetic character, one expects the variance to be four times that among open pollinated progeny groups, giving better discrimination in the face of plot errors or of within-family variation. However, if the characters concerned show appreciable non-additive genetic effects, identification of the breeding value of the parental genotypes is correspondingly imperfect, and the situation becomes similar in principle to that already discussed in connection with the use of clonal performance as a measure of breeding potential. Polycross progeny performance, on the other hand, gives an unbiased evaluation of the general combining ability of a parental genotype whether the inheritance of the character is additive or genetically complex.

In many outbreeding grass species, most plants are highly self-sterile and only a small proportion of the eligible genotypes could be tested by means of inbred progeny: typical examples are *Agropyron intermedium*, *Lolium perenne*, and *Phalaris tuberosa*. In a number of species of agronomic importance, however, the proportion of self-fertile plants is somewhat higher, as for example in *Dactylis glomerata*, *Phleum pratense* and *Bromus inermis*, and attention has been drawn to the possible value of inbred progeny tests in such species.[10, 15] These authors have emphasized the fact that, in an autotetraploid species, the loss of heterozygosity on self-fertilization is considerably less than that expected in functional diploids, and the reduction in vigour sustained by inbred individuals may be correspondingly less. This point is of considerable interest and it is worthwhile to review the present cytological, theoretical, and practical evidence.

The available cytogenetic evidence reviewed by Carnahan and Hill[1] suggests that *Dactylis glomerata* behaves in many ways as an autopolyploid, but that the tetraploid species has probably been produced by the hybridization of two closely related diploid species; there is also evidence to suggest that *Bromus inermis* has originated as an autoallo-octaploid, with two basic genomes represented in quadruplicate; and *Phleum pratense* is presumed to be autohexaploid in origin. *Lolium perenne* on the other hand is a strict diploid, and provides a useful comparison in evaluating the experimental evidence on the magnitude of the reduction in vigour observed on self-fertilization. For each level of polyploidy, the expected rate of loss of heterozygosity following one generation of self-fertilization can be derived theoretically, assuming strict autoploidy and random chromosome segregation. Since the figures which have been given in the grass breeding literature for this rate of decline are not strictly appropriate, it will be as well to set out the expectations here. It is well known that, in a random mating *diploid* population, one generation of self-fertilization leads to an average reduction in heterozygosity of 50 per cent: in a random mating *autotetraploid* population, the consequences of self-fertilization are not so readily summarized, but the average loss of heterozygosity in one generation is expected to lie between 17 and 25 per cent depending on the array of gene frequencies in the population: and for an *autohexaploid* the loss in heterozygosity is expected to lie between 7 and 25 per cent.

Though there is no reason to expect the decline in plant vigour at these different levels of ploidy to be strictly proportional to the reduction in hetrozygosity, one would certainly expect some sort of relationship to be observable. Wexelsen[17] has reported a 25 per cent reduction in vigour, measured as plant weight, in the hexaploid *Phleum pratense* after self-fertilization for one generation. McDonald *et al.*[13] recorded a 35 per cent reduction in vigour in S₁ plants by comparison with open pollinated progeny in *Bromus inermis*. Kalton *et al.*[10] and Schultz[16] observed a 40 per cent and a 55 per cent reduction respectively in plant yield following one generation of selfing in *Dactylis glomerata*, and Jenkin[9] found an average loss in vigour of 59 per cent in *Lolium perenne*. In view of the fact that all these polyploid species are almost certainly segmental allopolyploids, and that *Dactylis glomerata* is unlikely to have originated as a strict autotetraploid, the observations are suggestive. It is to be hoped that future comparative studies of species whose polyploid status is reasonably well understood, will provide more critical evidence along these lines.

Polycross Progeny

Though progeny testing by means of inbred progeny may be a practical proposition in some species, it is only under special circumstances that it can be an efficient procedure. Of far greater importance in pasture plant breeding is the polycross progeny test, for two main reasons: performance is a reflection of the general combining ability of the parental genotypes; and replication enables the production of sufficient open pollinated seed for comprehensive tests of sward performance. In the discussion to follow, the term progeny testing will be used to denote polycross progeny testing.

Let us return to a consideration of the phase of a breeding programme in which each of a small number of 'single plant characters' is under selection. An excellent discussion of the role of progeny testing and individual plant selection in such a situation has been given by Morley and Heinrichs,[14] and we can take the following procedure from their paper as an example to illustrate the steps involved. In the spring of Year 1, 5,000 single plants are set out in the field, and are scored in the following spring for degree of expression of the characters under selection (in this instance, winter injury and degree of creeping root development in lucerne); from each of the best 100 plants, clonal propagules are taken and planted in polycross blocks for seed production, the seed being harvested in the autumn of Year 2. In the spring of Year 3, the polycross progenies are planted out in a randomized blocks test and scored as individual plants in the following spring: of the 100 progeny groups under test, the best 20 are identified on the basis of their mean performance. The mother clones whose breeding value has been proven by this procedure, are retained in the original polycross blocks and the propagules of the remaining 80 genotypes are eliminated. In the autumn of Year 4, seed is harvested from the 'elite' polycross blocks for planting in the following spring. The cycle may then be repeated with a four-year generation interval.

The efficiency of this testing scheme may best be judged by comparing the predicted annual improvement under the optimal combination of individual selection and progeny testing with that expected under individual selection alone. Since individual selection involves a generation interval of only two years, one would expect it to be a superior method of selection for characters of high heritability: Morley and Heinrichs[14] have shown that for characters with a heritability as low as 20 per cent, the inclusion of a progeny testing phase in the selection programme leads to a reduction in annual improvement. It is only with characters of heritability in the vicinity of 10 per cent that individual selection + progeny testing is superior to individual selection alone.

As far as selection solely for single-plant characters is concerned, therefore, the role of progeny testing can be seen to be extremely limited: if heritability is known to be low for one or more of the important characters in the programme, or if a threshold character is involved, and something in addition to individual selection is obviously required, then the use of *family selection* is to be preferred to the progeny test. As we shall see in the next section, family selection is a procedure by which individuals are chosen on the basis of the mean performance of the full-sib and half-sib families to which they belong: the method involves no increase in generation interval, though it does entail the labour of controlled hybridization and complete pedigree recording.

Let us turn now to the discussion of a breeding programme which has as its immediate objective the improvement of sward productivity, no attention being given to selection for single-plant characters. The over-riding consideration in the choice of an efficient scheme of testing and selection here is the practical problem of producing sufficient seed of each progeny to sow a replicated sward-test in plots. The polycross method of progeny testing is admirably suited to cope with this difficulty, since a sufficient number of polycross blocks can be employed to provide the required seed of each progeny: polycross progeny testing is a particularly convenient scheme, when sward tests are to be conducted on a regional basis. However, when testing is to be carried out in only one location and the species concerned is such that sufficient seed can be produced for plot testing by means of controlled hybridization of selected genotypes (as for example with *Phalaris tuberosa*), consideration should be given to the alternative procedure of *sib-testing*. Sib-testing involves the selection of genotypes from a reserve nursery on the basis of the performance of their full- and half-sibs under sward test, and consequently leads to a reduction in generation interval by comparison with the progeny test: as a result, the scheme may often be more efficient in terms of annual improvement.

In an improvement programme involving both sward testing and selection for individual performance in spaced plants, polycross progeny testing is again extremely convenient and efficient, particularly where sward performance is to be measured over more than one season because of important genotype × season interactions. Scoring for the single-plant characters can usually be carried out in the first year of the cycle, prior to the selection of genotypes for inclusion in the polycross blocks; and sward testing is therefore confined to those genotypes which have passed the single-plant test. An excellent progress report of a programme of this sort devoted to the breeding of smooth bromegrass, with testing conducted on a regional basis, is to be found in a recent bulletin of the Cornell University Agricultural Experiment Station (No. 954, 1960).

Family Selection and Sib-Testing

Single-Plant Characters

We have seen in the preceding section that the use of progeny testing inevitably leads to a marked increase in the generation interval, which has to be weighed against the accuracy of the method in the identification of superior genotypes. As far as single-plant characters are concerned, the analysis of Morley and Heinrichs[14] has shown that it is only for characters with a heritability in the vicinity of 10 per cent or lower, that the increased accuracy more than compensates for the lengthening of the generation interval. However, it can readily be shown on the basis of quantitative inheritance theory that such characters will show greater progress per annum under a system of *family selection.* Under such a scheme, the price one has to pay for the increased response is the tedium of controlled hybridization under glasshouse conditions; fortunately many species are sufficiently self-sterile for pollination under bags or in pollen-proof glasshouse units to be all that is required.

As an illustration of the steps involved in a family selection programme for the improvement of single-plant characters, let us suppose that at the commencement of a typical cycle, 125 genotypes are removed from the field well before flowering, and the 25 largest plants broken up into four propagules each prior to potting for crossing in the glasshouse. It will be convenient to refer to these 25 genotypes as pollen parents, and to the remaining 100 genotypes as ovule parents, though in practice seed may be collected from each of the pair of plants entering into any particular cross. Each pollen parent is then crossed with four randomly chosen ovule parents to give a total of 100 full-sib families: the 25 sets, each of four families with a common pollen parent, will be referred to as sire groups (composed of half-sibs and full-sibs).

The 100 families are then set out in the following season in a randomized blocks design with 5 replications, using perhaps 10 plants per plot to give a total of 5000 spaced plants. Each plant is then to be scored for the characters of importance (e.g. winter injury and degree of creeping root development) and the 10 best families chosen on the basis of the mean performance of the 50 individuals in each: ideally, a method of scoring is adopted which gives the correct weight to the mean performance of each sire group, and to the deviation of each family from this mean, for each character under selection. From each of the 10 selected families 12 or 13 individuals are chosen on the basis of their own performance, to provide the 125 selected genotypes for a further cycle of the programme.

The generation interval under such a scheme is, of course, no longer than that under individual selection, but the accuracy with which the breeding value of a genotype is determined is considerably increased by the use of information on the performance of full-sib and half-sib relatives. A further consequence of the knowledge of family structure in the tested population is that estimates of the covariances among full-sibs and among half-sibs can be extracted each generation, and inferences drawn as to the composition of the genetic variance displayed by each character. It is beyond the scope of the present review to discuss, in detail, the procedures of estimation of these parameters, their use in the identification of elite families by means of a selection index, or their value in the prediction of optimal design in the testing regime: the reader is referred to Henderson [8] for an excellent account of the statistical methods involved.

However, since the method of family selection has received so little attention in the pasture breeding literature, it is worthwhile to discuss a simple example of its application. Heinrichs and Morley [7] have presented an analysis of the inheritance of creeping root in lucerne which is ideal for this purpose, and the mean squares and components of variance for one set of their observations are given in Table 10.1. The analysis is based on plot means, each plot containing the survivors of four spaced plants.

We shall denote the component of variance among replicates as $\sigma^2_R = 0\cdot031$; the component among sire group means as $\text{cov(H.S.)} = 0\cdot081$; that among full-sib families within sire groups as $[\text{cov(F.S.)} - \text{cov(H.S.)}] = 0\cdot115$; and the residual component (due to within-plot variation and plot effects) by $\sigma^2_E = 0\cdot343$.

TABLE 10.1

An Analysis of Variance of Scores for Creeping Root in Lucerne [7]

Source of Variance	d.f.	Mean Square	Component
Replications	2	4·110	0·031
Sire groups	29	1·589	0·081
Dams within sire groups	92	0·689	0·115
Sire groups × Reps.	58	0·295	−0·012
Residual	184	0·343	0·343
Total	365	0·542	0·558

To illustrate the use of these components of variance in the selection of elite full-sib groups, replicate effects will be neglected, and we shall assume that the numbers of ovule parents per pollen parent was constant, though in this material the number varied from 3 to 6 with a mean of 4·1. Let the observed mean of the ith sire group be denoted by x_i, and the mean of the full-sib group of offspring produced by the ith sire and the jth dam be denoted by x_{ij}. Then a score, which measures the potential mean breeding value of the genotypes in a full-sib group, can be given to each mating according to the expression

$$I = \alpha(x_i - \bar{x}) + \beta(x_{ij} - x_i) \qquad (1)$$

where $\bar{x}$ denotes the overall mean of the population. If we let the number of dams per sire be represented by d, and the number of replications by r, then

$$\alpha = \frac{r(d+1)[\text{cov}(\text{H.S.})]}{dr[\text{cov}(\text{H.S.})] + r[\text{cov}(\text{F.S.}) - \text{cov}(\text{H.S.})] + \sigma^2_E};$$

$$\beta = \frac{r[\text{cov}(\text{H.S.})]}{r[\text{cov}(\text{F.S.}) - \text{cov}(\text{H.S.})] + \sigma^2_E} \quad (2)$$

With $d = 4$ and $r = 3$, we find that $\alpha = 0.732$ and $\beta = 0.353$ in this example. Use of these values in equation (1) gives optimal weight to the information available on the sire's and dam's breeding values.

The optimal breeding structure in a family selection programme can be predicted from the formula given by quantitative inheritance theory for the expected progress per generation: the appropriate expression in the situation we are discussing is

$$\Delta G = \bar{i}\,\text{cov}(\text{HS})\sqrt{\frac{(s-1)(d+1)^2}{sd[d\text{cov}(\text{HS}) + \text{cov}(\text{FS}) - \text{cov}(\text{HS}) + \sigma^2_E/r]} + \frac{(d-1)}{d[\text{cov}(\text{FS}) - \text{cov}(\text{HS}) + \sigma^2_E/r]}} \quad (3)$$

where s denotes the number of sire groups under test, and $\bar{i}$ is the selection differential achieved.[12] Let us suppose that it is planned to use a total of 500 plots (i.e. $sdr = 500$) and that breeding individuals are to be chosen from the ten best families as judged by equation (1). The expected genetic improvement for alternative breeding structures (i.e. different values of s, d, and r) can then be calculated: in Table 10.2 are given a number of possible alternatives for comparison.

TABLE 10.2

Predicted Genetic Progress (ΔG) in a Family Selection Programme
[Based on Parameters in Table 10.1. ($sdr = 500$)]

Value of r	Value of d	$\Delta G/\bar{i}$	$\bar{i}$	ΔG
2	1	0·267	2·15	0·57
2	2	0·277	2·15	0·60
2	5	0·292	2·15	0·63
2	10	0·300	2·15	0·64
4	1	0·304	1·86	0·56
4	5	0·318	1·86	0·59
5	1	0·313	1·75	0·55
5	2	0·319	1·75	0·56
5	5	0·324	1·75	0·57

These calculations are of course only part of the story, but they highlight two important considerations in this example: (1) the inefficiency of an increase in replication at the expense of a reduction in the number of families tested; and (2) the inefficiency of some breeding plans which involve a series of unrelated pair-crosses ($d = 1$). With five dams per sire, one can anticipate making a 10 per cent greater gain per generation with 50 sire groups tested in two replications, than with 20 sire groups in five replications: one can then weigh this expected increase in response against the labour involved in the additional hybridization. Of perhaps greater significance is the indication that with two replications, each of 250 families, the use of 50 sire groups with five dams per sire will lead to a 10 per cent greater gain than the use of 250 sire groups each containing only one dam. However, if one chose to work at the five replication level, with 100 families under test, schemes involving from one to five dams per sire are almost equivalent as far as anticipated gains are concerned: consideration of the rates of inbreeding involved would then perhaps lead one to adopt a scheme involving only two dams per sire.

Sward Performance

In selecting for sward performance, a similar procedure known as *sib-testing* can be adopted, in which full-sib families are tested under sward conditions in replicated plots. A small nursery of spaced plants is also maintained with reserve members of each of the families, so that when superior families have been identified on the basis of their mean productivity, breeding individuals can be taken from the nursery for hybridization. In this way, maximum seed production from the chosen genotypes can be assured. The optimal number of ovule parents per pollen parent in such a scheme depends, as one might expect, on the degree of genetic complexity of the variation shown by the character; but, in general, four or five will be close to the most desirable number, because of the practical difficulties of hybridization if the pollen parent has to be split into a larger number of pieces.

Though such a scheme may be superior to progeny testing because of the shorter generation interval, it imposes two sorts of restriction on the breeding programme. In the first instance, the scope of the test is limited by the amount of seed which can be produced by mutual pollination: this will, in general, preclude the possibility of simultaneous tests at more than one location. In addition, the possibility of selection for characters other than sward productivity is restricted to a choice among the reserve plants of the elite families. Under a progeny testing regime, on the other hand, an extensive population can be produced from seed harvested from the 'elite' polycross blocks, and intense individual selection is possible prior to the establishment of family structure in the population. The incorporation of such a phase in a sib-testing programme immediately forfeits the advantage of the reduced generation interval.

REFERENCES

[1] Carnahan, H. L., and Hill, Helen, D. (1961). Cytology and genetics of forage grasses. *Bot. Rev.*, **27**, 1–162.

[2] Cooper, J. P. (1959). *Grasses in Agriculture.* (F.A.O. Agric. Studies, No. 42.) Rome. Chapters 13 and 14.

[3] Daday, H. (1962). Breeding for creeping root in lucerne. I. The initial response to selection. *Aust. J. Agric. Res.*, **13** (5), 813–20.

[4] Dewey, D. R. (1961). Response of orchardgrass clones to clipping frequency. *Crop Science*, **1**, 421–4.

[5] Hanson, A. A., and Carnahan, H. L. (1956). Breeding perennial forage grasses. *U.S. Dept. Agric. Tech. Bull.* No. 1145, pp. 1–116.

[6] Heinrichs, D. H. (1953). Methods of breeding *Agropyron intermedium*. *Can. J. Agric. Sci.*, **33**, 470–93.

[7] Heinrichs, D. H., and Morley, F. H. W. (1962). Quantitative inheritance of creeping root in alfalfa. *Can. J. Genet. Cytol.*, **4**, 79–89.

[8] Henderson, C. R. (1963). Selection index and expected genetic advance. In *Statistical Genetics and Plant Breeding*, (W. D. Hanson and H. F. Robinson) Nat. Acad. Sci. Nat. Res. Council Publ. **982**, 141–163.

[9] Jenkin, T. J. (1931). The method and technique of selection, breeding, and strain-building in grasses. *Imp. Bur. Plt. Genet.* (Herb. Plts.) Bull. No. 3, pp. 5–34.

[10] Kalton, R. R., Smit, A. G., and Leffel, R. C. (1952). Parent-inbred progeny relationships of selected orchardgrass clones. *Agron. Jour.*, **44**, 481–6.

[11] Keller, W. (1946). Designs and technic for the adaptation of controlled competition to forage plant breeding. *Amer. Soc. Agron. Jour.*, **38**, 580–8.

[12] Lush, J. L. (1945). *Animal Breeding Plans.* 3rd edn. Iowa State College Press.

[13] McDonald, E. D., Kalton, R. R., and Weiss, M. G. (1952). Interrelationships and relative variability among S_1 and open-pollinated progenies of selected bromegrass clones. *Agron. Jour.*, **44**, 20–5.

[14] Morley, F. H. W., and Heinrichs, D. H. (1960). Breeding for creeping root in alfalfa. *Can. J. Plt. Sci.*, **40**, 424–33.

[15] Murphy, R. P., and Atwood, A. A. (1953). The use of I_1 families in breeding smooth bromegrass. *Agron. Jour.*, **45**, 24–8.

[16] Schultz, H. K. (1941). A study of methods of breeding orchardgrass, *Dactylis glomerata* L. *Jour. Amer. Soc. Agron.*, **33**, 546–58.

[17] Wexelsen, H. (1940). Selection and inbreeding in red clover and timothy *Imp. Agric. Bur. Joint Pub. No.* 3, pp. 93–114.

11

Distribution of Grasslands

By C. W. E. Moore

A NATURAL grassland is a plant community in which the dominant species are perennial grasses, there are few or no shrubs, and trees are absent. Associated with the dominant grasses there are usually less abundant grass species and a variety of other herbaceous plants, both annual and perennial, which at certain times of the year give a characteristic aspect to the community.

Grasses, however, form a substantial proportion of the ground flora of many other plant communities, including savannahs, woodlands, shrublands, and forests. Many of these are utilized for stock raising either with or without prior modification to encourage better growth of grasses. In the following discussion, therefore, any community, whether natural or developed by man, in which grasses provide a substantial proportion of the feed for domestic stock will be included under the general term grassland.

Large areas of the natural grasslands of the world (e.g. the prairies of the United States and Canada, the pampas of Argentina, and the steppes of southern U.S.S.R.) have been destroyed by cultivation because, by reason of climate, soil, and topography, they are ideally suited for agriculture, especially for the production of grain crops such as wheat and corn.

Extensive areas of grassland still occur, however, in all the continental land masses and many of the larger islands. Figure 11.1 shows the distribution of natural communities in which grasses are prominent constituents, and these include grasslands, savannahs, woodlands and shrub communities. Figure 11.1 also shows the major areas where grazing lands have been developed from communities in which grasses were minor constituents in the natural state. Large areas of many of these communities have been destroyed or modified to enable the development of pastures, or to extend arable areas.

The extent and importance of grazing lands are indicated in Table 11.1, which shows the area under permanent pasture and the numbers of domestic grazing animals for each continent. In Oceania the high percentage of grasslands is due to the high proportions in Australia and New Zealand where they constitute 58 per cent and 47 per cent respectively of the total areas. The distribution of pastures in Australia is shown in Figure 11.2.

The distribution of grasslands will be discussed in relation to the major environmental factors, viz. climate, soil, topography, and biotic factors and fire. Before doing so, however, it must be pointed out that correlations between environmental factors and the occurrence of a particular kind of community do not necessarily indicate causal relationships, which can be established only by studying the effects and interactions of all the factors involved.[9,40] Nevertheless, the establishment of correlations is useful and is necessary to an understanding of environmental relationships.

The nature of a plant community will be determined in part by the assemblage of species which can establish, grow to maturity, and reproduce

MAJOR GRAZING AREAS OF THE WORLD
(Adapted from vegetation map by A.W. Küchler)

LEGEND

Grasses prominent in the natural communities which can be grazed with little or no modification.

Grasses not prominent in the natural communities, which have been more or less modified to produce grasslands.

Fig. 11.1. Major grazing areas of the world. (Adapted from Vegetation map by A. W. Küchler in *Weather and Climate*, 1958, by Koeppe and de Long; McGraw-Hill, New York.)

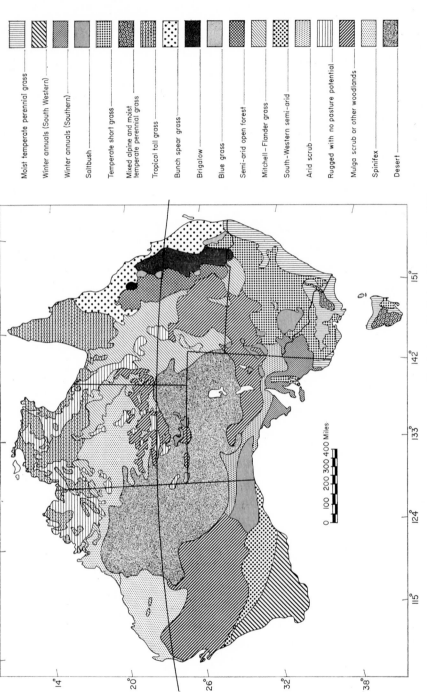

Moist temperate perennial grass

Winter annuals (South Western)

Winter annuals (Southern)

Saltbush

Temperate short grass

Mixed alpine and moist temperate perennial grass

Tropical tall grass

Bunch spear grass

Brigalow

Blue grass

Semi-arid open forest

Mitchell – Flinder grass

South-Western semi-arid

Arid scrub

Rugged with no pasture potential

Mulga scrub or other woodlands

Spinifex

Desert

0 100 200 300 400 Miles

FIG. 11.2. Pasture map of Australia. (After Christian, Donald, and Perry, 1955, in *Australian Environment*, 3rd ed.; C.S.I.R.O., Melbourne.)

CLIMATIC MAP
(Adapted from Köppen-Geiger Map)

LEGEND

A—Wet and dry tropical climates
s—Summer dry; w—Winter dry

BW—Desert climates
h—dry hot; k—dry cold

BS—Steppe climates
h—dry hot; k—dry cold

C—Humid mesothermal climates
s—Summer dry; w—Winter dry
f—wet; a—warm; b—cool; c—cold

D—Humid microthermal climates
s—Summer dry; w—Winter dry; f—wet
a—warm; b—cool; c—cold; d—very cold

A,E—Tropical and Polar climates
(Not under discussion)

FIG. 11.3. Climatic map of the world. (Adapted from Köppen-Geiger map in *Weather and Climate*, 1958, Koeppe and de Long; McGraw-Hill, New York).

TABLE 11.1

Areas of Grazing Land (sq. miles) and Percentage of Total Area, and Numbers
of Cattle, Sheep, and Goats in the Different Continents

(*Data from F.A.O. Production Yearbook*, 1960)

	Total Area (millions of sq. miles)	Permanent Meadows and Pastures		Stock Numbers (1958/59) (millions)		
		Millions of sq. miles	% Total area	Cattle	Sheep	Goats
Europe	1·9	0·3	16	111	134	19·5
U.S.S.R.	8·6	1·4	16	71	130	9·0
North and Central America	9·4	1·4	15	141	41	16·0
South America	6·9	1·1	16	153	122	25·0
Asia	6·7	1·0	15	232	144	126·0
China, Mainland	3·8	0·7	18	46	61	51·5
Africa	11·7	2·3	20	113	136	93·0
Oceania	3·3	1·8	55	22	200	0·2
TOTAL	52·3	10·0	19	889	968	340·2

under a particular set of climatic conditions. Broad correlations between
regional climates and plant formations will therefore be observed, but the
hypothesis that climate is the controlling factor in the development of plant
communities, and that for any climatic region there can be only one climax
formation, has been shown to be unsound.[31, 64, 68]

Beadle[7] has pointed out the error of assuming that the vegetation of a
region can be deduced from climatic data. The climate-soils-vegetation
correlations of North America, for instance, are not applicable in Australia.
Thus in Australia various communities, in which eucalypts and other woody
species are the dominants, occur in areas of supposed 'grassland climate' on
the basis of North American correlations. It is clear that an important factor
affecting the kind of community which develops is the species available for
colonization. Further, those who have attempted to define a grassland climate
have neglected the influence of man's activities, especially the use of fire, in
their development and maintenance.

Climate

Climate is composed of many elements which vary daily and from season to
season, so that a simple and accurate classification is difficult. Köppen
classified climates principally on annual and seasonal precipitation and annual
and monthly temperatures, the limits of both temperature and precipitation
being based originally on natural vegetation. A simple account of this system
of classification and its limitations, together with brief descriptions of the
climate, vegetation, soils, and land use for each climatic region, has been given
by Koeppe and Long.[38] A simplified map of world climates is given in
Figure 11.3.

Köppen's classification of climates, in spite of its limitations, is useful in a study of the broad relationships between climate and vegetation. The natural grasslands, as well as many of those which have been developed by man from woodlands and other communities, occur chiefly in regions having more or less well-marked wet and dry seasons. The climatic regions in which grasslands are of major importance are the wet and dry tropical (Aw), dry (BS and BW), humid mesothermal (C), and humid microthermal (D). Natural grasslands, or open tree and shrub communities, occur in all four of these climatic regions, but many other kinds of vegetation are also found.

1. The wet and dry tropical (Aw) climate has a winter dry season of 3 to 5 months followed by a rainy season and the mean temperature of the coldest month is not less than 64°F. This type of climate occurs over large areas in Africa, South and Central America, India, Pakistan, and northern Australia. In South and Central America where excessively dry and excessively wet seasons alternate, the vegetation is typically tropical savannah (e.g. *campos* of Brazil, the *llanos* of Venezuela, Columbia, northern Brazil, coastal Ecuador, the Guianas, and parts of coastal Central America). The savannahs are liable to flooding for long periods, but the surface soil dries out rapidly during the dry season.[57] In Africa there are various combinations of grasses and trees, such as tree savannahs with tall grasses up to 10 feet high, the *Acacia*-tall grass savannahs, and the *Acacia*-desert grass savannahs. In the wet and dry tropical region of northern Australia, the natural vegetation consists chiefly of grassy forests and *Eucalyptus* woodlands, with some tree savannah and tussock grassland.[17,]

2. The dry climates include the desert (BW) and steppe (BS) climates. Their chief characteristics are low and unreliable rainfall; potential evaporation always greater than precipitation; low relative humidity, with much sunshine and considerable wind; and a wide diurnal temperature range, usually exceeding the annual range. There is no temperature limitation, desert and steppe climates being classified as hot when the mean annual temperature exceeds 64°F, and cold when it is less than this. The differences between the dry and humid climates are shown in Figure 11.4.

The desert and steppe regions together occupy more than one-quarter of the world's land surface, covering large areas of Australia, Africa, Asia, and North and South America. Australia, with three-quarters of its area in this category, has a higher proportion of dry climate than any other continent. In these regions are found extensive areas of grazing lands of low carrying capacity; agriculture, because of the low and unreliable rainfall, is uncertain without irrigation.

Vegetation is sparse or even absent in deserts, and annuals, which appear only after rain, often predominate. Cacti, succulents, and xerophytic shrubs are characteristic of these regions and of the drier parts of the steppe climates. Scattered bunch grasses, which are best developed in the moister sites, are frequently the predominant perennial species in the herbaceous stratum. Sparse woodlands or other woody communities may develop in orographic areas where precipitation and temperature regimes are more favourable to plant growth, and permanent streams and oases may be lined with trees.

In the steppe climates grasses are prevalent, with bunch grasses predominating, usually associated with scrub trees or thorny bushes and annuals.

In Australia, the desert and steppe regions are occupied by a wide variety of vegetation types depending on the local soil, topographic conditions, or (especially in the deserts) on the microhabitat. Most of the desert region (BWh) is occupied by the desert complex,[69] but large areas of tussock grassland (Mitchell and Flinders grass, and part of the blue grass area of Fig. 11.2), hummock grassland (spinifex), shrub and tree savannah, shrub steppe, low layered woodland and mallee, also occur.

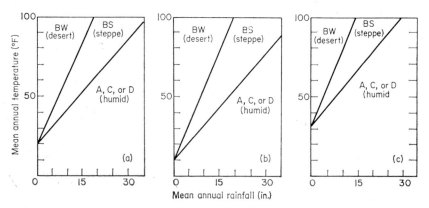

FIG. 11.4. Graphs to indicate the boundaries between humid and dry climates. (After Koeppe and de Long, 1958, in *Weather and Climate*; McGraw-Hill; New York.) (a) rainfall evenly distributed; (b) summer concentration of rainfall; (c) winter concentration of rainfall.

The lines for determining the boundary between humid and steppe climates are based on the following three formulae:

$r = 0.44 \ (t - 19.5)$ when rainfall is evenly distributed;

$r = 0.44 \ (t - 7)$ when there is a summer concentration of rainfall;

$r = 0.44 \ (t - 32)$ when there is a winter concentration of rainfall;

where r = mean annual rainfall in inches and t = mean annual temperature in degrees Fahrenheit. For the boundary between steppe and desert climates use $\frac{1}{2}r$ in each case. Precipitation is said to be concentrated in the winter when more than 70% of the total is received during the cooler six months (Oct.–Mar. in the Northern Hemisphere, Apr.–Sept. in the Southern Hemisphere); in the summer when more than 70% of the total is received during the warmer six months (Apr.–Sept. in the Northern Hemisphere, Oct.–Mar. in the Southern Hemisphere); evenly distributed if neither season receives more than 70% of the total.

In the steppe region, the most important vegetation forms in the north are tussock and hummock grasslands, shrub and tree savannah, and low layered woodland; in the south, low layered woodland, tall woodland, savannah woodland, shrub woodland, tree savannah, shrub steppe, and semi-arid and sclerophyllous mallee occur.[69]

The hummock grasslands of the desert regions of Western Australia, the Northern Territory, and Queensland occur where the mean annual rainfall is less than 8 inches and evaporation exceeds precipitation in each month of the year. They are mono- or multi-layered open communities of sclerophyllous grasses (*Triodia* and *Plectrachne*), with a marked seasonal development of

ephemeral herbs.[69] In the sandy deserts a complex of habitats is provided by
the very long parallel sand dunes separated by interdunal corridors, usually

PLATE 4 (a). Spinifex grassland (*Triodia longiceps*) on rocky hills and basal apron. Alice Springs area, Northern Territory, Australia.

(b) Spinifex grassland (*Triodia basedowii*) with scattered trees and shrubs on sand plains (coarse sandy soil), Willuna area, Western Australia.

less than one mile in width, having a clayey soil. Hummock grasslands develop
on the dunes, with shrubs and stunted eucalypts in the sandy hollows and
shrub steppe in the interdunal corridors. This type of grassland must be
adapted not only to withstand severe and prolonged drought, but also the
effects of wind and abrasion by moving sand particles.

Extensive areas of hummock grassland dominated by spinifex (*Triodia* and *Plectrachne*) in the northwest of Western Australia (see Fig. 11.2) have been described by Burbidge,[14,15] these grasslands include both climax and disclimax communities. Two types of hummock grassland occur in the Northern Territory.[50] Soft spinifex (*Triodia pungens* R.Br. and *Plectrachne schinzii* Henrard dominant) is found on flat to gently undulating plains, chiefly of coarse-textured sandy red earths, and receiving a mean annual rainfall of from 12 inches in the south to 25 inches in the north. In the higher rainfall areas spinifex forms the understorey in a low *Eucalyptus* woodland, but in the lower rainfall areas to the south it is the characteristic plant in a low tree savannah containing scattered *Acacia* spp. and *Eucalyptus* spp. Hard spinifex (*T. basedowii* Pritzel dominant) occurs on flat and gently undulating plains with sandy, infertile soils where mean annual rainfall is 5–13 inches. These areas are generally treeless but there is a sparse to medium cover of *Acacia* and *Eucalyptus* shrubs 2–6 ft high (see Fig. 11.2 and Plate 4).

Where the growth of grasses is adequate, and especially where the grasses can be supplemented by browse trees and shrubs, desert areas support sedentary or partly sedentary grazing by sheep or cattle as in Patagonia and some parts of the desert regions of Australia. Steppe regions are utilized chiefly for grazing by cattle, sheep, and goats. In the natural or near natural condition, the grasslands, savannahs, and woodlands often produce enough grass for stock at low carrying capacity without modification, but in many of the southern steppe communities of Australia (e.g. woodlands and mallee) thinning of the trees has been necessary to encourage the growth of grasses. In many places, perhaps especially in North America and southern Africa, grazing has resulted in a decrease in grasses and an increase in tree or shrub density, with consequent decreased animal production.

3. The humid mesothermal (C) climates have one or more months in which the mean temperature is below 64°F, at least one month in which the mean temperature exceeds 50°F, but no month with a mean temperature below 27°F. They are subdivided according to the distribution of the rainfall into moist (Cf) when the rainfall is well distributed throughout the year, winter dry (Cw), and summer dry (Cs). They may be further subdivided on the basis of the temperature of the warmest month, i.e. hot summer (Cfa or Cwa), warm summer (Cfb or Cwb), and cool summer (Cfc).

The humid mesothermal climates, in contrast to most tropical climates, have both a summer and a winter season and are generally exempt from continuous cold, continuous heat, and continuously dry conditions. The natural vegetation includes grassland, savannah, scrub (chaparral and maquis) and broadleaf, coniferous and mixed forests, and woodlands. In the regions of cool summers the vegetation is typically taiga or tundra, but in southern Chile and the Faeroes grasslands are well developed.

In the humid mesothermal regions, both agricultural and pastoral production are important activities. Extensive areas of forests and woodlands in Europe, North America, Asia, Australia, and New Zealand have been modified or destroyed to provide areas for cultivation or for the development of natural or sown pastures.

The vegetation of the humid mesothermal region of Australia includes a variety of forms, the most important of which are wet and dry sclerophyll forests, woodlands, shrub steppe, tree savannah, tussock grassland, mallee, and heath.[69] In Queensland, bunch spear grass (*Heteropogon contortus* (L.) Beauv. ex Roem. et Schult.) pastures occupy the greater part of the region, with brigalow (*Acacia harpophylla* F. Muell.) scrub in the drier western portion (see Fig. 11.2). In the natural condition, *Paspalidium caespitosum* C. E. Hubbard and members of the Chenopodiaceae form a sparse herbaceous stratum in the brigalow scrub but, on clearing, mixed grass pastures develop, with *Chloris*, *Eragrostis*, and *Dichanthium* as the most common genera. In New South Wales and Victoria temperate short grass pastures, in which *Danthonia* and *Stipa* are the dominant genera under grazing, develop in the cleared woodlands, while moist temperate perennial grass pastures occupy cleared areas of the wet and dry sclerophyll forests. *Themeda australis* (R.Br.) Stapf and *Poa caespitosa* * auctt. austral. are the principal perennial species in cleared wet sclerophyll forest. *Danthonia pallida* R.Br., a tall, unpalatable bunch grass, commonly dominates after clearing the dry sclerophyll forests, but in the moister and cooler localities a sparse cover of *Poa caespitosa* develops. In the humid mesothermal regions of South Australia, winter annuals predominate in the pastures developed in cleared mallee or heath, the major species being of Mediterranean origin, but native and sown perennial species achieve some significance. Smaller areas of temperate short grass and moist temperate perennial grass pastures also occur. In the south west of Western Australia, disturbed woodland and forest are typically occupied by pastures composed of volunteer Mediterranean annuals (*Erodium*, *Cryptostemma*, *Vulpia*, *Bromus*, *Hordeum*, *Trifolium* and *Medicago*). Because of the severe summer drought, native perennials are of little significance.[17]

4. The humid microthermal (D) climates also have one or more months in which the mean temperature is below 64°F, but are distinguished from the humid mesothermal climates in that the mean temperature of the coldest month is below 27°F. They are divided as for the mesothermal climates into moist, winter dry, summer dry, and hot, warm, or cool summer. There is in addition a fourth category, severe winter, in which the mean temperature of the coldest month is less than −36°F.

The humid microthermal climates are essentially confined to the northern hemisphere; in the southern hemisphere they are limited to high mountain regions such as the Andes. The natural vegetation includes extensive areas of prairie and steppe, broadleaved, mixed, and deciduous forests. In these regions the grazing animal generally takes second place to agricultural production, though dairying is an important activity in some of the more humid regions where rainfall is uniformly distributed throughout the year. Grasslands of humid microthermal climates at high altitudes are found in South America,[57] North America,[29] Africa,[1,55] New Guinea,[12,56] Australia,[22] New Zealand,[20] and elsewhere.

* This species complex is under revision and the number of taxa involved has not yet been determined.

Soil

The effect of climate, particularly rainfall, may be modified by the soil, especially heavy soils in which reduced moisture availability causes increased moisture stress during dry periods. In south-eastern Australia, a region of dominantly winter rainfall with a climate similar to that of grassland areas in other parts of the world, *Eucalyptus* dominant woodlands are generally found

PLATE 5. Dry tussock grassland on basalt, with narrow belt of *Eucalyptus pauciflora* woodland on outcrop of shale. Between Cooma and Nimmatibel, Monaro Region of New South Wales, Australia.

except where soil and topographic factors favour the development of forests.
[22,41,43,44,45] However, large areas of natural grassland occur on heavy textured soils in the Monaro Region of New South Wales [22] (see Plate 5), and on similar soils in Victoria.[48,49] Costin [22] recognized two distinct grassland sub-forms in the Monaro Region. Dry tussock grassland, in which the most common dominants are *Stipa scabra* Lindl., *S. bigeniculata* D. K. Hughes, and *Themeda australis*, is usually found on sierozems, chernozems, chocolate soils,

rendzinas and terra rossas. Wet tussock grassland, in which the dominant species are *Poa caespitosa* and *Themeda australis* associated with a number of species of *Juncus* and *Carex*, occurs on gley podzols, meadow, alluvial, and prairie soils. Forest and woodland communities in this region occur chiefly on light textured podzolic soils.

In northern New South Wales and Queensland, extensive areas of natural grassland occur in a region of summer rainfall and winter drought. The grasslands, which are interspersed with tree and shrub dominant communities, are found on grey and brown soils of heavy texture and black earths.[6, 8, 10, 33] In southern Queensland and the drier parts of northern New

PLATE 6. *Astrebla pectinata* (Mitchell grass) grassland on heavy grey calcereous soil, Barkly Tablelands, Queensland, Australia. The spaces between tussocks are commonly covered by annuals after rain.

South Wales the dominant grasses are the Mitchell grasses (*Astrebla* spp.) and *Dichanthium sericeum* (R.Br.) A. Camus. Under somewhat higher rainfall in the Macquarie Region the dominant species in the grasslands on the heavy textured soils is *Stipa aristiglumis* F. Muell. A similar relationship between the occurrence of natural grasslands and heavy textured soils has been reported for the Northern Territory [50] (see Plate 6).

In the coastal and eastern tablelands areas of northern New South Wales and southern Queensland, where moisture stress is less severe because of greater precipitation, the heavier soils on basic igneous rocks support wet sclerophyll forest in the cooler regions and sub-tropical rainforest on the warmer sites. These forests have been largely cleared and pastures established for dairy or beef cattle.

Soils developed from limestone may support a grassland while on neighbouring soils derived from other parent materials, woody communities are found. The effect of limestone soils in some areas appears to be confounded with the effect of temperature. In the warmer parts of New South Wales (e.g. Wellington and the Great Horseshoe Bend of the Shoalhaven River) the limestone supports an open woodland, while in colder areas (e.g. the Cooleman Plain in the subalpine region to the south-west of Canberra, and an area near Goulburn) grasslands develop on the limestone soils. The relationships between soil and vegetation on the Cooleman Plain are of interest. This plain

PLATE 7. Frost pocket grassland, with *Poa caespitosa* dominant, surrounded by *Eucalyptus pauciflora – E. rubida* woodland. Snowy Mountains area, New South Wales, Australia.

consists chiefly of limestone, with small outcrops of ferruginous sediments, andesite, and chert.[61] The whole area is a 'frost pocket', topographically similar to other areas of temperature inversion in the same district. The limestone soils are occupied by grassland with *Poa caespitosa* dominant, but subalpine woodlands, with *Eucalyptus stellulata* Sieb. ex DC., *E. pauciflora* Sieb. ex Spreng., and *E. rubida* Deane and Maiden, are found on the sediments, andesite and chert, even at topographic levels below the upper limit of grassland on limestone.

Rattray[55] includes in edaphic grasslands those which occur in areas subjected to periodic inundation and in perennial swamps. These include types similar to the tropical grasslands of Latin America. On this basis, the *llanos* of Latin America would be regarded as edaphic rather than climatic grasslands.

Topography

Grasslands are found where topographic conditions influence local climate, especially when this influence is in the direction of reduced temperatures. Topographic features which result in the development of 'frost pockets' may produce conditions suitable for the development of grasslands, usually on a somewhat limited scale. Such frost pockets are found in many subalpine regions and are well exemplified in the high mountains in southeastern Australia (see Plate 7). In these situations the phenomenon of temperature inversion causes a reversal of the usual altitudinal zonation of vegetation. Accumulation of a 'lake' of cold air in the floor of a valley may produce temperatures too low for the survival of tree seedlings. At any time of the year in the subalpine region of the Snowy Mountains in Australia, for example, cold air (20°F or less) may accumulate in the valleys to a depth corresponding to the tree line.[46] Actively growing seedlings of *Eucalyptus niphophila* Maiden and Blakely (snow gum) up to 2 years old are killed by short term exposure to temperatures of 18–20°F.

Topographic influences are also seen in the effect of aspect on vegetation, especially at relatively high latitudes or altitudes. In Idaho, for example, northerly slopes are forested, while southerly slopes support a grassland. These differences in the vegetation are correlated with significant climatic differences on the two aspects. On the south-facing slopes wind velocities are reported to be greater, average relative humidity 22 per cent lower, and evaporation 50 per cent greater, than on north-facing slopes.[30] Further, the range of air temperature is 44°F greater on the south than on the north slopes, and the soil at 6-inch depth is below wilting point for three weeks longer. Prairie openings in forests often occur on south and south-west slopes of valleys where insolation and dry south-west winds produce local xerophytism.[66] In the South Island of New Zealand, pockets of beech (*Nothofagus*) forest are found throughout the low-altitude tussock grasslands on cool and moist southern and eastern slopes.

The Biotic Factor and Fire

Of all the organisms influencing the development and maintenance of grasslands, man has by far the most widespread and significant effect, either directly by his own actions, or indirectly by the introduction of exotic plants and animals. In many parts of the world, and especially in those areas where increasing populations have necessitated the development of new methods of using natural resources, plant communities have been influenced by man's activities for many centuries. Few have escaped modification to a greater or lesser extent, and the type of community now present often bears little or no relation to that which would develop if uninfluenced by man. Man is capable of developing grasslands in almost any place where grasses will grow, and by suitable management can maintain such grasslands and prevent reversion to the original community. Conversely, mismanagement of grasslands, especially by civilized man, has too often caused deterioration of the original community and invasion by woody species or other weeds.

Probably the most ancient and important influence of man on vegetation has been through the use of fire.[58, 62] The effect of fire is so closely related to man's other activities that it cannot be fully separated from the biotic factor.

The morphology and growth rhythm of perennial grasses are eminently suited for resistance to burning. Perennating organs are usually close to or below the ground surface where they are least affected by fire. Seed production and seed fall are completed before the advent of hot, dry weather, so that much of the seed escapes combustion. When grasses are burnt only one season's growth is destroyed, and this is usually dead at the time of the burn. These characters are in marked contrast to those of most trees and shrubs, whose buds are exposed to the full intensity of the heat generated by the fire and whose seeds are often immature and lost; many years' growth is destroyed in a single burn.

Many woody plants have developed mechanisms which enable them to resist the effects of fire,[28] and grasslands do not always develop in response to regular burning. The majority of *Eucalyptus* spp. have a thick insulating bark which protects the cambium, and produce new shoots from epicormic buds even if all the naked buds have been destroyed.[35] Further, the seedlings of many eucalypts develop a lignotuber, usually below ground level, from which new shoots arise after destruction of the stem and leaves. This process can be repeated many times, and it is not unusual to find apparently young seedlings which are in fact many years old. Palms are able to resist fire because they are not dependent on a cambium layer near the surface.

Savannahs, or open woodlands, with grasses dominant in the herbaceous stratum, may therefore develop under the influence of fire. As the seedlings of the woody species have not developed fire resisting characters and grow largely within the herbaceous stratum, periodic fires kill the majority and the community is kept open. Protection from fire, especially when associated with grazing by domestic animals, often causes the development of dense, woody communities and a reduction in the grass component.[3, 21]

Contemporary primitive peoples in all parts of the world burn the vegetation to improve the yield of desired animals and plants. This is not destructive exploitation, since a protective cover of plants is maintained, moisture penetration is unimpaired, and possibly loss of moisture through evapotranspiration is reduced.[58] The practice of the Australian aborigine of burning many plant communities at more or less regular intervals has had a profound effect; it has often resulted in the development of open forest and woodland communities.[3] Over much of the continent of Africa, fire is important in controlling the density of the tree population, and many grasslands and much of the open savannah have developed under the influence of frequent burning.[1, 32, 55] In North and South America there can be little doubt that the frequent fires set by the Indians had a significant effect on the development and maintenance of grasslands and savannahs.

In tropical regions, clearing and burning of forest is practised by native tribes to provide areas for cultivation, and in time tropical grasslands may replace the original forests. These grasslands are maintained by frequent burning, and tend to extend in area due to destruction of the forest margins.[5, 57]

The grasslands of New Guinea and their relationships to environment have been discussed by Robbins.[56] The swamp grasslands of the low lying flood plains of the Lower Ramu and Sepik Rivers and the alpine grasslands above 10,000 feet in the central highlands are natural grasslands, i.e. their development and maintenance are not dependent on the influence of man. By far the greater part of the New Guinea grasslands, however, has developed as a result of man's activities over many centuries. The dry grasslands in both the lowland and highland (about 5000 feet) regions occur in habitats differing widely in soil, climate, and altitude, and are of varying extent, continuity, and floristic composition; they are considered to be induced disclimaxes. Two major disclimax types, tall grasslands and short grasslands, are recognized in both the lowlands and the highlands. The former is characterized by tall 'canegrasses' (*Saccharum* and *Miscanthus*) and kunai grass (*Imperata cylindrica* (L.) Beauv.) which form a dense cover from 6–12 ft or more in height. In the more extensive short grasslands the dominants are bunch grasses (*Themeda* and *Arundinella*) about 2 ft high, with a dense canopy. These grasslands have developed as a result of clearing the forest for native gardening, and have been maintained by frequent burning. The tall grasslands are of more recent origin and are still in a seral, dynamic phase, while the short grasslands indicate a further stage in the regression and have a long history of biotic and pyric interference (see Plates 8 and 9).

Civilized man has been responsible for marked changes in the botanical composition and structure of natural plant communities. In North and South America, Africa, and Australia, extensive areas of natural grasslands, open woodlands, and shrub communities were available for stock raising by European settlers. Prior to colonization, these areas were subjected to grazing by the native fauna and were influenced to varying degrees by the aboriginal populations chiefly through their use of fire. The European settler introduced domestic stock wherever the natural communities offered suitable grazing species, and, especially in the more favourable environments, introduced both useful pasture plants and weeds. The vegetation changes caused by exotic animals are accentuated by confining them to restricted areas by fences, or in the more arid areas by the distribution of watering points and by continuous grazing of these areas. Many woodlands and forests in Australia and New Zealand have been converted to pasture by the destruction of trees and shrubs, with or without the assistance of fire, thus allowing the native grasses to develop or the sowing of introduced pasture species.[6, 39, 42]

In the north-west of Western Australia many of the spinifex grasslands appear to be disclimax communities. On the deep red soils the original dominants prior to settlement were palatable perennial grasses such as *Chrysopogon* and *Eragrostis*, while *Dichanthium–Themeda* communities occurred on the river loams. Shallow soils supported climax spinifex grassland in which the dominants were probably both soft (e.g. *Triodia pungens*) and hard (e.g. *T. lanigera* Domin) species. Continuous grazing and winter burning have weakened the cover of palatable perennial grasses and encouraged the

PLATE 8. Tall *Miscanthus* grassland, 5–8 ft high, developed after clearing lower montane oak (*Lithocarpus*) forest and maintained by burning. Scattered regrowth of shrubs and trees can be seen. Near Mendi in the Southern Highlands of New Guinea.

PLATE 9. Short *Themeda–Imperata* grassland, (about 3 ft tall), on volcanic hills north of the Sepik Plain, New Guinea. Undisturbed lowland rainforest occurs in the background, and along drainage lines in the middle distance.

development of spinifex on the better soils. In the climax hummock grasslands the hard species of *Triodia* have been favoured at the expense of the soft species. Recent investigations on the effect of burning and grazing the soft spinifex communities have shown that summer burning (November–December) and 'deferred grazing' will reverse the process by killing most of the spinifex and encouraging the growth of the original dominants.[4, 13, 47, 63] The success of this method of pasture regeneration depends on the existence of scattered plants of *Chrysopogon*, *Eragrostis*, and other grasses in the community. It has not been successful in the Northern Territory because of the absence of these species in the spinifex grassland.[50]

Burning does not always assist in the maintenance of desirable plant communities. Bunch spear grass (*Heteropogon contortus*) pastures, in which annual burning is standard practice, occur in eastern Queensland from Brisbane to at least as far north as Townsville.[60] It has been shown that annual burning of grazed pastures promotes dominance of the undesirable spear grass. However, in areas burnt annually but protected from grazing (as in railway enclosures) *Themeda australis* is the dominant grass, indicating that the spear grass pastures develop in response to the combined effects of burning and grazing.[59]

When grazing by domestic stock and burning are imposed on a plant community developed in an area where these factors were not an integral part of the environment, especially where climatic conditions are unfavourable for plant regeneration, the results may be disastrous. After the introduction of sheep to the subalpine tussock grasslands of New Zealand, burning to remove old, unpalatable growth and to encourage young palatable growth, became standard practice. The effect has been the destruction of large areas of grassland with loss in grazing value, severe erosion, damage to forests at lower altitudes, siltation of river-beds and dams, and increased flooding. Regeneration of a plant cover on the unstable and unprotected soil is particularly difficult under the rigorous climate.[20, 65]

Similar effects in the high mountain communities of south-eastern Australia have been reported.[23, 24, 25] Here the problem of conservation of vegetation and soil is complex because of variation in the effects of grazing and burning on the different communities, and the effects of deterioration in one community on the stability of others. Further, in some communities deterioration can be arrested and regeneration initiated by removal of stock and control of fires, while in others degeneration can be arrested only by costly conservation measures (cf. Chapter 14).

The prevention of wild fires has commonly been an essential corollary of settlement. Reduction in fire frequency, combined with the effects of grazing, has often been followed by invasion of grasslands and savannahs by woody species. In South Africa, extensive invasion of such communities has resulted in the development of dense scrubs.[1, 55] In the United States vast areas of prairie and desert grassland have been invaded by woody species since they were settled by white man. Much of the prairie of Texas and the neighbouring States has been converted to mesquite jungle, while sagebrush and juniper have invaded parts of the drier grasslands from the west. Large areas of

o

Illinois and Wisconsin prairie are now heavily forested.[62] The desert grasslands have also been invaded by woody species in response to the combined
effects of grazing and reduction in fire frequency. Humphrey[34] considers that,
in the absence of frequent fires, possibly the whole area would have supported
a woody vegetation long before the first white man set foot in North America.

Because of the interaction between the effects of grazing and burning, the
two factors must generally be studied together. The dense grass cover in the
undisturbed prairie inhibits the establishment of woody species, and those
that do establish are subjected to severe competition from the grasses in the
early stages. Further, the large bulk of combustible material provided by the
grasses causes a hot fire which readily kills the seedlings. Few woody species
therefore have an opportunity of reaching maturity in the natural prairie.
Grazing by domestic stock reduces the amount of combustible material, thus
decreasing the intensity of subsequent fires, and the perennial grasses,
especially the more palatable species, are weakened. Domestic stock may also
spread the seed of woody species (e.g. mesquite) into the grassland. In the
open sward are many suitable sites for the establishment of seedlings of
woody plants, a large proportion of which survive and grow to maturity because of reduced competition from grasses and decreased effect of fires. Subsequently competition from shrubs further weakens the grass component,
fires become even less effective, and the final result may be a dense, woody
vegetation with a sparse herbaceous stratum.[28, 54]

The Ecological Status of Grasslands

The ecological status of grasslands has been the subject of much argument,
and there are still differences of opinion among ecologists as to whether grassland communities are a climatic climax. The fact that extensive areas of grassland occur in certain climatic regions has led to the conclusion that the major
grasslands of the world are climatically controlled. However, examination of
other environmental factors, such as soil, topography, biotic factors and fire,
and the availability of species for colonization, clearly indicates that factors
other than climate frequently determine whether the climax community will
be a grassland or a community dominated by woody species. It has even been
suggested that the vast steppe regions of Europe and Asia, for long considered
a classic example of climatic control of vegetation, were once forested, and
that the grasslands have developed as a result of the activities of man.[26]
Though the effect of climate on the distribution of grasslands cannot be
neglected, climate is seldom, if ever, the sole environmental factor determining
their distribution.

The difficulty would no doubt be largely resolved if there were agreement
on the concept of the climax. Much of the confusion probably arose because
of the initial widespread acceptance of the mono-climax theory as proposed by
Clements,[18,19] Phillips[51, 52, 53] and others, a concept still accepted by some
ecologists although it has been shown to be untenable.

In a climax community no further directional change takes place under the
prevailing environmental conditions, its composition being determined by all

the factors of the environment, not by any one factor.[31] Variations in topography, soil parent materials, and other factors produce a variety of habitats which are reflected in a mosaic of climax types. Climax vegetation is therefore not uniform within a climatic region, but is a pattern of populations corresponding to the pattern of environmental gradients.[68] If the attributes of a climax community as stated by Hanson and Churchill[31] can be applied to a grassland, then it is climax, whatever the particular environmental factors maintaining it.

The development of a soil is in part influenced by the vegetation,[36, 37] but at the same time it is one of the environmental factors influencing the development of vegetation. Grasslands are often associated with particular kinds of soil, such as the chernozems and prairie soils of North America and the steppe regions of southern U.S.S.R. It is, however, difficult and perhaps even impossible to determine the extent to which the soil properties have been influenced by the grasslands, and the extent to which the soils have influenced the development of the grasslands. There is the further problem that there are interactions between soil and climate. Under relatively low rainfall conditions, especially when there is a well-marked dry season, grasslands are found on heavy soils where reduced moisture availability increases moisture stress during dry periods, while on similar soils under more favourable rainfall conditions woodlands or forests occur. Thus the development of a grassland is commonly attributable to the interaction of soil and climate, rather than to the direct effect of either.

The influence of topography on the development of grassland is associated with its effect on other environmental factors, such as climate and soil. Where topographic conditions are such that frost pockets develop, the climate may be so altered as to make conditions unsuitable for the growth of trees, and grasslands are produced. Similarly, topography may influence soil conditions on valley floors through an increase in water supply causing frequent and prolonged waterlogging and the development of meadow and gley soils. If the regional flora contains tree species such as *Salix* and *Alnus* which can withstand such conditions, the wetter parts of the valley may be occupied by these species, while grasslands develop on the drier sites. Most species of *Eucalyptus*, however, cannot grow in these situations, and in the higher rainfall areas of southern Australia the wetter sites are occupied by wet tussock grassland and the drier sites by *Eucalyptus* woodland or forest. In the development of grasslands, therefore, the effects of topography must be considered in relation to the other environmental factors and to the species available for colonization.

Perhaps the most controversial subject in relation to the origin and maintenance of grasslands has been the effect of fire. Since this factor can be most readily modified on a large scale, it is useful to consider more fully the relationship of fire to natural grassland.

In the absence of fire, or where fire frequency and effectiveness are reduced, many grasslands rapidly change to shrub or tree communities. In tropical areas, fire appears to have been a major factor in converting forest to grassland, and frequent burning is necessary to prevent reversion to forest. Stewart[62] points out that the climate of the North American grassland region permits tree growth and reproduction, and suggests that, in the absence of fire and other disturbances, brush and trees could invade virtually all of the tall-grass prairie. Similarly, there is evidence that fire has been responsible for the maintenance of vast areas of grassland and savannah in South America and in Africa.

The effects of fire and climate on the development of grasslands are often inter-related. It has been pointed out above that grasslands and savannah commonly occur in regions having a definite dry season, during which the vegetation, especially the herbaceous species, dries off and becomes inflammable. In the absence of rain, fires may burn for days or weeks and affect extensive areas. Both climate and fire, and especially the combined effects of both factors, favour the development of grasses, while woody plants can persist only if they have developed efficient mechanisms for fire resistance, such as the majority of the species of *Eucalyptus*.

The proponents of the climatic climax have argued that the effects of fire on grasslands have been of minor importance, and that even in the absence of fire the grasslands would have developed in response to the climate.[11, 67] Fire is dismissed as being just a part of the environment, the major cause being by lightning strike. It is illogical to dismiss fire, whatever its cause, as being simply a part of the environment. If it is an environmental factor, its effect on the plant communities must be considered, and its significance evaluated in relation to all the other factors. Fire as an environmental factor reacts with all other factors in moulding species and vegetation, and the communities developed are climax. Its role in the development of vegetation and its value as a management tool are both inter-related with all the other factors.[32]

Some of the confusion which has arisen in respect to the effects of fire has been due to the fact that settlement of new areas has been accompanied by the introduction of domestic animals, as well as by changes in burning practices. The effects of grazing animals and fire are confounded, and contradictory results of burning experiments reported by different workers are in part due to the failure to realize this. Changes in vegetation following settlement must commonly be attributed to the combined effects of both factors.

The literature on the effects of fire on vegetation is full of contradictions.[2] This is not surprising in view of the many interacting factors, the difficulty of experimentation, and the fact that many conclusions must be reached on historical evidence without precise measurement. Some of the more obvious and important factors influencing the results obtained by burning are the season of the year, the amount of inflammable material, frequency of burning, weather conditions at the time of and following the burn, the time allowed after the burn before stock are permitted to graze, the effect of grazing on the regenerating plants, and the resistance of the plant species to fire. The results of burning experiments will not be comparable unless the conditions and treatments were the same or similar.

It is often difficult and sometimes impossible to determine whether a plant community has developed and is maintained without interference by man. Primitive man has been 'thoughtless of the future and therefore a natural ecological factor for millenniums'.[5] The effects of primitive man on vegetation should be considered as a part of the biotic factor, and a plant community as natural unless it has been influenced by civilized man. In the broad sense it is possible to distinguish between natural grasslands and those developed by civilized man, though the distinction between primitive and civilized man may be a subject for argument.

Natural or climax grasslands cover extensive areas of the earth's land surfaces. These communities are the result of the interactions of all the environmental factors on the vegetation, not of one factor alone. An understanding of the ecological status of grasslands and other communities utilized for grazing by domestic stock is of basic importance in determining sound management. A knowledge of the conditions under which the community was developed and the effects of changes in environmental factors, especially biotic factors and fire, enables the prediction of events following the imposition of certain management practices, and the avoidance of those which produce undesirable changes. Further, such knowledge enables us to determine the best methods of regenerating degraded communities, except when irreversible changes have been induced; i.e. when removal of the factor causing degradation does not result in a reversal of the change.

Marked deterioration of the habitat, with deflection of succession to the xeric, has followed pastoralism of domestic animals in wild lands. This is a profound and dangerous change.[27] Throughout extensive areas especially in the desert and steppe regions, reliance must be placed on the natural vegetation as a source of food for the grazing animal. To prevent further deterioration, management of this natural range must be based on a sound knowledge of the ecology of the plant communities, and should have as a principal objective the preservation of the grass cover.

REFERENCES

[1] Acocks, J. P. H. (1953). Veld types of South Africa. *Bot. Survey of S. Africa*, Mem. No. 28.

[2] Ahlgren, I. F., and Ahlgren, C. E. (1960). Ecological effects of forest fires. *Bot. Rev.*, **26**, 483–533.

[3] Andrews, A. (1920). *The First Settlement of the Upper Murray, 1835–1845*. Ford, Sydney.

[4] Anon. (1957). Spinifex school. Another pastoral innovation. *J. Agric. W. Aust.*, **6** (Third Series), 677–82.

[5] Bartlett, H. H. (1956). Fire, primitive agriculture, and grazing in the tropics. In *Man's Role in Changing the Face of the Earth*, pp. 692–720. Univ. of Chicago Press, Chicago.

[6] Beadle, N. C. W. (1948). *The Vegetation and Pastures of Western New South Wales with Special Reference to Soil Erosion*. Govt. Printer, Sydney.

[7] Beadle, N. C. W. (1951). The misuse of climate as an indicator of vegetation and soils. *Ecology*, **32**, 343–5.

[8] Biddiscombe, E. F. (1963). A vegetation survey in the Macquarie Region, New South Wales. *C.S.I.R.O. (Aust.), Div. of Plant Industry, Tech. Paper*, No. 18.

[9] Billings, W. D. (1952). The environmental complex in relation to plant growth and distribution. *Quart. Rev. Biol.*, **27**, 251–65.

[10] Blake, S. T. (1938). The plant communities of western Queensland and their relationships, with special reference to the grazing industry. *Proc. Roy. Soc. Queens.*, **49**, 156–204.

[11] Borchert, J. R. (1950). The climate of the central North American grassland. *Ann. Assoc. Amer. Geographers*, **40**, 1–39.

[12] Brass, L. J. (1941). The 1938–39 expedition to the Snow Mountains, Netherlands New Guinea. *J. Arnold Aboret.*, **22**, 297–342.

[13] Burbidge, N. T. (1944). Ecological succession observed during regeneration of *Triodia pungens* R. Br. after burning. *J. Roy. Soc. W. Aust.*, **28**, 149–56 (1941–42).

[14] Burbidge, N. T. (1945). Ecological notes on the De Grey-Coongan Area, with special reference to physiography. *J. Roy. Soc. W. Aust.*, **29**, 151–61 (1942–43).

[15] Burbidge, N. T. (1959). Notes on plants and plant habitats observed in the Abydos–Woodstock area, Pilbarra district, Western Australia. *C.S.I.R.O. (Aust.), Div. of Plant Ind. Tech. Paper*, No. 12.

[16] Cantlon, J. E. (1953). Vegetation and microclimates on north and south slopes of Cushetunk Mountain, New Jersey. *Ecol. Monog.*, **23**, 241–70.

[17] Christian, C. S., and Donald, C. M. (1960). In *The Australian Environment*, 3rd ed., pp. 85–104. C.S.I.R.O. (Aust.), Melbourne.

[81] Clements, F. E. (1928). *Plant Succession and Indicators.* Wilson, New York.

[19] Clements, F. E. (1936). Nature and structure of the climax. *J. Ecology*, **24**, 252–84.

[20] Cockayne, L. (1928). The vegetation of New Zealand. In *Die Vegetation der Erde*, Vol. 14, No. 2. W. Englemann: Leipzig.

[21] Cooper, C. F. (1960). Changes in vegetation, structure, and growth of south-western pine forests since white settlement. *Ecol. Monog.*, **30**, 129–64.

[22] Costin, A. B. (1954). *A Study of the Ecosystems of the Monaro Region of New South Wales, with Special Reference to Soil Erosion.* Govt. Printer, Sydney.

[23] Costin, A. B. (1957). *High Mountain Catchments in Victoria in Relation to Land Use.* Govt. Printer, Melbourne.

[24] Costin, A. B. (1958). The grazing factor and the maintenance of catchment values in the Australian Alps. *C.S.I.R.O. (Aust.), Div. of Plant Ind. Tech. Paper*, No 10.

[25] Costin, A. B., Wimbush, D. J., Kerr, D., and Gay, L. W. (1959). Studies in catchment hydrology in the Australian Alps. I. Trends in soils and vegetation. *C.S.I.R.O. (Aust.), Div. of Plant Ind. Tech. Paper*, No. 13.

[26] Darby, H. C. (1956). The clearing of the woodland in Europe. In *Man's Role in Changing the Face of the Earth*, pp. 183–216. Univ. of Chicago Press, Chicago.

[27] Darling, F. F. (1956). Man's ecological dominance through domesticated animals on wild land. In *Man's Role in Changing the Face of the Earth*, pp. 778–87. Univ. of Chicago Press, Chicago.

[28] Daubenmire, R. F. (1959). *Plants and Environment.* 2nd ed., Wiley, New York.

[29] Ellison, L. (1954). Subalpine vegetation of the Wasatch Plateau, Utah. *Ecol. Monog.*, **24**, 89–184.

[30] Gail, F. G. (1921). Factors controlling the distribution of douglas fir in the semi-arid regions of the north-west. *Ecology*, **2**, 281–91.

[31] Hanson, H. C., and Churchill, E. D. (1961). *The Plant Community.* Rheinhold, New York.

[32] Heady, H. F. (1960). *Range Management in East Africa.* Govt. Printer, Nairobi.

[33] Holland, A. A., and Moore, C. W. E. (1962). The vegetation and soils of the Bollon District in Southern Queensland. *C.S.I.R.O. (Aust.), Div. of Plant Ind. Tech. Paper*, No. 17.

[34] Humphrey, R. R. (1958). The desert grassland. A history of vegetation change and an analysis of causes. *Bot. Rev.*, **24**, 193–252.

[35] Jacobs, M. R. (1955). *Growth Habits of the Eucalypts.* Govt. Printer, Canberra.

[36] Jenny, H. (1941). *Factors of Soil Formation.* McGraw-Hill, New York.

[37] Jenny, H. (1958). Role of the plant factor in the pedogenic functions. *Ecology*, **39**, 5–16.

[38] Koeppe, C. E., and de Long, G. C. (1958). *Weather and Climate.* McGraw-Hill, New York.

[39] Levy, E. B. (1923). The grasslands of New Zealand. I. Principles of pasture establishment. *N.Z. Dept. Agr. Bull.*, No. 107.

[40] Major, J. (1951). A functional factorial approach to plant ecology. *Ecology*, **32**, 392–412.

[41] Moore, C. W. E. (1953). The vegetation of the south-eastern Riverina, New South Wales. I. The climax communities. *Aust. J. Bot.*, **1**, 485–547.

[42] Moore, C. W. E. (1953). The vegetation of the south-eastern Riverina, New South Wales. II. The disclimax communities. *Aust. J. Bot.*, **1**, 548–67.

[43] Moore, C. W. E. (1959). The nutrient status of the soils of some natural plant communities on the Southern Tablelands of New South Wales. *Ecology*, **40**, 337–49.

[44] Moore, C. W. E. (1959). Interaction between species and soil in relation to the distribution of eucalypts. *Ecology*, **40**,734–5.

[45] Moore, C. W. E. (1961). Competition between *Eucalyptus melliodora* and *E. rossii* at varying levels of exchangeable calcium. *Aust. J. Bot.*, **9**, 92–7.

[46] Moore, R. M. (1956). Natural phenomena and microclimate. Australia–UNESCO Symposium on Arid Zone Climatology with Special Reference to Microclimatology, Canberra. Paper No. 20.

[47] Nunn, W. M., and Suijdendorp, H. (1954). Station management. The value of 'deferred grazing'. *J. Agric. W. Aust.*, **3** (Third Series), 585–7.

[48] Patton, R. T. (1930). The factors controlling the distribution of trees in Victoria. *Proc. Roy. Soc. Vic.*, **42** (N.S.), 154–210.

[49] Patton, R. T. (1936). Ecological studies in Victoria. IV. Basalt Plains Association. *Proc. Roy. Soc. Vic.*, **48** (N.S.), 172–90 (1935).

[50] Perry, R. A. (1960). Pasture lands of the Northern Territory, Australia. *C.S.I.R.O. (Aust.), Land Res. Ser.*, No. 5.

[51] Phillips, J. (1934). Succession, development, the climax and the complex organism: an analysis of concepts. *J. Ecology*, **22**, 554–71.

[52] Phillips, J. (1935). Succession, development, the climax and the complex organism: an analysis of concepts. *J. Ecology*, **23**, 210–46.

[53] Phillips, J. (1935). Succession, development, the climax and the complex organism: an analysis of concepts. *J. Ecology*, **23**, 488–508.

[54] Phillips, J. (1959). *Agriculture and Ecology in Africa. A study of actual and potential development south of the Sahara.* Faber and Faber, London.

[55] Rattray, J. M. (1960). *The Grass Cover of Africa. F.A.O. Agric. Studies*, No. 49.

[56] Robbins, R. G. (1963). The anthropogenic grasslands of Papua and New Guinea. In *The UNESCO Symposium on the Impact of Man on Humid Tropics Vegetation, Goroka, New Guinea*, September 1960, pp. 313–29. UNESCO Science Cooperation Office for Southeast Asia, Djarkarta.

[57] Roseveare, G. M. (1948). The grasslands of Latin America. *Imp. Agric. Bur. Bull.*, No. 36.

[58] Sauer, C. O. (1956). The agency of man on the earth. In *Man's Role in Changing the Face of the Earth*, pp. 49–69. Univ. of Chicago Press, Chicago.

[59] Shaw, N. H. (1957). Bunch spear grass dominance in burnt pastures in south-eastern Queensland. *Aust. J. Agric. Res.*, **8**, 325–34.

[60] Shaw, N. H., and Bissett, W. J. (1955). Characteristics of a bunch spear grass (*Heteropogon contortus* (L.) Beauv.) pasture grazed by cattle in sub-tropical Queensland. *Aust. J. Agric. Res.*, **6**, 539–52.

[61] Stevens, N. C. (1958). Palaeozoic geology of the Cooleman Caves district, New South Wales. *Proc. Linn. Soc. N.S.W.*, **83**, 251–8.

[62] Stewart, O. C. (1956). Fire as the first great force employed by man. In *Man's Role in Changing the Face of the Earth*, pp. 115–33. Univ. of Chicago Press, Chicago.

[63] Suijdendorp, H. (1955). Changes in pastoral vegetation can provide a guide to management. *J. Agric. W. Aust.*, **4** (Third Series), 683–7.

[64] Tansley, A. G. (1935). The use and abuse of vegetational concepts and terms. *Ecology*, **16**, 284–307.

[65] Tussock Grassland Research Committee (1954). The high-altitude snow-tussock grassland in South Island, New Zealand. *N.Z. J. Sci. Tech.*, **36A**, 335–64.

[66] Vestal, A. G. (1920). Local inclusions of prairie within forest. *Ill. State Acad. Sci. Trans.*, **11**, 126–8 (1918). (Quoted by Cantlon[16].)

[67] Weaver, J. E. (1954). *North American Prairie*. Johnsen, Lincoln, Nebraska.

[68] Whittaker, R. H. (1953). A consideration of the climax theory: the climax as a population and pattern. *Ecol. Monog.*, **23**, 41–78.

[69] Wood, J. G., and Williams, R. J. (1960). In *The Australian Environment*. 3rd ed., pp. 67–84. C.S.I.R.O. (Aust.), Melbourne.

12

The Nutrition of Grasslands

By J. F. Loneragan

GRASSES flourish naturally on soils covering a wide spectrum of fertility, varying from the chernozems of the Russian steppes to the impoverished podzolic soils of many Australian grasslands. Soils originally carrying trees and shrubs, which have been cleared by man and replaced by grasses also vary greatly in fertility. Yet on such soils, grasses have flourished and persisted for centuries. In many situations, therefore, nutrient conditions cannot be a major factor determining the dominance of grasses over other forms of vegetation. These conditions are, however, of extreme importance in determining the species of grass which will dominate the grassland, the vigour of its growth, and its value in the diet of the grazing animal.

The application of plant nutrients to grasslands may therefore have profound effects upon the grasses growing in them. In these interactions between nutrients and grasses, nitrogen plays an important and unique role. It is especially important because of the severity and widespread nature of nitrogen deficiency in grasslands; it is unique because symbiotic fixation of nitrogen by pasture legumes provides a source of supply of the element as an alternative to expensive fertilizer dressings.

The value of legumes to grass production was known to Roman writers two thousand years ago. After a long period of neglect, interest in legumes in pastures was revived in England in the early seventeenth and the eighteenth centuries, when a number of new types of legumes were introduced and their incorporation into pastures encouraged. John Worlidge, for example, recommended in 1681 that clover and rye grass be sown together as a means of improving the soil and furnishing animals with a superior herbage (see 69). Appreciation of the reasons for the beneficial effect of legumes on grass production had to wait until the nature of the elements essential to plant growth was understood and the nature of the peculiar nitrogen nutrition of legumes was resolved. Thus, it was not until the end of the nineteenth century, when the necessary basic concepts had finally been resolved by the experiments of Hellriegel and Wilfarth, that the beneficial effect of legumes on grass growth could be understood.

Since that time, the legume has come to be accepted as an essential component of the grass-dominated pasture. Moreover, the legume, through its key position in the supply of nitrogen to grass, has assumed a dominant place in nutritional studies on pastures. Experience has shown that vigorous growth of symbiotically active legumes is particularly sensitive to nutrient deficiencies. Hence, when the nutrient requirements of legumes are met, it may be expected that associated grasses do not usually respond to additional nutrients other than nitrogen. For these reasons, improvement in the nutrition of grasses has always been intimately associated with the nutrition of legumes.

206

This situation is now changing in some areas of the world where nitrogenous fertilizers have become sufficiently cheap to replace symbiotic nitrogen.

In Australia, there are still relatively few situations in which it is profitable to replace legumes, even partly, by applying fertilizer nitrogen to grasses. Here, as in other parts of the world, advances in the nutrition of grasses have been dominated by advances in the understanding of legume nutrition. This chapter will therefore be mainly concerned with a discussion of some principles of legume nutrition which have proved important in the improvement of the productivity of Australian pastures.

Legume Nutrition

The majority of Australian soils are so severely deficient in both nitrogen and phosphorus that pasture improvement is rarely undertaken without the introduction of a legume and the application of superphosphate fertilizer (see, for example, 56). Extensive areas of grasslands have been improved in southern Australia by incorporating legumes, with no special treatment to achieve nodulation and satisfactory growth other than the supply of phosphatic fertilizer. Prior to 1939, pasture improvement was carried out almost exclusively on these soils. Since the war, pasture improvement has continued over large areas of these soils, but, in addition, vast areas with much more difficult nutritional requirements have been cleared and sown to legume-grass pastures.

Nutritional difficulties associated with the establishment of legumes on these problem areas have arisen both in the nodulation and in the subsequent growth of the legume.

Nodulation

Many nodulation problems have been encountered in the establishment of legumes in new areas. These problems have been primarily associated with the survival and growth of suitable strains of *Rhizobium*, but there is also evidence that in some areas nutritional factors prevent development of nodules, even when growth of *Rhizobium* is satisfactory.

Growth of Rhizobium

In soils where suitable *Rhizobium* is absent, difficulties in the establishment of clover have often been due to ineffectiveness of the inoculant. In Tasmania, for example, many areas with a history of slow clover establishment were found to give rapid and satisfactory establishment when effective strains of *Rhizobium* were used.[49, 50] The inadequacy of commercial inoculants has been emphasised by Vincent and co-workers.[63, 64] There has been a considerable improvement in commercial inoculants in recent years and legume inoculants of suitable quality are now readily available.

Toxicities of seed insecticides and of fertilizers to *Rhizobium* being introduced to some soils where suitable *Rhizobium* is absent, have resulted in failure of legumes to nodulate. Mixing superphosphate with seed has long been known to be harmful to *Rhizobium* on the seed[21] and has caused failures

in many areas (see review 59). Marked inhibition of nodulation of subterranean clover has also resulted when a trace element mixture ($CuSO_4$,
$ZnSO_4$, MoO_3)[34] or insecticides[17] were drilled with seed.

Toxicity of the seed coat of subterranean clover to *Rhizobium* has also been
demonstrated.[16, 57] This toxicity is believed to be partly responsible for the
failure of subterranean clover to nodulate satisfactorily on soils in the New
England region of New South Wales. Physical separation of the seed coat and
the *Rhizobium* by a variety of materials was effective in promoting nodulation.
It seems likely that soils vary greatly in their ability to inactivate the toxic
components in the seed coat.[58]

Competition between *Rhizobium* and other organisms in the rhizosphere
has also been suspected of depressing the survival of *Rhizobium* in some areas.
Ineffective strains of *Rhizobium* have been shown to compete with effective
strains sufficiently to inhibit nodulation.[32] In other areas, indigenous soil
organisms are believed to suppress *Rhizobium* growth. Sterilization of the soil
prior to introduction of *Rhizobium* to these areas has resulted in marked improvement in nodulation.[20] Antibiotic materials excreted from fungi indigenous to these soils have been shown to inhibit nodulation of subterranean
clover.[33]

Soil chemical and physical conditions which are unfavourable for the
survival and growth of *Rhizobium* may also lead to nodulation failure of
pasture legumes. Many soil conditions may, of course, limit *Rhizobium*
growth. However, the effects of these conditions on *Rhizobium* growth will
only be important to legume establishment when the *Rhizobium* is more
sensitive to the unfavourable condition than any other phase of the legume-
Rhizobium symbiosis. In all other situations the growth of the host legume
or the development of the nodule will be more important.

The differential effects of acidity on the growth of *Rhizobium* and of subterranean clover provide a good example of this principle. Faulty nodulation
of subterranean clover occurs on acid soils in many parts of Australia. Where
this problem occurs on the Southern Tablelands of New South Wales, it has
been shown to be due to an effect of soil acidity on the rate of growth of
Rhizobium. The problem was overcome either by using a heavy rate of ino-
culum or by treating the soil with carbonates of either calcium or magnesium.[6]
The plant, once nodulated, grew quite well under the existing soil conditions.
Moreover, where new pastures showed faulty nodulation there was a gradual
improvement over a period of years, suggesting that slow growth of *Rhizobium*
was occurring and that the problem was one of increasing its rate of growth
in the initial years of establishment.[9]

Thus, the problem appeared to be due to a greater sensitivity of the *Rhizobium* than the host plant to acid soil conditions. Water culture studies have
since shown that the two organisms differ sufficiently in their sensitivity to
hydrogen ions to explain the field results. *Rhizobium* was very sensitive to acid
conditions and made little or no growth at pH 4·0 or 4·5. Subterranean clover,
on the other hand, was not affected at these pH values.[38] Clearly, then, subterranean clover may flourish in a soil which is sufficiently acid to reduce
seriously the rate of growth of its *Rhizobium*.

The establishment of this principle of differential sensitivity to acidity suggested that nodulation of subterranean clover could be achieved on acid soils by providing a micro-environment around the seed favourable for *Rhizobium* growth. Legumes have, in fact, been established on such soils with minimal quantities of lime, either drilled with the seed [9] or coated on the seed.[39] Obviously, these techniques can only be applied to soils in which acidity is not so severe that growth of the host plant is affected.

Nodule Development

When conditions are favourable for *Rhizobium* growth and survival in soils, it is still possible for nodulation to fail. Boron deficiency, for example, has been shown to interfere quite specifically with nodule development. Under some conditions, vascular strands fail to develop in the nodules of boron-deficient plants.[18] However, the main effect of boron deficiency in the field appears to be on host plant metabolism rather than on nodulation or nitrogen fixation. Other factors, such as light, temperature, ineffective strains, and combined nitrogen, have also been shown to affect nodule development (see review 46). Like boron deficiency, few of these factors appear to cause nodulation problems in the field.

Calcium deficiency, which may also interfere specifically with nodule development, appears to be an exception in that it may affect nodulation of pasture legumes in some areas. *Rhizobium*, like most unicellular organisms, has only a trace requirement for calcium.[38, 45] On the other hand, calcium-deficient plants do not form nodules.[2, 53] Moreover, the process of nodulation has an even higher requirement for calcium than growth of the host plant.[38] This suggests that the process of either infection or nodule development has a particularly high calcium requirement.

This effect of calcium deficiency is believed to explain the failure of lucerne and subterranean clover to nodulate on deep podzolised sands in the south-east of South Australia. The problem in these soils is readily overcome if seed is drilled with either calcium sulphate or calcium carbonate. Thus calcium deficiency, rather than soil acidity, appears to be the dominant factor – a conclusion supported by the mild acidity of the soils and the action of magnesium carbonate in accentuating the problem.[59]

Growth of the Nodulated Legume

Nutrient Deficiencies and their Effects

Early work was concerned with the definition of nutrient deficiences. With the exception of iron and chlorine, field responses of Australian pastures have been recorded for all nutrient elements known to be essential to plants: N, P, K, Mg, S, B, Mo, Zn, Cu, Mn;[56] Ca;[14, 28] Co.[47, 51]

Whilst the majority of nutrient deficiencies influence legume growth through direct effects on the metabolism of the host plant,[5, 37] some influence it through their effects on the process of nitrogen fixation. Cobalt, for example has only improved the growth of legumes in the absence of nitrogen salts,[1, 24] and there is as yet no evidence that the host plant requires the element for its own metabolism. Field responses of pastures to cobalt have also been recorded in the absence of fertilizer nitrogen.[47, 51]

The widespread and striking responses of Australian pastures to molybdenum have also been mainly through effects of molybdenum on the reactions of nitrogen fixation. However, in contrast to cobalt, molybdenum is required for the growth of legumes even in the presence of adequate nitrogen salts.[42] Apparently the needs of the host legume for molybdenum are met on most Australian grassland soils.[6]

Calcium deficiency, like molybdenum deficiency, may depress the growth of the host legume when severely deficient, and interfere specifically with the process of nitrogen fixation when moderately deficient.[36] Unlike molybdenum deficiency, calcium deficiency of pastures is not widespread and, where it does occur, may be expressed as a combination of both effects.[28]

Where nutrient deficiencies influence legume growth through direct effects on the metabolism of the host, the plants are usually characterized by their failure to respond to the addition of nitrogen salts. They also frequently contain a higher percentage of nitrogen than healthy plants. However, some of these nutrient deficiencies affect the growth of the host plant by interference with its nitrogen metabolism after fixation has taken place. Subterranean clover deficient in sulphur, for example, appears nitrogen deficient and has a low percentage nitrogen. The plants do not respond to fertilizer nitrogen, so sulphur is not required for the process of nitrogen fixation; it is required for the conversion of non-protein nitrogen to protein.[10]

Phosphorus and copper deficiencies may also reduce the percentage of nitrogen in subterranean clover.[30, 40] However, it is not yet clear whether these effects are through interference with nitrogen metabolism of the host or specifically with the reactions of nitrogen fixation. In other circumstances phosphorus deficiency may increase the percentage nitrogen content of the plants, indicating a prime effect on host plant growth.[61]

The large number of nutrient deficiences which may be encountered in Australian grassland soils has frequently made the resolution of field problems exceptionally difficult. It led quite early to a recognition of the need to cover all other possible nutrient limitations in the investigation of a single nutrient response. However, this was often not accomplished, especially prior to the realization of the widespread occurrence of severe molybdenum deficiency. The recent demonstration of pasture responses to cobalt may also require that, in some areas, responses of pastures to soil additives be re-examined.

In the resolution of the complex interactions of soil additives and nutrients which resulted from the multiplicity of deficiencies, careful analysis of plant growth responses has proved exceptionally rewarding. The principles involved have been outlined by Anderson[7] and they have been used by him and his co-workers with outstanding success in the resolution of a variety of important problems in the growth of pastures. They warrant close examination.

Nutrient Response Curves

(*a*) Response to a single limiting nutrient. Where a single nutrient limits growth, the plant frequently responds to the addition of that nutrient with a curve in keeping with the law of diminishing returns as enunciated, for example, by Mitscherlich.[43] This law requires that each addition of a nutrient gives a successively smaller response, thus producing a curve asymptotic to the nutrient axis. The Mitscherlich-type curve does not hold as a nutrient is increased beyond optimal supply; when excess of nutrient is supplied, growth is depressed.

However, Steenbjerg[54, 55] has pointed out that the reaction of a nutrient with the soil may change the response curve from asymptotic to sigmoidal. Many examples of sigmoid response curves are known. Steenbjerg emphasizes that there is more chance of observing a sigmoid curve the lower the yield is from the optimal treatments; thus, where it applies, the exponential part of

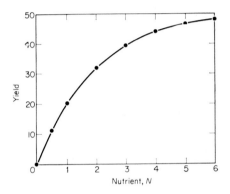

FIG. 12.1. Mitscherlich-type curve for yield of dry matter with increasing levels of nutrient N.

the sigmoid curve is restricted to fertilizers in low supply and becomes asymptotic at optimal supply. In these cases then, the Mitscherlich-type curve would apply only over the optimal part of the yield curve.

In situations where it is applicable, the Mitscherlich-type curve may be used to give information about the effect of soil treatments. Consider a soil on which Mitscherlich-type response curve has been obtained with increasing supply of nutrient N (Fig. 12.1). Clearly, any treatment which increases the supply of N will decrease the response of a given quantity of fertilizer N. Thus, the interaction between the treatment and increasing application of N will be negative.[23]

Anderson[7] has proposed that the converse may be taken as a generality; he postulates that, wherever a treatment and a fertilizer each produce a positive response and the interaction between them is negative, they correct the same deficiency. This interpretation of a number of negative interactions has, in fact, been used extensively by Anderson and co-workers to understand the effects of soil treatments on plant growth.

A negative interaction between molybdenum and fertilizer nitrogen was used to demonstrate the importance of molybdenum in the nitrogen fixation of legumes.[11,12] (Fig. 12.2.) A negative interaction between lime and molybdenum in the growth of legumes was used to support the claim that liming released molybdenum from soils.[13] A negative interaction between decreasing soil acidity and increasing *Rhizobium* numbers was interpreted to indicate that excess soil acidity had an adverse effect on *Rhizobium* growth.[7]

All these conclusions have had far-reaching practical consequences in the development of improved pastures over considerable areas of southern Australia.

(*b*) Response to two limiting nutrients. Where two essential nutrients for growth are in limiting supply, the response of the plant to each nutrient is modified by the supply of the other. Responses to two or more nutrients are described in general terms by the law of limiting factors, which requires that the effect of a factor is least when another factor limits growth, and greatest when all other factors are in optimal supply.

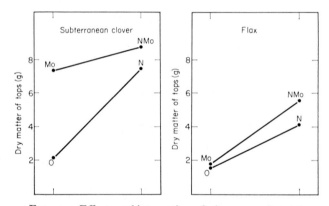

FIG. 12.2. Effects and interaction of nitrogen and molybdenum fertilizers on the yield of a legume (subterranean clover) and on a non-legume (flax) [11].

The application of the law of limiting factors to the effects of nutrients on plant growth was examined critically by Anderson and Thomas.[12] These authors presented diagramatically (Fig. 12.3) the logarithms of certain yield data obtained by Mitscherlich and co-workers on oats. Anderson and Thomas pointed out that, 'in these diagrams, if two levels of any two nutrients occurring in a 2 × 2 factorial arrangement are taken so that the yield obtained with the nutrients together at their high levels is not less than any one of the three remaining individual yields, the interaction is invariably positive or nil'.

This positive interaction between two essential nutrients is in marked contrast to the negative interaction between two elements which correct the same deficiency. This contrast was used by Anderson and co-workers[11,12] (Fig. 12.2) to support their conclusion that molybdenum is required for nitrogen fixation by legumes – a conclusion supported by all subsequent physiological and biochemical evidence.

Anderson[7] later suggested that the law of limiting factors has sufficient validity in the case of nutrients to allow its use in diagnostic analysis of soil treatments, i.e. where the interaction between a treatment and a known element is positive, he would expect that the treatment and the known element correct different deficiencies. He has certainly used it very effectively in this way.

Special cases of the effects of two limiting nutrients are met when the nutrients are added simultaneously in a constant proportion (as, for example,

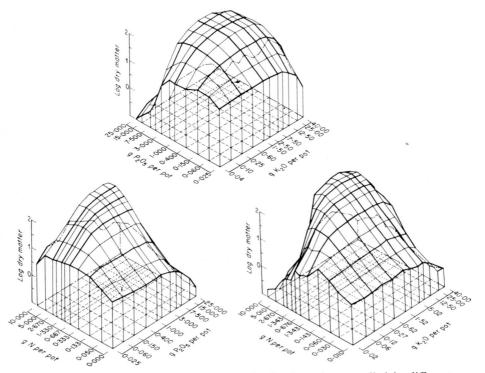

FIG. 12.3. The yield of oats with varying levels of nutrients applied in different combinations. The dry matter of the tops is plotted as logarithms[12].

in the case of calcium and phosphorus with the application of increasing levels of superphosphate). In this event, a linear response curve[31] or, more frequently, a sigmoid response curve will obtain.[29] Thus, response curves of these types must always be treated with caution if they are supposed to be due to the application of a single nutrient. For example, a sigmoid response curve to superphosphate was shown to be due to the presence of zinc impurity in the superphosphate.[4]

Grass-legume Relationships

In addition to effects on production of herbage, the introduction and stimulation of legumes in pastures produces marked changes in the chemical composition of the pastures and in their botanical components.

Chemical composition of the pasture may be affected directly through the presence of legumes which may differ from grasses in both organic and inorganic constituents, and it may be affected indirectly through the secondary effects which improved nitrogen supply has on both the composition of the original grasses and on botanical changes induced in the sward. All these effects may have important consequences on the health and productivity of animals grazing the pasture.

Botanical composition of a pasture may also undergo drastic changes as a consequence of introduction of a legume. The simplest situation is that encountered when grass and clover are sown on a soil low in available nitrogen but with an adequate supply of all other nutrients. In the first year of the pasture, legumes dominate the sward; apparently pasture grasses in the winter rainfall environment of southern Australia gain little or no nitrogen from nodulated legumes growing in association with them.[19, 62] In subsequent years, nitrogen from prior legume growth is available to grasses and enables them to compete with the associated legumes, so that by the third or fourth year grasses may become dominant.[8, 60]

Deficiencies of other nutrients may also have striking effects on the balance of grasses and legumes in pastures. Where they occur in association with a low supply of nitrogen, interactions between nitrogen and nutrient fertilizers on grass-legume balance may be expected. The principles have been studied in sand culture for the interaction of nitrogen and phosphorus supplies on the growth of Wimmera ryegrass and subterranean clover.[61] These plants were grown separately and together at varying levels of nitrogen and phosphorus. When grown alone, subterranean clover responded strongly to increasing phosphorus fertilizer and was not influenced at all by nitrogen fertilizer. The presence of ryegrass had little effect on subterranean clover growth when nitrogen fertilizer was absent; but, when nitrogen fertilizer was added, ryegrass grew vigorously and severely depressed subterranean clover growth. Competition between grass and legume for phosphorus was believed to be an important factor in the depression of clover growth.

The same relationships have been shown to exist in the field. On soils deficient only in nitrogen, legumes dominate mixed pastures in the first year of sowing. In subsequent seasons, the grass component increases and the increase depends on the amount of previous growth by legumes. On soils initially deficient in phosphorus and nitrogen the proportion of grass to clover therefore depends upon the prior dressings of superphosphate, heavy initial or annual dressings leading rapidly from clover to grass dominance.[8, 41, 60]

Where legumes are introduced into a pre-existing native pasture, changes in botanical composition may be even more marked than those described above. A good example of such an effect is described by Donald,[25] who outlines the behaviour of native Australian pastures composed principally of the perennial grasses *Danthonia* and *Stipa*, species of which are the principal components of many native pastures in southern Australia. With settlement, annual clovers may become introduced and spread throughout the pasture. However, under the extremely low phosphorus status of most Australian soils, the clovers make little growth and do not affect the dominance of the pasture by *Dan-*

thonia and *Stipa*. The application of superphosphate stimulates the growth of the clovers, leading to an increase in the nitrogen status of the soils. The increased soil fertility allows annual grasses such as *Festuca myuros* and *Bromus mollis* to flourish. These grasses, together with the clovers, may form a dense sward which may completely eliminate the original perennial native grasses.

Botanical composition of pastures may also be affected by nutrient deficiencies other than nitrogen and phosphorus. Potassium deficiency, for example, may severely depress clover and rye grass growth, leading to their replacement in the pasture by inferior grasses.[48] The specific effect of molybdenum on nitrogen fixation of legumes also leads to marked effects of this element on pasture composition.[3] Some pasture legumes are also more susceptible to copper deficiency than grasses, so that application of copper fertilizers may change the pasture from grass to legume dominance.[52] Subterranean clover may also be more sensitive to zinc deficiency than grasses in the same sward.[4] Thus, many of the changes in pasture composition which follow fertilizer application may be a direct result of the greater susceptibility of legumes to nutrient deficiencies than grasses. These fertilizers could thus be expected to interact with nitrogen in much the same way as phosphorus does.

There are, however, some situations in which the grass is more susceptible to a nutrient deficiency than the legume. For example, on a newly cleared area sown to a mixture of lucerne and *Phalaris tuberosa* the grass was found to be more susceptible to zinc deficiency than lucerne.[4] Since the area was copper deficient as well as zinc deficient, the differences between lucerne and *Phalaris* in their susceptibility to these deficiencies produced some interesting interactions. In the absence of zinc and copper fertilizers, *Phalaris* was dominant. Addition of zinc alone gave *Phalaris* dominance; addition of copper alone gave lucerne dominance. Addition of both trace elements also gave lucerne dominance but increased the content of *Phalaris*.[4] Apparently lucerne is very sensitive to copper deficiency but in some situations relatively insensitive to zinc deficiency.

The susceptibility of different species to nutrient deficiencies can thus produce large changes in botanical composition of pastures. The reasons for the different responses of species to the same nutrient element are generally not understood; they warrant further study.

Of all the nutrients which may affect the botanical composition of Australian pastures, nitrogen and phosphorus are the most important. These nutrients are important not only because they are the most widespread and severe of all nutrient deficiencies on virgin soils, but also because, to prevent reappearance of their deficiencies, they need to be continually replenished under most systems of pasture management. Phosphorus fertilizer is seldom supplied in excess; in addition, in the early phases of pasture development it has a limited residual value, so that phosphorus supply may fluctuate continuously from deficient to adequate. The vigour of legume growth may depend, as already described, on the interaction between nitrogen and phosphorus supply, so that, with fluctuating phosphorus supply, nitrogen supply, too, may fluctuate markedly. On the other hand, when deficiencies other than nitrogen and

P

phosphorus occur in pastures, it is normal practice to provide the deficient elements in excess. Difficulties are experienced in special situations for some nutrients, particularly copper and manganese.[35] Excess sulphur is readily leached so that, unless frequent applications of fertilizer are made, sulphur deficiency may, like phosphorus deficiency, reappear quickly and have marked effects on grass-legume balance.[68]

Nitrogen, sulphur, and phosphorus fertilizers have an especially low residual value when applied to newly improved pastures on soils of low organic matter content. This phenomenon is partly a direct result of the striking accumulation of organic matter which takes place under these conditions.[27, 65] Over a very wide range of conditions soil organic matter contains a remarkably constant amount of nitrogen, sulphur, and phosphorus.[15, 27, 65] Thus, the striking increase in the organic matter content of many native grass-

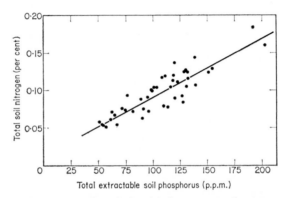

FIG. 12.4. The relationship between total extractable soil phosphorus and total soil nitrogen in podzolic soils under pasture. In these soils there was a direct relationship between total extractable soil phosphorus and the amount of superphosphate applied (27).

land soils is accompanied by increases in organic nitrogen, sulphur, and phosphorus. Large amounts of fertilizer may be consumed in supplying the organic form of these elements. For example, after superphosphate had been applied over a period of years to pastures on podzolic soils in New South Wales, organic phosphorus was found to account for about half the phosphorus applied in dressings of up to 13 cwt of superphosphate per acre; the remaining phosphorus was present in the soil as inorganic phosphorus.[27] In the same study, the accumulation of organic matter was directly proportional to the amount of phosphorus supplied and had not reached an equilibrium value after many years (see Fig. 12.4).

Walker[66, 67] has emphasized that this accumulation of nutrient elements in the organic matter represents a drain on the reserves of available elements. Thus, until the organic matter content of these soils reaches a new high equilibrium value, there will be a continual drain on the available forms of nitrogen, sulphur, and phosphorus. The residual value of fertilizers of these elements can therefore be expected to be lower before than after equilibrium is attained. Perhaps this principle may partly explain the recent report of a significant difference in the residual value of phosphorus fertilizer applied to pastures on granitic soils compared with that applied to pastures on basaltic soils of New South Wales.[41] Organic matter content showed striking increases with superphosphate applications in the granitic soils, but little change in the basaltic soils in which it was already high. The residual value of phosphorus was low in the granitic soils and high in the basaltic soils.

The evidence so far presented indicates the great importance of nutritional factors to the balance of grass and legumes in the early years of pasture establishment when deficiencies are severe. However, over extended periods of time, as the nutritional status of the soil is improved, other factors, such as grazing and the competition for light and water,[26] may become important, so that the simple relationships which hold for initial establishment become more complex. In many parts of New South Wales, for example, thistles have invaded older pastures and may make up a high proportion of the plants present. In Western Australia also, non-leguminous dicotyledons, such as cape-weed, may dominate pastures, relegating grasses to a minor status. The principles governing the botanical composition of these old pastures are not as well understood as they are for the early developmental phase of pasture establishment.

In other countries where more intensive use is made of pastures, legumes are extensively supplemented or even replaced in the pasture by the use of nitrogenous fertilizer. Recent investigations in Australia[22,44] have shown that payable increases in production of pastures may be obtained by using fertilizer nitrogen on suitable grasses at specific times of the year. Reduction in the cost of fertilizer nitrogen can be expected to increase greatly the area of pastures treated in this way. However, it has been stressed that nitrogen fertilizers can only be expected to give profitable increases in production during the winter period when mineralization of organic nitrogen is slow, and that legumes must be maintained in the pasture for profitable production at other times of the year. It is therefore clear that the need for a better understanding of the principles governing grass-clover balance in pastures will assume even greater importance in the immediate future.

REFERENCES

[1] Ahmed, S., and Evans, H. J. (1959). Effect of cobalt on the growth of soybeans in the absence of supplied nitrogen. *Biochem. and Biophys. Res. Com.*, **1**, 271–5.

[2] Albrecht, W. A., and Davis, F. L. (1929). Physiological importance of calcium in legume inoculation. *Bot. Gaz.*, **88**, 310–21.

[3] Anderson, A. J. (1946). Molybdenum in relation to pasture improvement in South Australia. *J. Coun. Sci. Ind. Res. (Aust.)*, **19**, 1–15.

[4] Anderson, A. J. (1946). Fertilizers in pasture development on peat soils in the lower south-east of South Australia. *J. Coun. Sci. Ind. Res. (Aust.)*, **19**, 394–403.

[5] Anderson, A. J. (1949). The influence of plant nutrients on symbiotic nitrogen fixation. *Brit. Com. Sci. Offic. Conf., Australia*, 190–9.

[6] Anderson, A. J. (1956). Molybdenum as a fertilizer. *Adv. Agron.*, **8**, 163–202.

[7] Anderson, A. J. (1956). Effects of fertilizer treatments on pasture growth. *Proc. 7th Internat. Grassl. Congr.*, 323–33.

[8] Anderson, A. J., and McLachlan, K. D. (1951). The residual effect of phosphorus on soil fertility and pasture development on acid soils. *Aust. J. Agric. Res.*, **2**, 377–400.

[9] Anderson, A. J., and Moye, D. V. (1952). Lime and molybdenum in clover development in acid soils. *Aust. J. Agric. Res.*, **3**, 95–110.

[10] Anderson, A. J., and Spencer, D. (1950). Sulphur in nitrogen metabolism of legumes and non-legumes. *Aust. J. Sci. Res. B.*, **3**, 431–49.

[11] Anderson, A. J., and Spencer, D. (1950). Molybdenum in nitrogen metabolism of legumes and non-legumes. *Aust. J. Sci. Res. B.*, **3**, 414–30.

[12] Anderson, A. J., and Thomas, M. P. (1946). Molybdenum and symbiotic nitrogen fixation. *Coun. Sci. Ind. Res. (Aust.) Bull.*, No. 198, 7–24.

[13] Anderson, A. J., and Oertel, A. C. (1946). Factors affecting the response of plants to molybdenum. *Coun. Sci. Ind. Res. (Aust.) Bull.*, No. 198, 25–44.

[14] Andrew, C. S., and Bryan, W. W. (1955). Pasture studies on the coastal lowlands of subtropical Queensland. I. Introduction and initial plant nutrient studies. *Aust. J. Agric. Res.*, **6**, 265–90.

[15] Barrow, N. J. (1961). Phosphorus in soil organic matter. *Soils and Fert.*, **24**, 169–73.

[16] Bowen, G. D. (1961). The toxicity of legume seed diffusates towards rhizobia and other bacteria. *Plant and Soil.*, **15**, 155–65.

[17] Braithwaite, B. M., Jane, A., and Swan, F. G. Unpublished data quoted by Vincent (64).

[18] Brenchley, W. E., and Thornton, H. G. (1925). The relation between the development, structure, and functioning of the nodules on *Vicia faba*, as influenced by the presence or absence of boron in the nutrient medium. *Proc. Roy. Soc. B.*, **98**, 373–99.

[19] Butler, G. W., and Bathurst, N. O. (1956). The underground transference of nitrogen from clover to associated grass. *Proc. 7th Internat. Grassl. Congr.*, 168–78.

[20] Cass Smith, W. P., and Holland, A. A. (1958). The effect of soil fungicides and fumigants on the growth of subterranean clover on light land. *J. Dept. Agric. W. Aust.* **7** (3rd Ser.), 225–31.

[21] Cass Smith, W. P., and Pittman, H. A. J. (1938). The influence of methods of planting on the effective inoculation and establishment of subterranean clover. *J. Dept. Agric. W. Aust.*, **16** (2nd Ser.), 61–79.

[22] Crofts, F. C. (1959). The commercial use of nitrogenous fertilizers and autumn sown oats for the production of winter dairy forage. *Univ. Sydney School of Agric. Report*, No. 4.

[23] Crowther, E. M., and Yates, F. (1941). Fertilizer policy in war-time; the fertilizer requirements of arable crops. *Emp. J. Exp. Agric.*, **9**, 77–97.

[24] Delwiche, C. C., Johnson, C. M., and Reisenauer, H. M. (1961). Influence of cobalt on nitrogen fixation by *Medicago*. *Pl. Physiol.*, **36**, 73–8.

[25] Donald, C. M. (1941). *Pastures and pasture research*. University of Sydney.

[26] Donald, C. M. (1956). Competition among pasture plants. *Proc. 7th Internat. Grassl. Congr.*, 80–91.

[27] Donald, C. M., and Williams, C. H. (1954). Fertility and productivity of a podzolic soil as influenced by subterranean clover (*Trifolium subterraneum* L.) and superphosphate. *Aust. J. Agric. Res.*, **5**, 664–87.

[28] Fitzpatrick, E. N. (1956). A study of the problems of establishment and nutrition of subterranean clover on acid peaty sands. M.Sc. Thesis, University of Western Australia.

[29] Goodall, D. W., and Gregory, F. G. (1947). Chemical composition of plants as an index of their nutritional status. *Imp. Bur. Hort. Plantation Crops, Tech. Comm.* No. 17.

[30] Greenwood, E. A. N., and Hallsworth, E. G. (1960). Studies on the nutrition of legumes. II. Some interactions of calcium, phosphorus, copper, and molybdenum on the growth and chemical composition of *Trifolium subterraneum* L. *Plant and Soil*, **12**, 97–127.

[31] Gregory, F. G. (1937). Mineral nutrition of plants. *Ann. Rev. Biochem.*, **6**, 557–78.

[32] Harris, J. R. (1954). Rhizosphere relationships of subterranean clover. I. Interactions between strains of *Rhizobium trifolii*. *Aust. J. Agric. Res.*, **5**, 247–70.

[33] Holland, A. A. (1962). *Antibiotics in Agriculture*. Ed. E. G. Hallsworth: Butterworths' Scientific Publications, London.

[34] Jenkins, H. V., Vincent, J. M., and Waters, L. M. (1954). The root nodule bacteria as factors in clover establishment in the red basaltic soils of the Lismore District, New South Wales. III. Field inoculation trials. *Aust. J. Agric. Res.*, **5**, 77–89.

[35] Leeper, G. W. (1952). Factors affecting availability of inorganic nutrients in soils with special reference to micro-nutrient elements. *Ann. Rev. Pl. Physiol.*, 3, 1–16.

[36] Loneragan, J. F. (1959). Calcium in the nitrogen metabolism of subterranean clover. *Aust. J. Biol. Sci.*, 12, 26–39.

[37] Loneragan, J. F. (1960). The legume-*Rhizobium* symbiosis. *J. Aust. Inst. Agric. Sci.*, 26, 26–31.

[38] Loneragan, J. F., and Dowling, E. J. (1958). The interaction of calcium and hydrogen ions in the nodulation of subterranean clover. *Aust. J. Agric. Res.*, 9, 464–72.

[39] Loneragan, J. F., Meyer, D., Fawcett, R. G., and Anderson, A. J. (1955). Lime pelleted clover seeds for nodulation on acid soils. *J. Aust. Inst. Agric. Sci.*, 21, 264–5.

[40] McLachlan, K. D., and Norman, B. W. (1961). Phosphorus and symbiotic nitrogen fixation in subterranean clover. *J. Aust. Inst. Agric. Sci.*, 27, 244–45.

[41] McLachlan, K. D., and Norman, B. W. (1962). Effects of previous superphosphate applications on the pasture environment and the response by pasture to a current dressing. *Aust. J. Agric. Res.*, 13, 836–52.

[42] Meagher, W. R., Johnson, C. M., and Stout, P. R. (1952). Molybdenum requirements of leguminous plants supplied with fixed nitrogen. *Pl. Physiol.*, 27, 222–30.

[43] Mitscherlich, E. A. (1909). Quoted by Goodall and Gregory (29).

[44] Newman, R. J., Allen, B. F., and Cook, M. G. (1962). The effect of nitrogen on winter pasture production in southern Victoria. *Aust. J. Exp. Agric. An. Husb.*, 2, 20–4.

[45] Norris, D. O. (1959). The role of calcium and magnesium in the nutrition of *Rhizobium*. *Aust. J. Agric. Res.*, 10, 651–98.

[46] Nutman, P. S. (1956). The influence of the legume in root nodule symbiosis. A comparative study of host determinants and functions. *Biol. Rev.*, 31, 109–51.

[47] Ozanne, P. G., Greenwood, E. A. N., and Shaw, T. C. (1963). The cobalt requirement of subterranean clover. *Aust. J. Agric. Res.*, 14, 39–50.

[48] Paton, D. F. (1956). The occurrence and significance of potassium deficiency in Tasmanian pastures. *Tas. J. Agric.*, 27, 189–204.

[49] Paton, D. F. (1957). Responses to seed inoculation of pasture legumes in Tasmania. *Tas. J. Agric.*, 28, 389–98.

[50] Paton, D. F. (1960). Problems in legume establishment with special reference to nodulation and nutrition. *J. Aust. Inst. Agric., Sci.* 26, 32–47.

[51] Powrie, J. K. (1960). A field response by subterranean clover to cobalt fertilizer. *Aust. J. Sci.*, 23, 198.

[52] Riceman, D. S., Donald, C. M., and Evans, S. T. (1940). Further investigations on copper deficiency in plants in South Australia. *Coun. Sci. Ind. Res. (Aust.)*, Pamph. 96.

[53] Spencer, D. (1950). The effect of calcium and soil pH on nodulation of *T. subterraneum* L. clover on a yellow podsol. *Aust. J. Agric. Res.*, 1, 374–81.

[54] Steenbjerg, F. (1954). Manuring, plant production, and the chemical composition of the plant. *Plant and Soil.*, 5, 226–42.

[55] Steenbjerg, F., and Jakobson, Sr. T. (1963). Plant nutrition and yield curves. *Soil Sci.*, 95, 69–88.

[56] Stephens, C. G., and Donald, C. M. (1958). Australian soils and their response to fertilizers. *Adv. in Agron.* 10, 167–256.

[57] Thompson, J. A. (1960). Inhibition of nodule bacteria by an antibiotic from legume seed coats. *Nature*, 187, 619–20.

[58] Thompson, J. A. (1961). Studies on nodulation responses to pelleting of subterranean clover seed. *Aust. J. Agric. Res.*, 12, 578–92.

[59] Tiver, N. S. (1960). The role of lime in pasture establishment on leached acid soils in southern Australia. *Proc. 8th Internat. Grassl. Congr.*, 93–8.

[60] Trumble, H. C., and Donald, C. M. (1938). The relation of phosphate to the development of seeded pasture on a podsolized sand. *Coun. Sci. Ind. Res. (Aust.) Bull.*, No. 116.

[61] Trumble, H. C., and Shapter, R. E. (1937). The influence of nitrogen and phosphorus treatment on the yield and chemical composition of Wimmera ryegrass and subterranean clover, grown separately and in association. *Coun. Sci. Ind. Res. (Aust.) Bull.*, No. 105, 25–36.

[62] Trumble, H. C., and Strong, T. H. (1937). On the nitrogen accretion of pasture grasses when grown in association with legumes. *Coun. Sci. Ind. Res. (Aust.) Bull.*, No. 105, 11–24.

[63] Vincent, J. M. (1954). The control of the quality of legume seed inoculants. *J. Aust. Inst. Agric. Sci.*, **20**, 247–9.

[64] Vincent, J. M. (1958). *Nutrition of the legumes.* Ed. E. G. Hallsworth. Butterworths' Scientific Publications, London.

[65] Walker, T. W. (1956). The accumulation of organic matter in grassland soils. *Trans. Internat. Congr. Soil Sci.*, 6th Congr., 409–16.

[66] Walker, T. W. (1957). The sulphur cycle in grassland soils. *J. Brit. Grassl. Soc.*, **12**, 10–8.

[67] Walker, T. W., Adams, A. F. R., and Orchiston, H. D. (1955). The effects and interactions of sulphur, phosphorus, and molybdenum on the growth and composition of clovers. *N.Z. J. Sci. Tech.*, **36A**, 470–82.

[68] Walker, T. W., and Adams, A. F. R. (1958). Competition for sulphur in a grass-clover association. *Plant and Soil*, **9**, 353–66.

[69] Wilson, P. W. (1940). *The biochemistry of symbiotic nitrogen fixation.* University of Winconsin Press, Madison.

13

The Effects of Grazing on Grasslands

By R. M. Moore and E. F. Biddiscombe

GRAZING involves not only reduction in leaf area of plants with concomitant effects on their storage of carbohydrate, tiller development, leaf and root growth but, in addition, alters their micro-environment, introduces such factors as trampling and return to soil of dung and urine, and modifies the dispersal of seeds and fruits. Further, the effects of grazing animals on grassland communities are not simple summations of their effects on individual species. Since species in such communities differ in germination, sprouting and flowering times, growth rhythms, and palatabilities, their inter-relationships may be profoundly altered by grazing.

For these and other reasons, grazing cannot be simulated in totality by cutting, particularly in greenhouse experiments, though such studies may be useful in elucidating the physiological effects of defoliation *per se* in individual species.

Effects of Defoliation

Cutting experiments on species grown alone generally show that the greater the proportion of leaf surface removed the lower the immediate growth potential. However, reaction to defoliation varies with the physiological age, geometry, and morphology of the plant, the intensity and frequency of cutting, and with ecological factors such as light, temperature, and soil properties.

Environmental conditions which promote leaf growth such as high temperature, low light intensity, and a high level of available nitrogen in the soil tend to reduce carbohydrate levels in grasses and may lessen their capacity to recover from repeated defoliation. On the other hand, under conditions less favourable to leaf growth, defoliation may not be deleterious. For instance, at high light intensities and low temperatures cutting enhances the tillering of grasses. A temporary decline in tiller production in *Lolium* after cutting is followed by a sharp increase, and frequent defoliation at high light intensities and low temperatures maintains tiller numbers.[27] Similarly, close cutting of *Phalaris tuberosa* in winter promotes tillering in spring,[43] and it is noteworthy that Alberda[1] found carbohydrate levels in *Lolium* highest in winter when growth is slow.

Frequent and severe cutting reduces the growth of roots[16, 68] and the amount of carbohydrate in perennating organs. There is evidence to suggest that these effects are most pronounced when plants are growing actively. For example, *Agropyron* is most susceptible to close cutting in the period of rapid growth immediately following winter dormancy.[50] Similarly, the subsequent growth of *Stipa* and *Astrebla* is depressed to the greatest extent by defoliation following drought-breaking rains when shoots elongate rapidly.[6, 53]

Grasses as a group react similarly to defoliation, but individual species vary in their tolerance to close and repeated cutting. Species with erect growth habit are generally more susceptible to close defoliation than rhizomatous or stoloniferous species,[26] but growth habit may be greatly modified by regular cutting or grazing. Grasses regularly cut or grazed tend to be semi-decumbent, to produce leaves close to the ground, and to have a relatively large number of nodes below the soil surface. These characteristics make them less easily defoliated by animals and less susceptible to grazing injury.

Many investigators have stressed the importance of high carbohydrate reserves in perennating organs on the persistence and productivity of plants subjected to defoliation. However, it may well be that high levels of reserves are of significance only when defoliated plants have to depend on stored energy for a relatively long time before their foliage regains access to light. Such a situation is most likely in grassland communities composed of species differing widely in palatability and in which the less utilized shade the preferred and, therefore, defoliated species. Grazing, therefore, may alter levels of competition among species in communities, and there is some evidence to suggest that the modifying effects of grazing on the micro-environment of plants may be of greater significance than the direct effects of defoliation.

Effects of Grazing on the Micro-environment

In sown pastures of few species similar in palatabilities, regular grazing generally increases the penetration of light and reduces mutual shading. Under these conditions, reduction in photosynthetic area by grazing may be compensated in part by a better light environment. In addition to stimulatory effects on tiller production in grasses, high light intensities are necessary for maintaining clover productivity in grass–clover communities. Regrowth of clovers which have horizontally placed leaves is maximal when the area of green leaves is about five times the area of ground surface, that is, when the leaf area index is about 5.[12, 18] The attainment of such a leaf area is dependent upon a high intensity of light.[60]

High light intensities within pasture communities may result from hard grazing or restriction of plant density and growth by low levels of soil nutrients especially water and nitrogen. Common invaders of grasslands under high light conditions are rosette forming perennials, some of which may be important weeds.[30]

Advantage has been taken of the horizontal leaf arrangement of clovers and of their independence of soil nitrogen in the control of St. John's Wort (*Hypericum perforatum*)[42] and Skeleton Weed (*Chondrilla juncea*),[43] two deep-rooted perennial weeds common under conditions in which they are not liable to shading when in the rosette form.

Close grazing reduces the insulating effect of vegetation and its buffering effect on temperature changes at the soil surface, thereby increasing the chances of stem and leaf meristems being exposed to extremes of temperature.[34] In this respect it is interesting to note that the commonly used pasture species have wide climatic tolerance ranges. Reduction of mulch or surface litter through complete or near complete consumption of herbage by grazing animals also may widen amplitudes of soil temperature and reduce the infiltration of water into soils. It has been shown that moisture infiltration in an *Andropogon* grassland protected from grazing is increased and evaporation reduced by the presence of surface litter.[69] Other consequences of reduction of plant cover by grazing are increased run-off of precipitation and liability to erosion.

In arid and semi-arid areas, loss of surface soil through wind erosion is a common consequence of heavy grazing and the resultant reduction in density of perennial herbs and shrubs.[3, 21] It has been suggested[13, 24] that the failure of Mulga (*Acacia aneura*) to regenerate in many areas in Australia is due to un-favourable conditions for germination resulting from the disappearance of perennial grasses following sheep grazing and consequent erosion of the soil surface by wind. Loss of surface soil markedly reduces levels of plant nutrients such as nitrogen and, for this reason, erosion is an important factor in the slow recovery of perennial vegetation in overgrazed communities of arid and semi-arid regions even in the absence of further grazing.[7, 8, 15, 20, 48, 74]

In mesophytic communities, wind erosion may not be important but heavy grazing, by increasing precipitation run-off and by widening soil temperature ranges, tends to make such environments more arid. This is exemplified by the ingress of species characteristic of more arid communities into grazed mesophytic woodlands in eastern Australia.[38] The importance of managing vegetation to maintain a protective cover on the soil and thus prevent erosion is discussed in Chapter 14.

Grazing affects the depth to which moisture penetrates in soil not only by reduction of the vegetative cover but also by consolidation of the soil surface by trampling. The new environment so created is more favourable to surface than to deep-rooted species and marked changes in life forms as well as floristics may commonly result.

Vegetation Changes Due to Grazing

In Australia, changes in vegetation resulting from grazing by domestic animals have been striking in character and extensive in distribution. Virtually the whole of the State of New South Wales was settled for pastoral purposes by 1880, and few plant communities in southern Australia have not been subjected to grazing. The depasturing of confined domestic animals intro-duced a new factor into the environments of Australian plant communities and produced marked changes in their species composition and predominant life forms. Changes in vegetation noted by early settlers such as J. G. Robert-son in 1853[11] occurred rapidly and extensively following the introduction of sheep. Nevertheless, the relatively short period of pastoral occupation makes it still possible to determine the nature of such changes.[38,40]

Mesophytic Communities

Even in the mesophytic temperate woodlands of Australia where replace-ment of native vegetation by communities of introduced pasture species is possible most livestock are carried on native pastures. The most striking single effect of sheep grazing in these woodland communities is the disappearance of

Kangaroo grass (*Themeda australis*), the presettlement dominant over extensive areas of southern Australia.[38] In northern Australia where the rainfall has a summer incidence and where the pastoral industry is based on cattle rather than sheep, Kangaroo grass has persisted better than in southern areas, although there is evidence that it was a dominant in sub-tropical woodlands, now mainly bunch spear grass (*Heteropogon contortus*). Regular burning is a feature of sub-tropical woodlands and its effects on the dominance of such species as *Heteropogon contortus* have been described in Chapter 11. A decrease in *Themeda* following grazing has been reported also in South Africa.[58]

In general, the tall warm season grasses of the herbaceous climax of temperate woodlands on both pedalfers and pedocals have been replaced under grazing, firstly by short cool season perennials and finally by annuals. The latter are often in two distinct communities, one of cool and the other of warm season species.[38, 40] On podzolic soils, the change in composition has been aided and accelerated by application of superphosphate and the consequent increase in annual legumes belonging to the genus *Trifolium*. On pedocals such as red-brown earths, black earths, and grey brown soils of heavy texture, changes similar in character have occurred but the predominant introduced annual legumes are species of *Medicago*.

The general pattern of change in the herbaceous components of woodland and grassland communities in south-eastern Australia as a result of disturbance by grazing has been determined by Moore.[38]

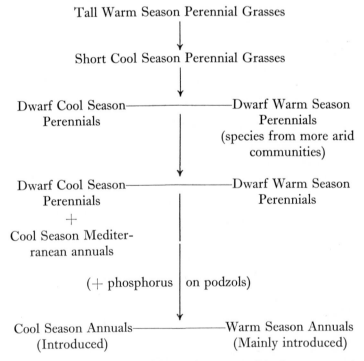

Tall Warm Season Perennial Grasses

Short Cool Season Perennial Grasses

Dwarf Cool Season——————————Dwarf Warm Season
Perennials   Perennials
                                (species from more arid
                                 communities)

Dwarf Cool Season——————————Dwarf Warm Season
Perennials   Perennials
+
Cool Season Mediter-
ranean annuals

(+ phosphorus on podzols)

Cool Season Annuals——————————Warm Season Annuals
(Introduced)   (Mainly introduced)

As densities and areas occupied by native perennials decrease, so do light, water, and nutrients such as nitrogen become available for other plants.

Mineral nitrogen is generally low under perennial grasses but fluctuates seasonally with increasing amplitudes as the area occupied by such species decreases. In heavily grazed communities in southern Australia, therefore, the availability of space, light, water, and nitrogen may be relatively high in autumn and conditions are thus favourable for the establishment of nitrophilous cool season annuals.

On leached soils such as the red-yellow podzolics of the Tablelands of New South Wales and Victoria, the change from perennials to annuals is influenced by increases in soil nitrogen following the use of superphosphate and its consequent effects on the establishment and growth of introduced clovers. Subterranean clover (*Trifolium subterraneum*), the most productive of the introduced annual clovers, is particularly effective in promoting and hastening the change from perennials to annuals.

A feature of the utilization of temperate Australian communities for pastoral purposes is their ultimate convergence irrespective of differences in original composition, to basically similar communities composed principally of introduced annuals.[38] The application of superphosphate and consequent increase in the nitrogen, sulphur, phosphorus, and calcium levels of podzolic soils, combined with the direct effects of grazing, tend to make disclimax communities on podsols similar in many respects to those on pedocals. All converge to similar disclimax communities under grazing.

Detailed changes in composition following grazing have been described for a number of communities in Australia,[3, 5, 14, 33, 34] and the most commonly occurring species in winter aspect communities of heavily grazed woodlands and grasslands in temperate Australia have been listed by Moore.[38]

In general, the palatable plants of heavily and regularly grazed communities tend to have similar growth curves and maturation times. Less palatable species which enter the communities when soil nitrogen levels are higher, are later maturing and frequently weeds, e.g. *Cirsium vulgare*, *Carduus pycnocephalus*, *Onopordum acanthium*, and *Carthamus lanatus*.

The overall trends under grazing in the mesophytic areas of southern Australia are, therefore, from summer to winter growing species, from perennials to annuals and from native to introduced species.

Xerophytic Communities

In arid and semi-arid regions livestock production is almost entirely from native species which vary markedly in accessibility and palatability. As a result, grazing pressures on some species may be high even though the stocking rate on an area basis is low. Under these circumstances the less desirable species predominate and their control is often a major problem in dry regions. Commonly, perennial grasses decrease and unpalatable shrubs increase as a result of grazing. Increases in unpalatable species of *Artemisia* as a result of grazing steppe communities have been reported in Israel,[9] Turkey,[62] Russia,[63] and Western U.S.A.[49] The shrub vegetation of the South African Karoo is believed similarly to be a grazing disclimax.[66] Other examples of grasslands changing to shrublands as a consequence of grazing are the creosote bush (*Larrea divaricata*) communities of New Mexico,

Arizona, and Texas. These are considered to have been originally grasslands composed principally of species of *Bouteloua*.[72]

An analogous situation exists on desert sandplains in the 8–15-inch rainfall zone of north-west Western Australia where the predominant species are xerophytic grasses collectively called Spinifex but belonging to the genera *Triodia* and *Plectrachne*. In the absence of regular burning, heavy grazing increases the density of an unpalatable native shrub (*Acacia translucens*).

Increases in unpalatable shrubs often make the continued utilization of arid and semi-arid lands for livestock production possible only by repeated burning. Sweet and sour veld in Rhodesia has to be fired every two or three years to prevent encroachment of thorny species of *Acacia*.[70] Similarly, the invasion of large areas of grassland in other parts of Africa by *Dichrostachys* and *Acacia* is thought to be a consequence of the withholding of fire.[51] The effects of fire on grasslands have been discussed in detail in Chapter 11.

In Australia, unpalatable native shrubs have spread and increased in density through the felling of woodland trees and subsequent grazing of the herbaceous community by sheep. Palatable species of the climax shrub-steppe have been similarly replaced by less readily eaten species characteristic of earlier stages of succession[25, 67, 74] and overgrazed shrub steppe is dominated commonly by *Kochia aphylla*, *Bassia paradoxa*, *Bassia divaricata*, and *Nitraria schoberi* and other relatively unpalatable species.

In comparison with mesophytic communities there are few introduced species in more arid communities following grazing. This difference is not entirely due to the application of phosphate fertilizers in the higher rainfall areas since there are many introduced species in grazed communities of these areas even in the absence of phosphate. In the drier areas colonizers of denuded areas come from within the original communities. In such communities perennials are spaced widely and the inter-tussock areas are normally vegetated for only a short period after rain by native species adapted to the colonization of bare areas. Unless erosion of the surface soil has occurred, these same species occupy areas denuded of perennials by overgrazing. The colonizers include both cool and warm season species, some of which are characteristic of disclimax stages of grazed mesophytic communities.

The grazing of native plant communities by confined animals changes the species' composition. Some of these changes may be harmful to continued pastoral production and others, while ultimately beneficial, entail changes in animal husbandry. Some form of management may be necessary, therefore, to control these changes or to make use of them in the most effective ways.

Grazing Management

Systems of management and utilization of pastures, both sown and native, have been and still are subject to scientific enquiry and controversy. Objectives of management systems range from protecting a resource for continued, albeit restricted, utilization to increasing the output of a pasture and the degree to which it may be utilized. In some instances the management is for the maintenance of the pasture community while in others it is for the needs of the grazing animal including the special requirements of breeding females and of young growing animals.

The simplest form of management involves only the control of stock numbers but in more complex systems the timing and duration of grazing periods are controlled. Management systems vary from continuous, year-long, and various forms of alternate resting and grazing, to no grazing at all. The latter, more applicable to fodder crops than to pastures, is known as zero grazing and involves daily cutting and stall-feeding during the growing season.

Evaluation of grazing systems and comparisons of the results obtained from similar systems in different countries are complicated by economic considerations, such as agricultural prices, national farm policies, labour costs, fertilizer subsidies, and by environmental factors including length of growing season, severity of winter cold, liability to fouling, and soil pugging. From a scientific viewpoint greatest interest is centred on the proposition that perennial pastures grazed rotationally, i.e. grazed in sections with periods of rest between grazings, will produce more dry matter and therefore more meat, wool, or milk per acre than the same pasture grazed continuously as one unit. In American usage 'rotational' or 'rotation grazing' is applied as well to systems in which native ranges are rested for a year or more between grazings. It would seem preferable, however, to restrict the term to grazing systems involving repeated utilization and rest in a single growing season. It is in this latter sense that it has been the subject of greatest controversy.

In the northern hemisphere the viewpoint is widely held that productivity is increased by allowing intervals of rest between grazings. Nevertheless the field experimental evidence for this viewpoint is slight and in the main unconvincing. In some instances it has been assumed at the outset that rotational grazing, including strip and all other variants of this system, would give greater animal production than continuous, and stocking rates were adjusted accordingly.

Recent studies on grazing behaviour and field investigations on the physiology of grazed pastures have not produced evidence in support of rotational grazing and, indeed, it has emerged that severe defoliation is more harmful to grasses than more frequent but less severe reduction in leaf area.

It would seem that the concept of rotational or intermittent grazing is based largely on frequency of cutting experiments and that it is regarded by many as having a physiological basis. Continuous grazing is often wrongly equated with both severe and frequent defoliation whereas defoliation is most likely to be complete under the rotational system in which all the animals are confined in rotation to small sections of the total area being grazed. Grazing pressures are therefore high for short periods, reducing to zero for the period of rest. Shortening the period of grazing shortens the period of rest and in a rapid cycle of grazing, rotational approximates continuous grazing.

Long periods of rest in times of rapid pasture growth mean that, at the recommencement of grazing, there is a wider range in the quality of feed available, and as sheep, in particular, tend to ignore older parts of plants in favour of the younger, the grazing pressure on the latter is thereby increased. The greater selectivity of animals grazing long pasture and their preference for young actively growing tissue may result in the defoliation of young tillers to such a degree that their regeneration is affected.[73] Recent work indicates similarly that grazing pressures on younger parts of plants, in this case, *Phalaris tuberosa*, increase as the plant matures.[2] It was found that sheep tend to select those parts of the plant highest in nitrogen. With more frequent but less severe defoliation, the proportion of young protein-rich parts of plants is higher, there is less variation in the quality of feed available, and correspondingly less grazing pressure on young rapidly growing tissues.

The more complete the defoliation of a plant the lower its subsequent yield of dry matter. Pastures grazed to one inch give lower yields of dry matter than those grazed to a height of five inches.[12] The rate of regrowth following close grazing is slower at the beginning but faster at the end of the recovery period in comparison with more leniently grazed grass. The more severe the defoliation the longer the period of recovery necessary and this is possibly a reason for the lack of clear cut differences between rotational and continuous grazing.

In field experiments conducted on both sown and native pastures in Australia, continuous year-long grazing has not shown to disadvantage in comparison with other systems, including rotational grazing.

Native Pastures

The management of native pastures is usually directed to the control of botanical composition and to the conservation of vegetation. The more arid the community being grazed the more important it is to regulate stocking so as to protect the plant's micro-environment. This may mean maintaining the community at its ecological climax and this in turn predicates a low level of utilization of the dry matter produced. In dry regions this is complicated by the frequent but irregular occurrence of droughts which, without changes in stock numbers, increase grazing pressures.

American investigators have stressed the importance of range condition as a guide to management.[50, 61] Range condition is determined by the relative abundance and vigour of desirable and undesirable species, the amount of litter, and the extent of soil erosion. Particular plants are used as indicators of different degrees of condition and, in theory, stocking rates are adjusted to relieve grazing pressures on the most useful species. Adjustment of grazing pressures on particular species is facilitated by grazing systems based on under-utilization and by the presence on one holding of a number of different communities.

Grazing management of arid communities has amongst its objectives not only the maintenance of a suitable environment for the germination of seeds and the protection of young seedlings but also the avoidance of heavily grazing regrowth following rains or fire, and the maturation of seed by desirable species. The various systems devised to achieve these objectives are based mostly on so-called deferment, the setting aside of part of the grazing area during a critical period.

Deferment is most likely to benefit perennials when new growth is being made and plants are being defoliated as fast or faster than new tissue is being produced. The possibility of this is greatest at the commencement of the growing season and following drought and fire. The advantages to be gained from deferment depend on the severity of the grazing pressure on the plants of the community and this, in turn, depends on stocking rate, the condition of the community and the favourableness or otherwise of the season. When conditions for growth are favourable and plants are growing faster than they are being eaten, deferment is unlikely to be beneficial. In the course of five unusually favourable seasons at Trangie, New South Wales, deferring grazing for three weeks after the opening rains in spring or autumn did not affect the botanical composition of a *Stipa falcata–Chloris acicularis* disclimax grassland differently to that of continuous grazing.[6]

In the rotation–deferred system of American investigators[23, 49] one portion of the range is grazed only in the autumn after seed of the most useful species has matured. Since there is no grazing on this section during the spring there is no possibility of damage to young seedlings. Sections of the range are deferred in sequence, the period of deferment depending on the degree of rehabilitation considered necessary. An important feature of the system is that stock numbers are determined not by the whole of the range but by that portion which has to be grazed during the growing season. A similar system, designed to change the period of use annually and allow seed setting, is the so-called 5-year-5-field rotation in use in drier parts of the U.S.S.R.[29]

In the north-west of Western Australia a deferred grazing system has been described for spinifex[47] in which part of the area is burnt before the opening of the summer rains to check spinifex, and left ungrazed until more desirable species have set seed. This system has been described more fully in Chapter 11. All of these deferment systems are designed to protect the plant community and its capacity to regenerate itself.[39]

Systems of grazing designed to increase animal productivity would seem to have little application to arid and semi-arid plant communities which characteristically fluctuate markedly in forage production.[36] An experiment in southwestern Queensland, where the mean annual rainfall is 15 inches, showed that grazing a community of Mitchell grasses (*Astrebla* spp.) rotationally was no more advantageous than continuous or set stocking at the same stocking rates.[53]

In the higher rainfall areas of Australia greater production is generally possible from pastures of introduced species than from any system of managing native pastures. However, rotational grazing has been of some interest in the Northern Tablelands of New South Wales because of its possible influence on the incidence of internal parasitism in sheep. This aspect of rotational grazing was investigated on a *Themeda–Bothriochloa* community at Armidale, New South Wales.[54] No differences were found between rotational and continuous grazing in their effects on botanical composition and productivity of the pastures or on the health and production of the sheep. There are data from other parts of the world which indicate that native grasslands do not respond differently to rotational and continuous grazing at similar stocking levels.[31, 55, 58]

The changes in composition of woodland communities under grazing already described increase their potential for animal production. The trend from native perennials to introduced annuals is accompanied and influenced by a rise in the level of nitrate nitrogen in the surface soil.[38] At the same time there is also an increase in the level of protein in the feed available to animals which, in a sense, improve the quality of their own food supply. On podzolic soils this improvement is further enhanced and accelerated by applications of phosphatic fertilizer, and large increases in sheep carrying capacity have resulted from the use of superphosphate. Disclimax *Danthonia* grasslands in southern Australia normally carry three quarters to one sheep per acre per annum but within a few years annual applications of superphosphate increase carrying capacities three and one half fold.[66] The greater production is not due to enhanced growth of native species but to increases in the densities and growth of introduced annuals particularly species of *Trifolium*.

The beneficial effects of adventitious species of *Trifolium* on pasture production stimulated the sowing of better species, notably *T. subterraneum*. In the presence of this species, native perennials are completely suppressed and the resultant community is composed essentially of *T. subterraneum*, and annual species of *Bromus*, *Hordeum*, *Vulpia*, and *Erodium* with one or more composites such as *Cryptostemma calendula* or thistles belonging to the genera *Cirsium*, *Carduus*, *Onopordum*, *Carthamus*. Such communities are unstable in composition and may pose problems in animal husbandry. In the drier parts of the temperate woodland zone in southern Australia, the species best adapted to annual re-establishment bear spiny fruits which are deleterious to wool.

In the higher rainfall woodlands, clover may be almost completely dominant and a continuing diet of subterranean clover high in oestrogens may lower the fertility of ewes. In addition, at the high levels of soil nitrogen common under annual pastures composed mainly of clover, there is the already mentioned problem of weeds. Both of these problems are less serious in pastures containing a perennial grass. In perennial grass pastures, clover is seldom dominant[18] and levels of available nitrogen are generally low.

The use of superphosphate and the intensive grazing of native pastures in high rainfall areas of temperate Australia therefore would seem to make perennial pasture an eventual necessity for good animal husbandry.

Sown Pastures

The possibilities of improving the utilization of sown pastures and of overcoming the problems of animal husbandry created by high stock numbers have been studied by various management systems.

Perhaps the most detailed Australian comparison of continuous and rotational grazing is an experiment[41] conducted at Canberra, A.C.T. over a period of five years and in which pastures were sampled at weekly intervals. Two rotational systems, one week's grazing and three and seven weeks' rest respectively, were compared with continuous grazing on a year-long basis and at similar rates of stocking with sheep.

During the experiment there were droughts and periods of above average rainfall so that grazing pressures varied widely. No evidence was obtained to suggest that rotational was superior to continuous grazing except in maintaining a preferentially grazed plant, lucerne, in small proportion in a community with two other species, *Phalaris tuberosa* and subterranean clover. It is perhaps significant that lucerne, a warm season species, may complete a cycle of growth in several weeks. In the experiment, therefore, being normally the only plant green in the summer, it was subjected to complete defoliation at a time when it grows rapidly. *Phalaris* grows slowly in the winter and produced about eighty per cent of its total leaf and stem dry matter in three spring months (Figure 13.1). Grazing pressures were highest, therefore, when growth rates were slow, and least when growth was rapid. Close defoliation in winter tends to accentuate the spring peak of production[45] which further

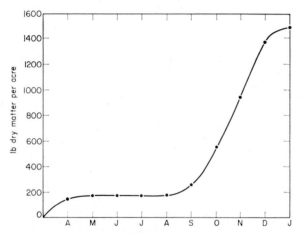

FIG. 13.1. Seasonal changes in dry weights of green *Phalaris tuberosa* present under continuous grazing. Pounds dry matter per acre.

serves to 'protect' *Phalaris* from severe defoliation when growing rapidly and therefore most sensitive to defoliation. Subterranean clover, because of a more favourable light environment near the ground, tended to produce most under continuous grazing. However, differences in botanical composition were not large enough to affect differentially pasture and animal production.

Similarly, no differences in pasture production were found in a Western Australian experiment comparing continuous grazing with a rotational system involving one week's grazing and five weeks' rest.[56] Freer[19] also showed that grazing method has little effect on the efficiency of utilization of a ryegrass-white clover pasture as measured in terms of animal production.

There is abundant evidence to indicate that the botanical composition of pastures can be altered by grazing management. This is particularly the case in pasture communities containing many species varying in their periods of maximum growth. In those parts of the northern hemisphere where animals are housed in the winter, the composition of pastures may be controlled to a degree by the earliness or lateness of the commencement of grazing in the spring. Where grazing is year-long, as in most of Australia and other countries

Q

of the southern hemisphere, deferment of one part of a pasture means a several fold increase in the grazing pressure on the remainder at a time when growth is rapid and the pasture sensitive to close defoliation. The effect of this heavy grazing on subsequent productivity later in the same or early in the next season has to be weighed against any short-term benefits from deferment.

Withholding grazing at the beginning of the growing season favours species which begin growth early and are normally subjected to heavy grazing pressures. Rossiter[57] found that autumn deferment or saving in south-western Western Australia, increases the proportion of the early germinating grass *Bromus rigidus*, in pastures. In Britain, ryegrass is favoured in pastures not grazed at the beginning of the spring growing season.[26] Similarly, it is a practice in New Zealand to graze hard in spring to suppress ryegrass and thereby promote the growth of clover.[59] Autumn or the end of season deferment in Britain favours the perennial grasses, *Dactylis glomerata* and *Festuca arundinacea*.[4]

The usefulness of managing pastures to control the proportions of the component species will depend on the contributions of individual species to animal production. Deferring the grazing of a portion of a pasture at the opening of the growing season – autumn in southern Australia – to save pasture for ewes during the later stages of pregnancy in late winter or early spring, or to allow annual pastures to regenerate,[57] has not generally proved better than continuous grazing. The greater stress to which animals are subjected while part of their pasture is being saved may not always be compensated for by the greater amount of feed available to them subsequently on the saved portion. Deferment, however, does offer scope for rationing pasture during periods when growth is slow. For example, deferment during dry autumns ensures that some pasturage is available to livestock in winter. It may well be that systems of management which limit the intake of non-fattening animals such as wool-producing wethers will allow greater numbers to be carried per unit area and thus increase animal production. In general, however, the experimental evidence for greater production on mesophytic pastures by conventional systems of management is not convincing.

REFERENCES

[1] Alberda, Th. (1957). The effects of cutting, light intensity, and night temperature on growth and soluble carbohydrate content of *Lolium perenne* L. *Plant and Soil*, **8**, 199–229.

[2] Arnold, G. W. (1960). Selective grazing by sheep of two forage species at different stages of growth. *Aust. J. Agric. Res.*, **11**, 1026–33.

[3] Beadle, N. C. W. (1948). *The Vegetation and Pastures of western New South Wales with Special Reference to Soil Erosion*. (Govt. Printer, Sydney).

[4] Beddows, A. R., and Jones, L. I. (1958). Grasses in Winter. 1. Observations at Aberystwyth. 2. Suggestions regarding winter herbage. *J. Brit. Grassld. Soc.*, **13**, 170–6.

[5] Biddiscombe, E. F. (1953). A survey of the natural pastures of the Trangie District, New South Wales, with particular reference to the grazing factor. *Aust. J. Agric. Res.*, **4**, 1–28.

[6] Biddiscombe, E. F., Hutchings, R. J., Edgar, G., and Cuthbertson, E. G. (1956). Grazing management of natural pastures at Trangie, New South Wales. *Aust. J. Agric. Res.*, **7**, 233–47.

[7] Blydenstein, J. (1957). Effect of domestic livestock exclusion on vegetation in the Sonoran Desert. *Ecology*, **38**, 522–6.

[8] Booth, W. E. (1944). Revegetation of abandoned fields in Kansas and Oklahoma. *Amer. J. Bot.*, **28**, 415–22.

[9] Boyko, H. (1952). On regeneration problems of destroyed pasture areas in arid regions. *Proc. 6th Int. Grassld. Congr.*, 632.

[10] Boyko, H. (1954). Plant Ecological Problems in increasing the productivity of arid areas. In *Biology of Deserts*. Instit. of Biology, London.

[11] Bride, T. F. (1898). *Letters from Victorian Pioneers*. Melbourne.

[12] Brougham, R. W. (1956). Effect of intensity of defoliation on regrowth of pasture. *Aust. J. Agric. Res.*, **7**, 377–87.

[13] Christian, C. S., and Slatyer, R. O. (1958). Some observations on vegetation changes and water relationships in arid areas. Climatology and microclimatology. *Proceedings of Canberra Symposium* 1956, pp. 156–8. UNESCO, Paris.

[14] Clark, L. R. (1948). Observations on the plant communities at 'Bundemar', Trangie District, New South Wales, in relation to *Chortoicetes terminifera* (Walk.) and *Austroicetes cruciata* (Sauss.). *Coun. Sci. Ind. Res. Aust. Bull.*, No. 236.

[15] Costello, D. F. (1944). Natural regeneration of abandoned plowed land in the mixed prairie association of north-eastern Colorado. *Ecology*, **25**, 312–26.

[16] Crider, F. H. (1955). Root-growth stoppage resulting from defoliation of grass. *U.S. Dept. Agric. Tech. Bull.*, No. 1102.

[17] Davies, H. Lloyd (1958). Pasture management for the breeding and lactating ewe. *Aust. Agrostology Conference, Univ. New England, Papers*, Vol. 1, part 2, pp. 55–1/55–11. C.S.I.R.O., Melbourne.

[18] Donald, C. M. (1956). Competition among pasture plants. *Proc. 7th Int. Grassld. Congr.*, **1**, 80–91.

[19] Freer, M. (1959). The utilization of irrigated pastures by dairy cows. I. A Comparison of rotational and strip grazing. *J. Agric. Sci.*, **52**, 129–36.

[20] Gardner, J. L. (1950). Effects of thirty years of protection from grazing in desert grassland. *Ecology*, **31**, 44–50.

[21] Gilliland, H. B. (1952). The vegetation of eastern British Somaliland. *J. Ecol.*, **40**, 91–124.

[22] Haskell, H. S. (1945). Successional trends on a conservatively grazed desert grassland range. *J. Amer. Soc. Agron.*, **37**, 978–90.

[23] Hyder, D. N., and Sawyer, W. A. (1951). Rotation-deferred grazing as compared to season long grazing on sagebrush-bunch-grass ranges in Oregon. *Jour. Range Mangt.*, **4**, 30–4.

[24] Jessup, R. W. (1946). The ecology of the area adjacent to Lakes Alexandrina and Albert. *Trans. Roy. Soc. S. Aust.*, **70**, 3–34.

[25] Jessup, R. W. (1951). The soils, geology, and vegetation of north-western South Australia. *Trans. Roy. Soc. S. Aust.*, **74**, 189–273.

[26] Jones, M. G. (1933). Grassland management and its influence on the sward. I. Factors influencing the growth of pasture plants. *Emp. J. Expt. Agric.*, **1**, 43–57.

[27] Klapp, E. (1938). Principles governing the value of herbage plants for hay and pasture use. *Herbage Rev.*, **6**, 57–63.

[28] Langer, R. H. M. (1959). Growth patterns of grasses in the sward. *Proc. N.Z. Inst. Agric. Sci.*, pp. 53–9.

[29] Larin, I. V. (1956). Rotation of pastures as a system of planned utilization and management of pastures. *Proc. 7th Int. Grassld. Congr.*, 303–12.

[30] Levy, E. B. (1940). Pasture weeds. I. Their ecological relationship to the pasture sward. *Imp. Bur. Pasture and Forage Crops, Herbage Publ. Series, Bull.*, No. 27, pp. 144–52.

[31] McIlvain, E. H., and Savage, D. A. (1951). Eight years' comparisons of continuous and rotational grazing on the Southern Great Plains Experimental Range. *J. Range Mangt.*, **4**, 42–7.

[32] McMeekan, C. P. (1956). Grazing management and animal production. *Proc. 7th Int. Grassld. Congr.*, **1**, 146–56.

[33] McMeekan, C. P. (1960). Grazing Management. *Proc. 8th Int. Grassld. Congr.*, **1**, 21–6.

[34] Mitchell, K. J. (1958). The influence of temperature on the growth of pasture plants. Climatology and microclimatology. *Proceedings of Canberra Symp.*, 1956. UNESCO, Paris.

[35] Moore, C. W. E. (1953). Vegetation of the south-eastern Riverina, N.S.W. II. The disclimax communities. *Aust. J. Bot.*, **1**, 548–67.

[36] Moore, R. M. (1940). The southern pastures of Australia. *Herb. Publ. Series Bull.*, No. 29.

[37] Moore, R. M. (1958). Natural phenomena and microclimate. Climatology and microclimatology. *Proceedings of The Canberra Symp.*, 1956, pp. 172–4. UNESCO, Paris.

[38] Moore, R. M. (1959). Ecological observations on plant communities grazed by sheep in Australia. In *Biogeography and Ecology in Australia*. Monographiae Biologicae Series, Vol. 8, pp. 500–13.

[39] Moore, R. M. (1961). The management of native vegetation in arid and semi-arid regions. UNESCO, Paris. pp. 173–90.

[40] Moore, R. M. (1962). The effect of sheep grazing on Australian vegetation. In *The Simple Fleece – Studies in the Australian Wool Industry*. Ed. by A. Barnard, Melb. Press and A.N.U.

[41] Moore, R. M., Barrie, N., and Kipps, E. H. (1946). A study of the production of a sown pasture in the Australian Capital Territory under three systems of grazing management. *Coun. Sci. Industr. Res. Aust. Bull.*, No. 201.

[42] Moore, R. M., and Cashmore, A. B., (1942). The control of St. John's wort (*Hypericum perforatum* L. var. *angustifolium* DC.) by competing pasture plants. *Coun. Sci. Industr. Res. Aust. Bull.*, No. 157.

[43] Moore, R. M., and Robertson, J. A. (1960). Studies on skeleton weed (*Chondrilla juncea* L.) in the New South Wales wheatbelt. *2nd Aust. Weeds Conf.*, Canberra, Vol. 1, pp. 41/1–42/8.

[44] Moore, R. M., Arnold, G. W., Hutchings, R. J., and Chapman, H. W. (1961). Poisoning of Merino sheep on *Phalaris tuberosa* L. pastures. *Aust. J. Sci.*, **24**, 88.

[45] Moore, R. M. Unpublished data.

[46] Naveh, Z. (1955). Some aspects of range improvements in a Mediterranean environment. *J. Range Mangt.*, **8**, 265–70.

[47] Nunn, W. M., and Suijdendorp, H. (1954). Station management – the value of deferred grazing. *Jour. Dept. Agric. W.A.*, **3** (N.S.), 585–7.

[48] Osborne, T. G. B., Wood, J. G., and Paltridge, T. B. (1931). On the autecology of *Stipa nitida*, a study of a fodder grass in arid Australia. *Proc. Linn. Soc. N.S.W.* **56**, 299–324.

[49] Pechanec, J. F. (1956). Rangeland development in difficult environments of the sagebrush-grass type in the western United States. *Proc. 7th Int. Grassld. Congr.*, **1**, 588–97.

[50] Pechanec, J. F., and Stewart, G. (1949). Grazing spring-fall sheep ranges of southern Idaho. *U.S. Dept. Agric. Circular*, No. 808.

[51] Phillips, J. (1956). Aspects of the ecology and productivity of some of the more arid regions of southern and eastern Africa. *Vegetatio*, **7**, 38–88.

[52] Pidgeon, I. M., and Ashby, E. (1940). Studies in applied ecology. I. A statistical analysis of regeneration following protection from grazing. *Proc. Linn. Soc. N.S.W.*, **65**, 123–43.

[53] Roe, R., and Allen, G. H. (1945). Studies on the Mitchell grass association in south-western Queensland. 2. The effect of grazing on the Mitchell grass pasture. *Coun. Sci. Industr. Res. Aust. Bull.*, No. 185.

[54] Roe, R., Southcott, W. H., and Turner, H. N. (1959). Grazing management of native pastures in the New England Region of New South Wales. I. Pasture and sheep production with special reference to systems of grazing and internal parasites. *Aust. J. Agric. Res.*, **10**, 530–54.

[55] Rogler, G. A. (1951). A 25-year comparison of continuous and rotation grazing in the Northern Plains. *J. Range Mangt.*, **4**, 35–41.

[56] Rossiter, R. C. (1952). The effect of grazing on a perennial veldt grass – subterranean clover pasture. *Aust. J. Agric. Res.*, **3**, 148–59.

[57] Rossiter, R. C. (1958). Utilization of annual pastures in a Mediterranean environment with special reference to autumn deferment. *Aust. Agrostology Conf. Univ.*, *New England Papers*, Vol. 1, part 2, pp. 56–1/56–15. C.S.I.R.O., Melbourne.

[58] Rowland, J. W. (1937). Grazing management. *Dept. Agric. and Forestry, Union of S. Africa. Bull.*, No. 168.

[59] Sears, P. D. (1956). The effect of the grazing animal on pasture. *Proc. 7th Int. Grassld. Congr.*, **1**, 92–103.

60 Stern, W. R., and Donald, C. M. (1962). Light relations in grass-clover swards. *Aust. J. Agric. Res.*, **13**, 599–644.
61 Stoddart, L. A. (1952). Problems in estimating grazing capacity of ranges. *Proc. 6th Int. Grassld. Congr.*, **2**, 1367–73.
62 Tarman, O. (1952). Forage resources and ecology of the high steppes area of Turkey. *Proc. 6th Int. Grassld. Congr.*, **1**, 646–9.
63 Terenozkin, I. (1934). Grazing: Its role and significance for pastures of the dry steppe and semi-desert regions of the lower Volga. *Sovetsk. Bot.*, No. 4, pp. 42–61.
64 Theron, G. C. (1946). Research in connection with veld control at the Potchefstroom College of Agriculture. *Dept. of Agric., Union of S. Africa, Sci. Bull.*, No. 266.
65 Tidmarsh, C. E. (1948). Conservation problems of the Karoo. *Farming in S. Afr.*, **23**, 519–30.
66 Trumble, H. C. (1935). The relation of pasture development to environmental factors in South Australia. *Agric. J. S. Aust.*, **38**, 1460–87.
67 Trumble, H. C., and Woodroffe, K. (1954). Influence of climatic factors in the reaction of desert shrubs to grazing by sheep. In *Biology of Deserts*. Instit. of Biology, London.
68 Weaver, J. E. (1950). Effects of different intensities of grazing on depth and quantity of roots of grasses. *J. Range. Mangt.*, **3**, 100–13.
69 Weaver, J. E., and Rowland, N. M. (1952). Effects of excessive natural mulch on development, yield, and structure of native grassland. *Bot. Gaz.*, **114**, 1–19.
70 West, O. (1947). Thorn bush encroachment in relation to the management of veld grazing. *Rhodesian Agric. J.*, **44**, 488–97.
71 Wheeler, J. L. (1960). Field experiments on systems of management for mesophytic pastures. *C.S.I.R.O. Div. Pl. Ind., Div. Rep.* No. 20, C.S.I.R.O., Canberra.
72 Whitfeld, C. J., and Anderson, H. L. (1938). Secondary succession in the desert plains grassland. *Ecology*, **19**, 171–80.
73 Willoughby, W. M. (1958). A relationship between pasture availability and animal production. *Proc. Aust. Soc. Anim. Prod. 2nd Biennial Conf.*, Vol. 2, pp. 42–5.
74 Wood, J. G. (1937). *The vegetation of South Australia*. Govt. Printer, Adelaide.

14

Grasses and Grasslands in Relation to Soil Conservation

By A. B. Costin

SOIL conservation philosophy has developed rapidly over recent years. It is no longer pre-occupied with specific problems of soil erosion such as gully control, or even with determining how a particular form of land use should be applied so that economic and soil conservation needs are satisfied. Both issues are, of course, still very important and will remain so, but increasingly soil conservation is becoming associated with broader issues of correct land use as well. In discussing grasses and grasslands in relation to soil conservation, therefore, the following considerations are involved:

1. The use of grasses for specific types of soil erosion control.
2. The management of grasslands with the dual purpose of producing plant and animal crops and of maintaining an adequate protective cover on the soil.
3. The application of broad conservation principles to decide whether an area should be developed primarily for grassland rather than for some other type of land use.

Before considering each of these topics, it is necessary to review briefly:

(*a*) The effects of grasses and grasslands on soil properties significant in soil conservation.
(*b*) The development of cover standards for grassland management.

Effects of Grasses and Grasslands on Soil Properties

Some of the best-known work on the effects of grasses and grasslands on the chemical properties of the soil has been done at Rothamsted, England, where different fields have been used in the same manner for long periods. Here it was found that under permanent pasture soil nitrogen increased for about 200 years before equilibrium was reached.[53] However, about half the equilibrium value was attained within 25 years and, even within a few years, appreciable increases in soil nitrogen occurred (Fig. 14.1).

Grazing of improved pastures topdressed with superphosphate mobilizes soil nutrients and concentrates them near the surface in available form. Increases in available potassium, calcium, magnesium, nitrogen, and organic matter have been demonstrated [54, 55, 62, 63] (Table 14.1). In the annual-type pastures examined, however, these increases are virtually confined to the surface two inches,[64] so that in the event of heavy overgrazing or pasture failure due to drought, erosion losses are potentially greater than from perennial native vegetation in which the nutrients are less mobile and more evenly distributed throughout the soil.

TABLE 14.1

Effect of Degree of Pasture Improvement on Soil Nutrients as Exemplified
by Nitrogen and Potassium, Crookwell, New South Wales
(Williams and Lipsett[63])

Site Number	Pasture Improvement	Total Nitrogen (%)	Total Potassium (me %)	Exchangeable Potassium (me %)
1	Nil	0·057	19·7	0·123
2	Slight	0·062	19·0	0·132
3	Medium	0·093	38·2	0·164
4	Medium	0·129	40·5	0·164
5	Medium	0·112	18·5	0·190
6	High	0·147	25·1	0·487
7	High	0·152	25·9	0·627

From the soil conservation viewpoint, the effects of grasses on the ability of
the soil to absorb water and resist erosion are more important than their
chemical effects. Soil structure and ground cover are of most significance in
this regard. It has long been recognized that grasses produce a stable, crumb-
structured soil, presumably because of their dense, fibrous root system.[41, 61]

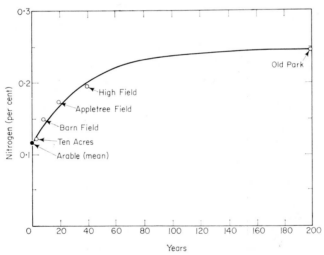

FIG. 14.1. Relationship between total soil nitrogen and
age of grassland at Rothamsted. (From Richardson, 1938, in
J. Agric. Sci., **28**, 78. Fig. 9.)

The Park Grass Plots at Rothamsted have 76–83 per cent of the soil in aggregates greater than 1 mm diameter, compared with the Broadbalk Wheat Plots
with only 6 per cent.[21] Low[43] examined the rate of improvement of soil
structure resulting from the sowing of improved pastures on a wide range of
British soils. Using the stability of air dry aggregates to wetting as an index of
improvement, he found there was considerable variation depending on soil
type and site conditions, for example, texture and drainage. On some clay
soils, 50 years or more were required for a full return to original conditions

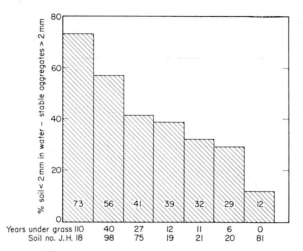

FIG. 14.2. Influence of number of years under grass on water-stable aggregation of clay loam surface soil, Northamptonshire, England. (From Low, 1955, in *J. Soil. Sci.*, **6**, 179. Fig. 7.)

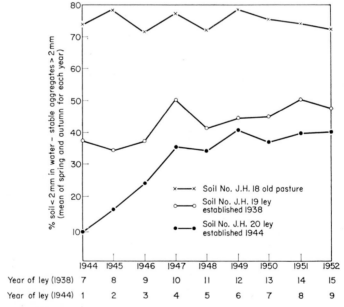

FIG. 14.3. Annual changes in water-stable aggregation of clay loam surface soil under leys established in 1938 and 1944, in relation to old pasture, Northamptonshire, England. (From Low, 1955, in *J. Soil Sci.*, **6**, 179. Fig. 6.)

(Fig. 14.2), but in coarse sandy soils 5–10 years may be enough and substantial structural improvement was apparent within shorter periods (Fig. 14.3). In Russia, the time required for full reconditioning is given as only 2–4 years; Low[43] suggests that a very sandy texture for the Russian soils would account for the shorter interval.

Greacen[30] compared structure profiles, as measured by aggregation, under conditions of continuous cultivation, improved pastures of various age, and virgin pasture in South Australia. He showed that continuously cultivated areas have very low aggregation values compared with virgin pasture where high values are maintained with depth (Fig. 14.4). Ten-year old perennial pastures of *Phalaris* showed high values at the surface, but a gradual decline with depth to considerably lower levels than those under virgin conditions.

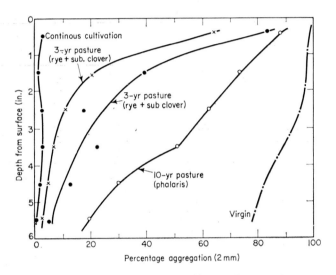

FIG. 14.4. Soil structure profiles under continuous cultivation, pastures, and virgin conditions, South Australia. Standard deviation 4·4. (From Graecen, 1958, in *Aust. J. Res.*, **9**, 129. Fig. 2.)

Both the 3- and 6-year old annual-type pastures of Wimmera ryegrass (*Lolium rigidum*) and subterranean clover (*Trifolium subterraneum*) showed a high degree of structural reconditioning at the surface, but below 1–2 inches there was a rapid decrease towards the low values of the continuously cultivated soils. Under South Australian conditions, therefore, it might be concluded that up to 10 years under pasture are needed for effective structural improvement of the topsoil, although considerable improvement in the surface inch will occur within 3 years. Greacen emphasizes the need for care in standardizing field and laboratory procedures, otherwise the results obtained in different experiments and by different workers may be difficult to compare. Some of the variation in the time required for effective reconditioning in different countries[43] may result from the different procedures used, as well as from differences in environmental conditions.

The reverse change, i.e. deterioration of structure with cultivation of grassland soils, has often been measured. Typical data are given by Downes and
Leeper[22] for Victoria, Australia (Table 14.2). The decline in structure is usually
associated with a decrease in organic matter and nitrogen content and an
increase in volume weight as illustrated in Table 14.2 and in Fig. 14.5.[38] In
many parts of the world, as for example in the wheat producing areas of
southern Australia, it has been found essential to alternate cropping with ley-
pasture to conserve soil fertility and structure.

TABLE 14.2

Physical Changes in Some Victorian Soils Due to Cultivation
(Downes and Leeper[22])

Soil	Treatment	Disaggrega-tion (%)	Organic Carbon (%)	Volume Weight
Merrigum	Improved pasture	32	2·04	1·24
	Native grassland	46	2·18	1·34
	Orchard, much cultivated	96	1·33	1·40
Werribee	Native grassland	26	2·09	1·18
	Thirty years cultivated	91	1·34	1·34
Wimmera	Native grassland	25	1·50	1·13
	Wheat stubble	44	—	1·07
	Wheat crop	58	—	0·99

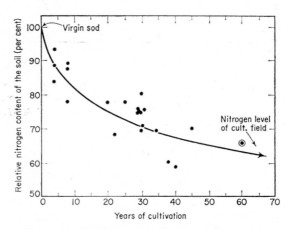

FIG. 14.5. Decline of soil nitrogen under average
farming conditions in the Central United States.
(From Jenny, 1941, in *Factors of Soil Formation.*
Fig. 122.)

The value of grass cover in minimizing surface run-off and soil erosion is
also well established. The data of Duley and Miller[23] are typical for the United
States (Table 14.3).

TABLE 14.3

Relation Between Type of Cover and Surface Run-off and Erosion,
Missouri, U.S.A.
(Duley and Miller[23])

Cover	Run-off (%)	Soil Loss (tons/acre/annum)
Bluegrass sod	11·55	0·3
Corn–wheat–clover rotation	14·14	2·3
Wheat	25·19	6·7
Corn	27·38	17·7
Bare soil, uncultivated	48·92	34·6

Cameron[4] summarizes results for south-east Australia (Table 14.4)

TABLE 14.4

Relation Between Type of Cover and Surface Run-off and Erosion,
New South Wales, Australia
(Cameron[4])

Station	Cover	Run-off (inches/annum)	Soil loss (lb/acre/annum)
Wagga	Wheat ley	0·22	38
	Ley	0·45	46
	Ley fallow	0·66	592
	Wheat stubble	0·72	127
	Stubble fallow	1·06	1739
	Permanent pasture	0·11	7
Cowra	Wheat ley	0·78	179
	Ley	0·58	69
	Ley fallow	0·80	1435
	Wheat stubble	1·38	450
	Stubble fallow	1·61	5234
	Permanent pasture	0·31	20
Wellington	Wheat stubble	1·34	744
	Stubble fallow	0·64	593
	Permanent pasture	0·23	23
Gunnedah	Wheat stubble	0·22	161
	Stubble fallow	0·28	148
	Permanent pasture	0·10	4

It is not always clear from such work whether the reduced surface run-off and
soil loss are due to special properties of the grass cover itself, or to the fact that
the other types of cover studied happened to expose more bare ground.
Osborne[50] sheds light on this question. He found that the order of decreasing
resistance to soil splash caused by raindrop impact was short sod grasses,
mixed range grasses, ordinary crops and grasses, and tall coarse crops and
weeds (Table 14.5). This question had also been clarified in forest, woodland,

TABLE 14.5

Amounts of Cover of Various Types Required for Different Levels of
Control of Erosion by Raindrop Impact
(Osborne [50])

Effectiveness of erosion control (%)	Total weight of cover (lb/acre)			
	Short sod grass	Mixed range grasses	Ordinary crops and grasses	Tall, coarse crops and weeds
98	4000	5000	6000	—
97	3000	3750	5000	—
95	2000	3000	3500	6000
90	1500	2000	2500	4000
85	1200	1600	2000	3000
80	1000	1400	1750	2250
75	850	1200	1500	1800
70	700	1100	1300	1500
60	500	900	1000	1100
50	400	750	800	900
35	250	500	600	600
25	175	400	400	400

and grassland areas of the Australian Alps.[15] Regression analyses relating amount of cover of different types to surface run-off and soil loss showed that, on oven-dry weight basis, herbs and herbaceous litter are twice as effective as forest litter or shrubs. Surface run-off and soil loss were effectively controlled by herbs and herbaceous litter at the rate of about 0·2 lb per square foot compared with about 0·5 lb for shrubs or forest litter. Langbein and Schumm[42] in the United States also concluded that, on a weight basis, a grass cover was most effective. It is thought that the superiority of grass leaves and litter results from their large surface area which affords maximum protection against the sealing of soil pores by raindrop splash and maximum opportunity for infiltration through high detention storage capacity (cf. 44). The high proportion of root growth made by grasses also contributes to soil stability.[41]

Grasslands and Cover Standards

Notwithstanding the value of grasses for soil conservation, most grazed grasslands show various degrees of soil erosion (Plate 10) including some of the most serious in the world (e.g. in New Zealand.[29,67]) Considerable effort has therefore been directed towards ascertaining how much cover is required for effective soil protection, and how this cover can be maintained. A variety of criteria has been employed, e.g. percentage cover of the soil (basal area or foliage cover, plus litter) weight of cover, density, height, etc.[50] Percentage cover and weight of cover have been most successfully used.

The cover requirements can rarely be decided from average meteorological values and normal catchment conditions, since it is usually the high intensity storms falling at times of maximum depletion of cover which cause highest surface run-off and soil loss.[15] The data of Marston[46] from Utah illustrate

PLATE IC. Gully erosion at Wagga Wagga, New South Wales, Australia, due to depletion of the grass cover. (*Photo by courtesy of the Soil Conservation Service of New South Wales.*)

PLATE II. Run-off and soil loss experiment at Scone, New South Wales, Soil Conservation Research Station, where the effects of various forms of land use and management practices are being measured. (*Photo by courtesy of the Soil Conservation Service of New South Wales.*)

how cover requirements increase with rainfall intensity (Fig. 14.6); in the environment studied a 5 per cent storm run-off was considered acceptable, since soil losses were very small below this level.

From such work using run-off plots and small catchments (Plate 11), cover standards in respect of storm rains of selected frequencies (e.g. once in 5–10 years) have been developed for some areas. In south-central Idaho the minimum cover requirements (basal area plus litter) are 70 per cent for wheat-grass range (*Agropyron inerme*) provided the diameter of the largest bare spaces does not exceed 4 inches, and 70 per cent for wheatgrass range (*Bromus tectorum*) with bare spaces of not more than 2 inches;[51] extra cover is needed when the bare spaces are larger. On mountain range in northern Utah, the cover requirements are 65 per cent and on subalpine herbaceous range in central Utah 70–75 per cent.[45, 46] On the high rainfall snowgrass pastures (*Poa*

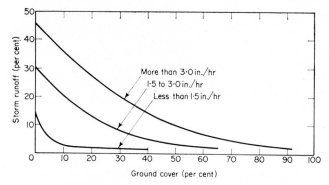

FIG. 14.6. Relation of summer storm run-off to total ground cover under the impact of low, moderate, and high intensity rainfall rates, Utah, U.S.A. (From Marston, 1952, in *J. Forestry*, **50**, 303. Fig. 5.)

caespitosa) of the Australian Alps, virtually continuous ground cover (foliage plus litter) at the rate of about 0·2 pounds per square foot has been found necessary.[15]

Quantitative cover standards such as these which are simple to estimate or measure in the field should be available to livestock managers for various soil, pasture, and slope conditions as readily as information on fertilizer require-ments, so that stocking rates can be adjusted as required. Unfortunately, there are very few areas for which these important data exist and still fewer where they are applied. The collection of such data is a world-wide need.

The Use of Grasses in Soil Erosion Control

Ecologically, grasses are one of the most successful groups of plants, having adapted themselves to most types of environment including the dry, wet, cold, and windy extremes, and to a wide range of unfavourable soil conditions (cf. Chapter 3). This versatility gives grasses a special value for erosion control, in which the amelioration of locally extreme conditions is an essential step to-wards complete reclamation. The ideal grass for erosion control should be easy to establish, quick to make growth despite unfavourable site conditions, persistent, and capable of rapid reproduction and spread. Special attributes may also be necessary depending on the nature of the erosion problem. A degree of unpalatability is often an advantage, since it may not always be possible to exclude grazing animals from the reclamation project. However, few species possess all these qualities.

Grasses are used to control erosion induced by wind, water, frost, salt, and to a less extent, gravity. Some basic problems and techniques associated with each type of erosion are outlined below, but no attempt is made to formulate complete species lists, as these vary widely from place to place: for example, very few North American grasses have been found useful in soil conservation work in Australia.[5]

Wind Erosion

Wind erosion is most serious in arid and semi-arid areas and along sandy shore-lines, and usually follows depletion of the original plant cover. The sand and soil material stripped from the most exposed sites is deposited in more protected situations where the vegetation may be killed. The problem is to minimize wind velocity near ground level and thus reduce the effects of sand blast, desiccation and (along sea coasts) salt spray. The pioneer plants must be able to withstand alternate burial and exposure due to continual deposition and erosion of soil and sand material; hence species capable of vigorous vegetative reproduction and spread, and with a lax rather than compact habit of growth, are most likely to succeed.

In coastal sand-dune areas, marram-grass (*Ammophila arenaria*) and sand spinifex (*Spinifex hirsutus*) have been widely used (Plate 12). Both species are usually established vegetatively at intervals of about 3 × 2 feet; spinifex is sometimes seeded also. Where conditions of exposure are very severe, mechanical protection must be afforded as with matting of brush or straw, and in extreme cases the dune area requires reshaping by bulldozer to modify sharp dune crests and severe blowouts. In coastal sand dune work the achievement of a grass cover is rarely the end-point of reclamation. Heath, scrub or low forest usually develop following the initial stabilization.[34, 57, 58]

Under arid and semi-arid conditions there are usually two distinct types of erosion areas: those from which topsoil has been removed leaving relatively hard 'scalded' surfaces, and those in which sand has accumulated in drifts.[1] The scalds rarely respond to replanting or re-seeding in the absence of supplementary mechanical work such as ripping or checkerboard ploughing. After such treatment, cereals may be sown as a cover crop for native species like saltbushes (Chenopodiaceae), the seed of which may be sown or left to blow in.[9, 10, 11] Cereal rye, because of its persistent straw, general hardiness, and ability to produce a volunteer crop the following year, is widely used as the cover crop. In areas of moving sand, mechanical measures may be unnecessary and the cover crop treatment, using cereal rye, is often sufficient.[8, 52] As in the control of coastal sand-dunes, the grasses are usually employed as a pioneer stage to a more persistent type of cover, for example scrub or saltbush (shrub-steppe).

PLATE 12. Wind-eroded sand dune on New South Wales coast being stabilized by marram grass and sand spinifex. (*Photo by courtesy of the Soil Conservation Service of New South Wales.*)

PLATE 13. Grassed water-way, in the Tamworth district of New South Wales, Australia. In addition to their main purpose of safe transport of run-off water, waterways can provide valuable hay crops and limited grazing. (*Photo by courtesy of the Soil Conservation Service of New South Wales.*)

Water Erosion

Grasses are used to minimize erosion by water in a variety of situations. They are used for the general improvement of cover and infiltration over large areas, the safe transport of intermittent high-volume flows along contour banks, waterways, grassed chutes, and spillways, and the local stabilization of disturbed sites such as road-side gravel pits, batters, canals, and dam walls (Plate 13). Their use in the first problem aims to secure and maintain an adequate amount of cover to minimize surface run-off and soil loss; this involves correct land use and grazing management as described earlier. The

PLATE 14. Advanced erosion in an alpine area of the Snowy Mountains of New South Wales, Australia. At these high levels, frost action largely prevents the establishment and growth of seedlings on bare areas. In the reclamation work seen in the foreground, protection from frost is obtained by a thin straw mulch applied after sowing, which is held to the ground by wire netting or bitumen. The diversion banks convey surface run-off to steep water-ways paved with stone. (*Photo by courtesy of the Soil Conservation Service of New South Wales.*)

second and third problems usually call for specialized species and special establishment techniques.

In contrast to the grasses used for the control of wind erosion, where an erect habit of growth is often an advantage, the best plants for the control of water erosion usually have a dense, compact habit of growth. Phalaris (*Phalaris tuberosa*), kikuyu (*Pennisetum clandestinum*) and rhodes grass (*Chloris gayana*) are 'standards' in areas of south-eastern Australia with an average rainfall of 20 inches or more.[5] Various techniques may be used to protect the young plants during establishment and they mostly take the form of applying mulches of straw, hessian, or bitumen by hand or by special machines. Satisfactory perennial species for drier areas have not yet been found.

Frost Erosion

Problems of water erosion in colder areas are complicated by the effects of freezing and thawing of the soil and revegetation of bare surfaces is made increasingly difficult by the continual frost-heave of developing plants.[12, 67] Species with a vigorous rhizomatous habit such as brown top (*Agrostis tenuis*) and kentucky bluegrass (*Poa pratensis*) are better able to cope with these conditions than tussock forming species. Special mulching techniques are usually necessary to minimize frost heave (Plate 14).

Erosion of Salted Lands

Areas of excessive salt accumulation also present difficult problems of soil conservation. High soil salinity (more than about 0·5 per cent total soluble salts) reduces or prevents plant growth, and thus often provides a focal point for water erosion. The three main types of area affected are salt marshes, irrigation areas, and catchments with slightly saline soils in which the vegetation is changed to one with a lower water use, for example, forest to pasture. Artificial drainage and the controlled use of water to flush out excess salts are the most effective remedial measures, although reclamation by vegetation including grasses is often necessary.

The reclamation of salt marshes, as in Holland and other parts of Europe, is hastened by growing high-yielding hay crops of salt-tolerant species such as hybrid rice-grass (*Spartina townsendii*), perennial rye-grass (*Lolium perenne*) and cereals.[7] Similarly, in salted irrigation areas, the growth of salt-tolerant crops for hay and grain permits otherwise unproductive land to be profitably used and improved. On the heavy saline soils of the Murrumbidgee Irrigation Area of New South Wales, rice is widely grown.

Saline conditions may develop sporadically, though on an extensive scale, following the replacement of forest with a relatively high water use by pasture or agricultural crops, as in southern Australia.[3, 11] The excess soil water leaches out the small quantities of salt from most of the more freely drained parts of the catchment and concentrates it around seepage areas and along valleys. These areas become bare, both because of excessive salinity and the preferential grazing of livestock, and are the focal points of serious gully erosion. Ideally, the steeper parts of this country should be returned to forest, but this is rarely possible for practical reasons. Instead, pastures with higher water use are recommended for the catchment as a whole, with special treatment for the salted areas in the form of ripping to encourage through-drainage of the salt, mulching to reduce evaporation and increase infiltration and leaching, and sowing of salt-tolerant species. In southern Australia, Wimmera ryegrass (*Lolium rigidum*) has been most successfully used on salted areas and several other species are sufficiently promising to merit further trial.[11]

Mass Movement

In the above problems of wind, water, and frost erosion, grasses have special value because of the large amounts of fine leaf and root material produced near ground level. By contrast, they are less useful in the control of erosion by mass movement, such as earthflows and landslips, where deep-rooting species with a high water use are required. Trees and shrubs are more generally used in such work.

Grassland Management and Soil Conservation

Assuming the best form of land use for a particular area is grassland, the usual approaches to its management are to fit the animal to the plants available, or modify plant composition to suit the type of livestock to be grazed. These are not necessarily compatible with the conservation approach, which is to fit both plant and animal to the basic productive capacity of the land. This is particularly important in pasture lands such as those in Australia, where unpredictable periods of environmental stress (e.g. droughts) are common.

If a broad view is taken of grassland problems, pasture and livestock must be regarded as the replaceable resources, and soil as the irreplaceable resource in the soil–plant–animal system. It would thus seem logical that principles governing the use of pastures should first satisfy soil conservation needs. This viewpoint is not always accepted, or if it is, it is often argued that a pasture which produces high livestock yields for most of the time automatically meets soil conservation needs. In the United States it is, in fact, found that the near-climax grassland communities which afford the best soil protection often provide the highest livestock yields. The greater the departure from climax condition the lower the carrying capacity and the more the range is exposed to soil erosion. Thus, management which is based on a recognition of the degree to which a range departs from climax conditions helps to achieve conservation needs.[24, 25, 59] Basing management on this principle, it has been found in Montana that 75 per cent of the growth should be left ungrazed at the end of spring and 50 per cent at the end of autumn to maintain perennial grasslands in good condition.[37] For the annual grasslands of California a linear regression of production at the end of the growing season on amount of mulch at the beginning of the season indicated that a substantial residue of mulch should be carried over each year.[32] Unfortunately, it is not always possible to apply these criteria successfully, for instance, where the climax or near-climax pastures have a low carrying capacity for all or part of the year. The spear grass (*Stipa* spp.) pastures of southern Australia, the tussock grasslands (*Danthonia* and *Festuca* spp.) of New Zealand,[60] and the *Phragmites-Saccharum* tall grasslands of India[17] fall into this category.

In the spear grass areas of Australia the relatively unpalatable climax grasses are being replaced by palatable sown species, the annuals Wimmera ryegrass (*Lolium rigidum*) and subterranean clover (*Trifolium subterraneum*) and the perennial grass *Phalaris tuberosa*. This preoccupation with finding species palatable to livestock and giving high livestock yields has led to neglect of soil conservation needs. Thus, on the basis of grazing trials on sub-terranean clover-*Phalaris* pastures on flat land, continuous grazing has been recommended in preference to other forms of management involving deferred and rotational grazing.[49, 66] With continuous grazing, however, bare soil is frequently exposed during the cold winter and dry summer periods, and on sloping land the danger of soil erosion with the onset of heavy rains is high.

The attitude that native pasture plants are liabilities to be replaced by more palatable species has contributed to the widespread deterioration of semi-arid and arid grazing lands. In Australia, these pastures, which occupy about 75 per cent of the continent and support about one-third of the livestock, have undergone progressive depletion since white occupation. Some agricultural scientists believe that the introduction of more palatable pasture plants is the answer to further decline in stock numbers; buffel grass (*Cenchrus ciliaris*) has done well in some places. However, it is unlikely that the bulk of the country can be rehabilitated in this fashion. If productivity is to be stabilized against further decline and soil erosion reduced, the maintenance and where possible the improvement of the native vegetation through range management is required. Ideally, a system of nomadism needs to be devised to maintain ade-

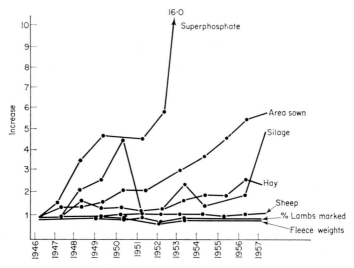

FIG. 14.7. Annual changes in sheep production in relation to pasture improvement practices, Southern Tablelands Statistical Division, Australia. (Private communication from Moule, 1959.)

quate cover in arid and semi-arid pastures, but under modern conditions this seems difficult to achieve.[18, 48]

Even in the 'safer' grazing areas, production methods and conservation needs do not always go hand in hand. In the favoured Coleraine and Dookie districts of Victoria, soil erosion reduces annual production by as much as 2·64 lb wool and 0·25 lb fat lamb per acre.[47] In the Southern Tablelands Statistical Division of New South Wales, where pasture improvement is being widely practised, there has been a 16-fold increase in the amount of superphosphate used since 1946, a 6-fold increase in the area sown to pasture, a 5-fold increase in the amount of silage conserved, and a 2- to 3-fold increase in the amount of hay. Yet the increases in numbers of sheep carried, percentage lambs marked and average fleece weights have been comparably slight (Moule, private communication, Fig. 14.7). A possible explanation for this situation is not that the measures have not been effective on the areas to which they have been applied, but that deterioration of the large areas of steeper unimproved pasture has masked the gains.[14] Statistics such as these are disturbing and indicate that our targets in grassland management and research may require re-assessing. Some of the problems are outlined below.

Pasture Evaluation

The usual method of pasture evaluation is by production per unit area per unit of time, either of livestock or of desirable pasture plants.[21] These production figures may then be expressed in economic terms. A corollary is that as much as possible of the available pasture should be consumed.[16] Management on the basis of these widely used criteria has so far been economically success-

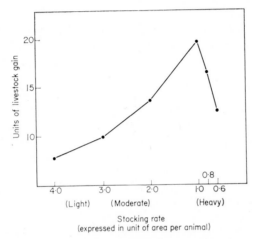

FIG. 14.8. Calculated curves for livestock gains per unit area at two stocking rate differentials, Sonora, U.S.A. (From Harlan, 1958, in *J. Range Management*, **11**, 140. Fig. 5.) There is a steady increase in gain per unit area from light to heavy rates but a crash in production (and range condition) when heavy rates are slightly exceeded.

ful, although production is often variable, with occasional heavy livestock losses in 'bad' seasons. Analysing this kind of situation in the United States, Harlan[31] showed that the economically most successful stocking at present is at 'heavy' rates. However, these rates are so close to peril point that only a slight further increase in stock numbers or a reduction in forage produces crashes in the condition of livestock and pasture alike (Fig. 14.8).

Similar conditions obtain in much of the grazing land in Australia. Under normal conditions – or rather those approximating to the mean – productivity is satisfactory and enough pasture remains uneaten to protect the soil against erosion. Recurrent droughts are, however, a regular feature of the environment. In the last century there have been 7 major droughts virtually on an Australia-wide scale and many more on a regional basis.[28] On these occasions stock losses have been very high. If these conditions were to recur today, it is considered that economic losses would be even worse and more far-reaching.[28]

Unfortunately, the recuperative power of many plant communities and soils is very slow. In south-western New South Wales stock carrying capacity has never recovered from the severe droughts at the turn of the century and it is now only half the average for the 1870–80 period.[65] The spinifex pastures (*Triodia* spp.) of north-west Western Australia have undergone similar depletion.[26] It is not generally recognized that certain downgrade trends in soils, once initiated, are virtually irreversible, even though the original disturbing agents are removed. Examples are the initiation and deepening of creeks in valleys containing deep soil,[2] and the continued erosion of once heavily stocked but now stock-free land.[1, 14, 27] It seems to be a characteristic of soil erosion that, although the processes of deterioration tend to be continuous and cumulative, their visible effects are discontinuous and may sometimes be unique events.

Another approach to pasture evaluation is in terms of overall stability of production rather than total yield. Production then tends to be geared as much to the bad years as to the average and good. This means that in the better seasons much of the forage remains uneaten, to be returned to the soil unless hay or silage is made. In general, perennial pastures are more likely to stabilize production than annuals, although total yield is often less.[36]

From here it is only a short step to evaluation of pastures in terms of forage remaining as well as in terms of forage (or livestock) removed.[33] The residual cover should be adequate to protect the soil during stress periods of a given probability (e.g. once in 5 to 10 years) rather than during average conditions (cf. section on Cover Standards). The following methods are available to help ensure that adequate cover for stress periods is maintained.

1. By development of pastures of different species, each to be used under various predetermined conditions, in accordance with a land use capability approach.

2. By adjustment of effective stocking rates, *in anticipation of deteriorating conditions*, through feeding conserved fodder or reducing livestock numbers.

3. By development of pastures better able to persist during unfavourable periods, even at the expense of total yield.

Land Use Capability

One of the main stumbling blocks to safe, long-term pasture production is the subdivision of land on a geometrical rather than a natural basis. The resultant management units often bear little relation to basic production factors such as soil, aspect, and slope, or to animal behaviour. Under these conditions the capacity of the pasture to withstand grazing varies from place to place over the paddock and a pattern of under-and-over-use develops. Livestock increasingly concentrate on the bare areas which extend and become worse.[13, 35] Many flood source areas and gullies originate in this way.

Subdivision, development, and management, in terms of land use capability groups, is largely the answer to this problem (Plate 15). Even on apparently well managed properties the potential for improvement is usually considerable. For example, the Westgate Farm Planning Project of 800 acres.

undertaken by the Soil Conservation Authority of Victoria, involved an increase from about 10 to 20 paddocks in the first 5 years, and provided for the ultimate development of 25.[20] The Soil Conservation Service of New South Wales has shown that in many parts of the State standard soil conservation measures can treble the amount of storm rainfall retained on the farm.[39] Increases in soil moisture of this order are likely to overshadow any increases which might result from successful rainmaking, or from breeding more efficient strains of particular pasture plants.

PLATE 15. A general view of balanced land use on the Wellington, New South Wales, Australia, Soil Conservation Research Station. Adequate ground cover is maintained, woodlots and watering places are judiciously located, and run-off water is safely disposed of along well-placed water-ways. (*Photo by courtesy of the Soil Conservation Service of New South Wales.*)

Readjustment of Effective Stocking Rates

Readjustment of effective stocking rates, achieved either by supplementary feeding or by removing livestock, becomes easier as the property is developed in terms of land use capability groups. Much has been written concerning supplementary feeding and some have questioned its value on purely economic grounds. Viewed as a soil conservation measure, however, supplementary feeding is often the only alternative to disposing of livestock.

The time at which excess livestock are withdrawn is usually determined by the more or less complete removal of forage or by loss of livestock condition. This is often far too late, particularly when sheep are being grazed. The critical time is when minimum cover conditions for storm rains, wind, or frost are being approached on the most vulnerable part of the paddock.

Persistence Under Stress

Persistence is a more desirable characteristic in difficult environments than productivity and it may never be possible to combine the two. For example, the persistent but unpalatable arid zone grass spinifex (*Triodia* sp.) has a root/shoot ratio of more than 1·0 compared with about 0·2–0·3 for most crop plants.[56] In fact, species capable of vigorous response to favourable conditions may be dangerous to the long-term stability of arid-zone pastures. Williams[65] found that aggresive annual legumes eliminated the slow growing persistent species during favourable seasons with the result that no vegetation remained when drought conditions returned. Stocking should be geared to stress periods regardless of whether the extra pasture in favourable seasons can be eaten or not.

In all but the small proportion of high rainfall pasture land in Australia, persistence under stress is synonymous with drought-resistant perennials. In this respect, a deep-rooting habit, as with phalaris,[6] helps the plant reach moisture reserves which often exist at depth in the soil. Species of only moderate palatability are an additional advantage.

Another relevant proposition is that for any habitat there is a community which is most efficient in circulating energy. Such communities, in addition to protecting the soil against erosion, would show maximum utilization of solar energy and soil water, and maximum circulation (as distinct from exhaustion) of nutrients. There may come a time when, especially in Australia, phosphatic fertilizers are not so readily or cheaply available, and in this event, information on the relative efficiency of various pasture plants in circulating a limited soil nutrient capital would be most important.

Grasslands and Optimum Land Use

Increasing competition for land during the twentieth century has made it clear that land is no longer an unlimited resource. The development of an area for a particular purpose often precludes its development for something else and alternative areas are not always available. It is therefore important that land should be used for its most suitable purposes, according to basic principles of land use. In the case of grassland, the following principles are proposed.

1. The permanent productive capacity of the land should be maintained and if possible increased.

2. The value of competitive types of production (e.g. timber) should not be reduced by more than the value of the grassland.

3. Use of grassland should be economically sound itself.

4. Other things being equal, use as grassland should not exclude other uses for which fewer alternative areas are available.

5. Changes should not be brought about in the environment or in the pattern of land use which cannot easily be reversed.

By and large, the maintenance of the large prairie and steppe areas of the world as grassland is capable of conforming to these requirements. Economic returns are not high, but grazing permits the utilization of otherwise unharvestable plant material. The application of sound range management principles, considered earlier, enables a moderate level of production and long-term stability to be harmonized. Many areas of heath, scrub, woodland, and forest have also been successfully converted to pasture. In some cases, the addition of small amounts of trace elements to normal fertilizers has resulted in a pasture revolution on formerly unproductive soils, and increased carrying capacity almost 50-fold.[19]

However, there are also many situations in which the development of grassland has been contrary to land use principles. Millions of acres of potentially high quality forest have been cleared to pasture, often with unfortunate results. For example, it is virtually impossible to apply proper grazing management where the area includes a large proportion of steep, uneven ground. Secondary succession to scrub and regrowth forest usually follows a few years after clearing, as in much of the steep mountain ash (*Eucalyptus regnans*) country of Victoria, and rainforest areas of northern New South Wales. With its relatively shallow rooting habit, grassland is incapable of utilizing the soil environment in these deep, moist soils as effectively as other forms of vegetation, and in the absence of continual checks on secondary succession, as by spraying or clearing, it becomes overgrown. The shallower root system and lower water use of grasses also facilitates soil mass movement, and erosion by flowage and slippage may become serious. Many such areas develop serious economic and social problems: the large investment in clearing and pasture development is not easily written off. Much marginal dairying in Australia is kept alive by Government subsidies, despite compelling ecological reasons for replacing it by other types of land use, for example forestry. The application of sound land use capability methods to determine the best uses for different areas, whether at the local or national level, can do much to obviate such mistakes.

Conclusion

In conclusion, therefore, it seems appropriate to ask whether some of the current specialist research into grassland problems is in danger of losing touch with important conditions in the field. Such conditions for most pasturelands include periods of severe stress. It is at this time that soil conservation problems reach their peak. Consequently, it can be argued that the basic pasture plants for these environments should be adaptable rather than specialized, persistent rather than highly productive, and preferably not too palatable. Higher yielding annuals might then be visualized as providing the extra cream to the milk, during the more favourable seasons.

There is also need to apply established land use capability principles to the grazing industry. This would require rather fundamental changes in subdivision and management. A detailed farm plan for every property and every catchment area should be the objective.

Thereafter, successful long-term management requires the establishment of minimum cover criteria for various land classes on the property and the adjustment of stocking rates through supplementary feeding and/or the removal of livestock so that minimum cover conditions are maintained.

R

REFERENCES

1 Beadle, N. C. W. (1948). *The Vegetation and Pastures of Western New South Wales.* Govt. Printer, Sydney.
2 Bride, T. F. (1898). Letter written by John G. Robertson to Governor C. LaTrobe, in *Letters from Victorian Pioneers.* Govt. Printer, Melbourne.
3 Burvill, G. H. (1950). The salt problem in the wheat belt. *J. Agric. W.A.,* 27, 174.
4 Cameron, D. G. (1955). Effects of soil cover and soil fertility on run-off and soil loss. *J. Soil Cons. Serv. N.S.W.,* 11, 115.
5 Cameron, D. G. (1956). Perennial grasses tested for soil conservation. *J. Soil. Cons. Serv. N.S.W.,* 12, 177.
6 Cashmore, A. B. (1934). A comparative study of *Lolium perenne* and *Phalaris tuberosa* at varying stages of growth. *C.S.I.R. (Aust.) Bull.,* No. 81.
7 Chapman, V. J. (1960). *Salt Marshes.* Leonard Hill, London.
8 Condon, R. W. (1954). Sand drift control on Coomealla Irrigation Area. *J. Soil. Cons. Serv. N.S.W.,* 10, 109.
9 Condon, R. W. (1958). Scald reclamation with primary cover crops. *J. Soil Cons. Serv. N.S.W.,* 14, 264.
10 Condon, R. W. (1959). Scald reclamation with primary cover crops. Part II. *J. Soil. Cons. Serv. N.S.W.,* 15, 125.
11 Cope, F. (1958). *Catchment Salting in Victoria.* Govt. Printer, Melbourne.
12 Costin, A. B. (1954). *A Study of the Ecosystems of the Monaro Region of New South Wales.* Govt. Printer, Sydney.
13 Costin, A. B. (1958). The grazing factor and the maintenance of catchment values in the Australian Alps. *C.S.I.R.O. (Aust.) Div. Plant Ind., Tech. Paper,* No. 10.
14 Costin, A. B. (1959). Replaceable and irreplaceable resources and land use. *J. Aust. Inst. Agric. Sci.,* 25, 3.
15 Costin, A. B., Wimbush, D. J., and Kerr, D. (1960). Studies in catchment hydrology in the Australian Alps. II. Surface run-off and soil loss. *C.S.I.R.O. (Aust.), Div. Plant Ind., Tech. Paper* No. 14.
16 Cotsell, J. C. (1958). Assessment of some of the factors involved in the formulation of an animal/pasture pattern for high production. *Aust. Agros. Conf. Univ. of New England.* Vol. 1, Paper No. 58. C.S.I.R.O., Melbourne.
17 Dabadghao, P. M., and Patil, B. D. (1956). Ecological basis of grassland conservation in India. *J. Soil and Water Conservation in India,* 5, 7.
18 Darling, F. F. (1956). Man's ecological dominance through domesticated animals on wild lands. *Man's Role in Changing the Face of the Earth.* Ed. W. L. Thomas. Pp. 778–87. Univ. Chicago Press, Illinois.
19 Davies, J. G. (1952). Pastures in the Australian economy. *J. Aust. Inst. Agric. Sci.,* 18, 60.
20 Dickinson, H. R., and Downes, R. G. (1953). *The Westgate Farm Planning Project.* Govt. Printer, Melbourne.
21 Donald, C. M. (1941). *Pastures and Pasture Research.* University of Sydney.
22 Downes, R. G., and Leeper, G. W. (1940). The measurement of soil structure. *Proc. Roy. Soc. Vic.,* 52, 1.
23 Duley, F. L., and Miller, M. F. (1923). Erosion and surface run-off under different soil conditions. *Missouri Agr. Expt. Sta. Res. Bull.,* No. 63.
24 Dyksterhuis, E. J. (1949). Condition and management of range land based on quantitative ecology. *J. Range Management,* 2, 104.
25 Dyksterhuis, E. J. (1958). Range conservation as based on sites and condition classes. *J. Soil and Water Consv.,* 13, 151.
26 Ealey, E. H. M., and Suijendorp, H. (1959). Pasture management and the euro problem in the north-west of Western Australia. *J. Agric. W.A.,* 8, 273.
27 Ellison, L. (1951). Indicators of condition and trend on high range watersheds of the inter-mountain region. *U.S.D.A. Agric. H'book,* No. 19.
28 Foley, J. C. (1957). Droughts in Australia. *C'wealth (Aust.) Bureau Meteorology Bull.,* No. 43.
29 Gibbs, H. S., Raeside, J. D., Dixon, J. K., and Metson, A. J. (1945). Soil erosion in the high country of the South Island. *D.S.I.R. (N.Z.) Bull.,* No. 92.
30 Greacen, E. L. (1958). The soil structure profile under pastures. *Aust. J. Agric. Res.,* 9, 129.
31 Harlan, J. R. (1958). Generalised curves for gain per head and gain per acre in rates of grazing studies. *J. Range Management,* 11, 140.

[32] Heady, H. F. (1956). Changes in a Californian annual plant community induced by manipulation of natural mulch. *Ecology*, **37**, 798.

[33] Hedrick, D. W. (1958). Proper utilization – a problem in evaluating the physiological response of plants to grazing use: A Review. *J. Range Management*, **11**, 34.

[34] Hewitt, B. R. (1954). Coastal sand drift investigations in New South Wales. *J. Soil Cons. Serv. N.S.W.*, **10**, pp. 45 and 90.

[35] Hormay, A. L., Evanko, A. B. (1958). Rest-rotation grazing. *Calif. Forest and Range Expt. Sta. Miscell.*, Pap. No. 27.

[36] Humphries, A. W. (1958). *Aust. Agros. Conf. Univ. of New England*. Vol. 1, Paper No. 13. C.S.I.R.O., Melbourne.

[37] Hyder, D. N. (n.d.). Rotation – deferred grazing at Squaw Butte. *Squaw Butte-Harney Range and Livestock Expt. Sta. Res. Paper*, No. 4.

[38] Jenny, H. (1941). *Factors of Soil Formation*. McGraw-Hill, New York.

[39] Kaleski, L. G. (1956). Soil conservation and its relation to the flood problem in New South Wales. *J. Aust. Inst. Agric. Sci.*, **22**, 19.

[40] Knowles, G. H. (1954). Scald reclamation in the Hay District. *J. Soil Cons. Serv. N.S.W.*, **10**, 149.

[41] Kramer, J., and Weaver, J. E. (1936). Relative efficiency of roots and tops of plants in protecting the soil from erosion. *Univ. Nebr. Conservation Dept. Bull.*, No. 12.

[42] Langbein, W. B., and Schumm, S. A. (1958). Yield of sediment in relation to mean annual precipitation. *Trans. Amer. Geophys. Union*, **39**, 1076.

[43] Low, A. J. (1955). Improvements in the structural state of soils under leys. *J. Soil Sci.*, **6**, 179.

[44] Lowdermilk, W. C. (1929). Further studies of factors affecting surficial run-off and erosion. *Proc. Internat. Cong. Forestry Expt. Stations*.

[45] Marston, R. B. (1952). Ground cover requirements for summer storm run-off control on open sites in northern Utah. *J. Forestry*, **50**, 303.

[46] Marston, R. B. (1953). Guide to Davis County Experimental Watershed, Farmington. Utah. *U.S.D.A. Forest Service Publication*.

[47] Molnar, I. (1955). *Relationships between soil erosion, land values and production in two areas in Victoria*. Govt. Printer, Melbourne.

[48] Moore, R. M. (1960). The management of native vegetation in arid and semi-arid regions. *Arid Zone Research*, **15**. (UNESCO.)

[49] Moore, R. M., Barrie, N., and Kipps, E. H. (1946). A study of the production of a clover pasture in the Australian Capital Territory under three systems of grazing management. *C.S.I.R. (Aust.) Bull.*, No. 201.

[50] Osborne, B. (1954). Effectiveness of cover in reducing soil splash by raindrop impact. *J. Soil and Water Consv.*, **9**, 70.

[51] Packer, P. E. (1951). An approach to watershed protection criteria. *J. Forestry*, **49**, 639.

[52] Phillips, J. R. H. (1955). Wind erosion at Berrigan. *J. Soil Cons. Serv. N.S.W.*, **11**, 82.

[53] Richardson, H. L. (1938). The nitrogen cycle in grassland soils: with special reference to the Rothamsted Park Grass Experiment. *J. Agric. Sci.*, **28**, 73.

[54] Russell, J. S. (1960). Soil fertility changes in the long-term experimental plots at Kybybolite, South Australia. I. Changes in pH, total nitrogen, organic carbon, and bulk density. *Aust. J. Agric. Res.*, **11**, 902.

[55] Russell, J. S. (1960). Soil fertility changes in the long-term experimental plots at Kybybolite, South Australia. II. Changes in phosphorus. *Aust. J. Agric. Res.*, **11**, 925.

[56] Slatyer, R. O. (1960). Principles and problems of plant production in arid regions. *Arid Zone Tech. Conf. Warburton*, Vol. 2, Paper No. 7. C.S.I.R.O., Melbourne.

[57] Sless, J. B. (1955). Coastal sand drift control – Recent progress at experimental centres. *J. Soil Cons. Serv. N.S.W.*, **11**, 172.

[58] Sless, J. B. (1958). Coastal sand drift. *J. Soil Cons. Serv. N.S.W.*, **14**, 50.

[59] Stoddart, L. A., and Smith, A. D. (1943). *Range Management*. McGraw-Hill, New York.

[60] Tussock Grassland Research Committee (1954). The high altitude snow-tussock grassland in South Island, New Zealand. *N.Z. J. Sci. and Techn.*, **36A**, 335.

[61] Weaver, J. E., and Harmon, G. W. (1935). Quantity of living plant materials in prairie soils in relation to run-off and soil erosion. *Univ. Nebr. Conserv. Dept. Bull.*, No. 8.

[62] Williams, C. H., and Donald, C. M. (1957). Changes in organic matter and pH in a podzolic soil as influenced by subterranean clover and superphosphate. *Aust. J. Agric. Res.*, **8**, 179.

[63] Williams, C. H., and Lipsett, J. (1960). The build-up of available potassium under pasture. *Aust. J. Agric. Res.*, **11**, 473.

[64] Williams, C. H., and Steinbergs, A. (1958). Sulphur and phosphorus in some eastern Australian soils. *Aust. J. Agric. Res.*, **9**, 483.

[65] Williams, O. B. (1960). The selection and establishment of pasture species in a semi-arid environment – An ecological assessment of the problem. *J. Aust. Inst. Agric. Sci.*, **26**, 258.

[66] Willoughby, W. M. (1959). Limitations to animal production imposed by seasonal fluctuations in pasture and by management procedures. *Aust. J. Agric. Res.*, **10**, 248.

[67] Zotov, V. D. (1938). Survey of the tussock-grasslands of the South Island, New Zealand. *N.Z. J. Sci. and Techn.*, **20**, 212A.

Index of Families, Genera, and Species

Subject Index

*Printed in Great Britain by
Richard Clay and Company, Ltd.,
Bungay, Suffolk.*